Low-Level
Light Therapy:
Photobiomodulation

Tutorial Texts Series

(For a complete list of Tutorial Texts, see http://spie.org/publications/books/tutorial-texts.)

Low-Level Light Therapy: Photobiomodulation

Michael R. Hamblin
Cleber Ferraresi
Ying-Ying Huang
Lucas Freitas de Freitas
James D. Carroll

Tutorial Texts in Optical Engineering
Volume TT115

SPIE PRESS
Bellingham, Washington USA

Library of Congress Cataloging-in-Publication Data

Names: Hamblin, Michael R., author. | Ferraresi, Cleber, author. | Huang, Ying-Ying,
  author. | Freitas, Lucas F. de (Lucas Freitas), author | Carroll, James D. (James
  Duncan), author.
Title: Low-level light therapy : photobiomodulation / Michael R. Hamblin, Cleber
  Ferraresi, Ying-Ying Huang, Lucas Freitas de Freitas, and James D. Carroll.
Description: Bellingham, Washington, USA : SPIE Press, [2018] | Series: Tutorial texts
  in optical engineering ; volume TT 115 | Includes bibliographical references and index.
Identifiers: LCCN 2017051028 (print) | LCCN 2017039318 (ebook) | ISBN
  9781510614161 (pdf) | ISBN 9781510614178 (epub) | ISBN 9781510614185 (mobi)
  | ISBN 9781510614154 | ISBN 9781510614154 (softcover) | ISBN 151061415X
  (softcover)
Subjects: LCSH: Phototherapy. | Lasers–Therapeutic use. | Lasers in medicine.
Classification: LCC RM837 .H26 2018 (ebook) | LCC RM837 (print) | DDC
  615.8/31–dc23
LC record available at https://lccn.loc.gov/2017051028

Published by

SPIE
P.O. Box 10
Bellingham, Washington 98227-0010 USA
Phone: +1 360.676.3290
Fax: +1 360.647.1445
Email: books@spie.org
Web: http://spie.org

The content of this book reflects the work and thought of the author. Every effort has
been made to publish reliable and accurate information herein, but the publisher is not
responsible for the validity of the information or for any outcomes resulting from
reliance thereon.

Printed in the United States of America.
First Printing.
For updates to this book, visit http://spie.org and type "TT115" in the search field.

Introduction to the Series

Since its inception in 1989, the Tutorial Texts (TT) series has grown to cover many diverse fields of science and engineering. The initial idea for the series was to make material presented in SPIE short courses available to those who could not attend and to provide a reference text for those who could. Thus, many of the texts in this series are generated by augmenting course notes with descriptive text that further illuminates the subject. In this way, the TT becomes an excellent stand-alone reference that finds a much wider audience than only short course attendees.

Tutorial Texts have grown in popularity and in the scope of material covered since 1989. They no longer necessarily stem from short courses; rather, they are often generated independently by experts in the field. They are popular because they provide a ready reference to those wishing to learn about emerging technologies or the latest information within their field. The topics within the series have grown from the initial areas of geometrical optics, optical detectors, and image processing to include the emerging fields of nanotechnology, biomedical optics, fiber optics, and laser technologies. Authors contributing to the TT series are instructed to provide introductory material so that those new to the field may use the book as a starting point to get a basic grasp of the material. It is hoped that some readers may develop sufficient interest to take a short course by the author or pursue further research in more advanced books to delve deeper into the subject.

The books in this series are distinguished from other technical monographs and textbooks in the way in which the material is presented. In keeping with the tutorial nature of the series, there is an emphasis on the use of graphical and illustrative material to better elucidate basic and advanced concepts. There is also heavy use of tabular reference data and numerous examples to further explain the concepts presented. The publishing time for the books is kept to a minimum so that the books will be as timely and up-to-date as possible. Furthermore, these introductory books are competitively priced compared to more traditional books on the same subject.

When a proposal for a text is received, each proposal is evaluated to determine the relevance of the proposed topic. This initial reviewing process has been very helpful to authors in identifying, early in the writing process, the need for additional material or other changes in approach that would serve to strengthen the text. Once a manuscript is completed, it is peer reviewed to ensure that chapters communicate accurately the essential ingredients of the science and technologies under discussion.

It is my goal to maintain the style and quality of books in the series and to further expand the topic areas to include new emerging fields as they become of interest to our reading audience.

James A. Harrington
Rutgers University

Contents

Preface

For almost 50 years, the medical therapy formerly known as "low-level laser therapy" and now known as "photobiomodulation" has had a somewhat checkered history. This approach has been promoted by some of its aficionados with almost missionary zeal, while doubters and skeptics have regarded it as "junk science" and "alternative and complementary medicine." This Tutorial Text intends to convey to the contemporary scientific reader that photobiomodulation is becoming increasingly well-founded based on the accepted principles of photochemistry, cellular and molecular biology, and physiology.

The text covers in some detail the basic mechanisms of action of photobiomodulation at the cellular and molecular level because we have found that by far the question posed most often by scientists outside the field is "How does it really work?" The well-known biphasic dose response is covered because we believe that failure to take account of this phenomenon contributes to many of the negative studies that have been published. The ability of photobiomodulation to be used as a pre-conditioning regimen before some medical or surgical procedure or for performance enhancement is intriguing.

This Tutorial Text (larger than most) includes original and previously published material. The majority of the book focuses on a critical analysis of the various diseases and disorders of different human and animal tissue and organ systems that can be beneficially treated by photobiomodulation therapy. Chapters cover well-established applications in muscles and orthopedic conditions (bone, tendon, cartilage). Applications of photobio-modulation in dentistry have historically been important because dentists are accustomed to using lasers and light sources in their clinical practice. In addition to the foregoing, more systemic disorders are addressed, such as stem cells, lymph flow and edema, and laser irradiation of blood. One of the most important growing areas of medical application is photobiomodulation to the brain. Many common disorders—such as stroke, traumatic brain injury, psychiatric diseases, and dementia—may all benefit. Finally, one of the commercially successful areas of photobiomodulation involves its applications to aesthetic medicine, including skin appearance, hair regrowth, and fat removal.

Michael R. Hamblin
Cleber Ferraresi
Ying-Ying Huang
Lucas Freitas de Freitas
James D. Carroll
January 2018

List of Contributors

James D. Carroll
THOR Photomedicine Ltd.

Eduardo Machado de Carvalho
Center for Lasers and Applications,
IPEN-CNEN/SP, Campinas,
São Paulo, Brazil

Roberta Chow
Brain and Mind Centre,
The University of Sydney,
Camperdown, NSW, Australia

Tingting Dong
Wellman Center for Photomedicine,
Massachusetts General Hospital

Asheesh Gupta
Defence Institute of Physiology and
Allied Sciences (DIPAS), DRDO,
Delhi, India

Cleber Ferraresi
Universidade do Sagrado Coração,
Brazil

Leila Soares Ferreira
Center for Lasers and Applications,
IPEN-CNEN/SP, Campinas,
São Paulo, Brazil

Fernanda Freire
Department of Biosciences and Oral
Diagnosis, Institute of Science and
Technology, UNESP - Universidade
Estadual Paulista, São José dos
Campos, Brazil

Lucas Freitas de Freitas
University of São Paulo, Brazil

Michael R. Hamblin
Wellman Center for Photomedicine,
Massachusetts General Hospital

Harvard Medical School

Ying-Ying Huang
Wellman Center for Photomedicine,
Massachusetts General Hospital

Daiane Thais Meneguzzo
Center for Lasers and Applications,
IPEN-CNEN/SP, Campinas,
São Paulo, Brazil

Cássia Fukuda Nakashima
Center for Lasers and Applications,
IPEN-CNEN/SP, Campinas,
São Paulo, Brazil

Qi Zhang
Wellman Center for Photomedicine,
Massachusetts General Hospital

Chang Zhou
Wellman Center for Photomedicine,
Massachusetts General Hospital

Chapter 1
Introduction

1.1 General

Low-level laser (light) therapy (LLLT), or photobiomodulation therapy (PBMT), is a general term that refers to therapeutic approaches based on the photobiomodulation (PBM) principle that causes biological alterations in organisms, secondary to interactions of photons in the visible or infrared spectral regions with molecules in the cells or tissues.

Therapeutic PBM has received many names over the years. Low-level laser therapy led to the adoption of the acronym "LLLT," which is an official Medical Subject Heading (MeSH) as defined by the U.S. National Library of Medicine. LLLT now retrieves 4161 citations on PubMed (Jan 2016). In 2015, the term "photobiomodulation" also became an official MeSH term and now retrieves 215 citations. It has been agreed that "photobiomodulation" or "photobiomodulation therapy" should be adopted as the preferred term going forward. However, there exists a plethora of alternative terminology that have been used in one form or another: low-level laser therapy, low-level light therapy, low-intensity laser irradiation, low-reactive laser therapy, cold laser, nonthermal laser, soft laser, biostimulation laser, photobiomodulation laser, or even light-emitting diode (LED) therapy and organic LED therapy. The adjectives in these phrases emphasize a comparison with surgical lasers, which can cut, ablate, and coagulate biological tissues due to a photothermal effect. LLLT and photobiomodulation do not generally increase the macroscopic tissue temperature because the power density used is much smaller than the threshold needed for photothermal effects.

The most common LLLT procedures are performed by the irradiation of tissue with relatively low-powered lasers or LED arrays. The light is generally applied to sites of injury in order to hasten cellular processes, leading to better healing, decreased inflammation, and reduced pain. Almost all LLLT treatments are conducted with red or near-infrared (NIR) light (600–1100 nm), with a total output power of 1–10,000 mW using a power density that does not heat the tissue (<1 W/cm^2, depending on the wavelength and tissue type). These LLLT procedures are generally noninvasive because light can penetrate through skin and overlying tissues to reach the underlying target tissue. The light is nonthermal; just like photosynthesis, it causes photochemical reactions, and it has a wide scope of different clinical applications.

The range of PBM applications has increased exponentially in recent years. The vast and ever-increasing body of literature in PBM provides many creative ways of using different light sources and some innovative ways to deliver light to target cells or tissues. In contrast with the past well-established terminology that was inextricably linked to the use of lasers (low-level laser therapy), LLLT or PBM is now performed with a wide variety of different light sources, such as LEDs, organic LEDs (OLEDs), and lamps that are filtered by bandpass filters or by monochromators. A question that is often asked is, "if light is so beneficial for all these different diseases, why can a person not just absorb sunlight?" For some superficial indications requiring PBM, sunlight is in fact beneficial, but because the peak emission is in the green wavelengths (500 nm), the light does not penetrate well. Moreover, sunlight contains a fair amount of harmful UVB radiation, so if one exposed oneself for a long enough time to get sufficient photons of the correct wavelength to the target tissue, the result would include a nasty sunburn.

Some biological processes can be modulated by photochemical reactions triggered by photons with a wavelength that is either shorter or longer than the optical window of 600–1100 nm, e.g., blue light (400–520 nm), green light (520–560 nm), or yellow light (560–600 nm); mid-infrared radiation (1100–3000 nm); and far-infrared radiation (>3000 nm). These intriguing observations are one of the driving forces behind the search for the chromophores (light-absorbing molecules) responsible for the biological effects of PBM. It has been suggested that because a relatively broad range of wavelengths have been shown to have beneficial biological effects (at the correct doses), it is therefore unlikely that there can only be a single chromophore (for instance, cytochrome c oxidase) responsible for absorbing the photons.

The optimal dosimetric parameters for PBM are usually 1–1000 mW/cm^2 for power density and 0.1–100 J/cm^2 for energy density. The time exposure is primarily measured in minutes rather than seconds or hours. However, good results can occasionally be found with parameters that fall outside these ranges. Interestingly, there are many ways to deliver light to a specific tissue: a focused laser spot on the skin; a large-area LED array, contact or not; a light source introduced inside a body cavity (mouth, ear, nose, vagina, etc.); or even intravenous or interstitial irradiation (where an optical fiber inside a needle (or a catheter) is inserted into the tissues). Taking all of these possibilities into account, PBM could have even more clinical applications than are obvious at first glance, given this is a developing field of knowledge with significant room to progress.

PBM does not often cause any visible or tangible changes in the tissue during the moment of light delivery, which leads some patients to doubt that a real effect could be evoked by that "little light," as they might say. It can be difficult to make them understand, or even accept, the photochemical and photobiological events that occur inside them during the therapy. Moreover, PBM still remains to some extent controversial, even among researchers and clinicians; sometimes this skepticism is related to lack of knowledge or previous distrust of unconventional (alternative and complementary) medicine. In these cases, personal experience of the effectiveness of PBM will remove the uncertainty. There are three fundamental points of controversy:

- even though the biochemical mechanisms behind PBM have been investigated, our understanding remains incomplete;
- a large number of parameters related to PBM, about which there is no consensus; and
- the effectiveness of PBM varies among individuals depending on genetic, epigenetic, and phenotypic differences that are poorly understood, and thus treatments may need to be personally tailored.

Today it is generally accepted that PBM is triggered by photon absorption by the complex enzyme called cytochrome c oxidase, located inside mitochondria; however, the chain of reactions that follows this initial photon-absorption event remains incompletely understood. To fully define a specific PBM procedure, it is necessary to specify many parameters, such as the wavelength, fluence, power density, pulse structure, and timing. The choice of such parameters must be adapted to each patient because the skin color, age, gender, amount of hair, and state of the tissue can all influence the light absorption and scattering throughout the tissues. A mistake in the selection of parameters for each patient can lead to a less-effective (or even negative) outcome of the therapy.

1.2 Light Sources

The first PBM procedures were performed using lasers, and in the early days of this field researchers were not sure if the biomodulation processes triggered by PBM depend on the special properties of laser light, e.g., monochromaticity (narrow bandwidth), coherence, or polarization, or whether similar therapeutic benefits can be achieved by other light sources. Considerable evidence has accumulated over the last decades that suggest other light sources can produce PBM effects and that the major determining parameters for the effectiveness of PBM are the wavelength and the dose. The wavelength must be capable of being absorbed by a photoacceptor molecule in the cell or organism. Noncoherent light sources, such as LEDs, or halogen or other incandescent lamps connected to filters can be equally effective. Even more recent are organic LEDs (OLEDs), which extend the possibilities of PBM because an OLED can emit light uniformly from a flexible surface.

The term "laser" originates from an acronym that stands for "light amplification by stimulated emission of radiation." The physical concept of stimulated emission was proposed by Einstein in 1916,[1] but it was only in 1960 that the first working laser was built by Maiman (see Chapter 2).[2] The key concept in the mechanism of laser action is "population inversion." The laser medium must be able to be excited into a state in which the majority of the atoms or molecules exist in higher excited states compared to those in lower unexcited energy states. Only then can the excited states be stimulated by spontaneously emitted photons to release even more photons and lasing can take place (see Fig. 1.1). Only a few materials can meet this criterion, including certain crystals, glasses, gases, semiconductors, and dye solutions. The laser has interesting properties, such as a high degree of spatial and temporal coherence, that make this light source unique. A laser acts as a point source that can be focused into a small spot, kept as a collimated narrow beam that can travel over long distances, or expanded by lenses to form a large spot, if necessary. Although light from gas and crystal lasers is naturally collimated, light from diode lasers is divergent and requires a lens to focus and to couple it into an optical fiber. In addition, the coherence property allows lasers to have a very narrow spectral-emission bandwidth (that can reach as narrow as approximately 10^{-3} nm) and can also allow the production of

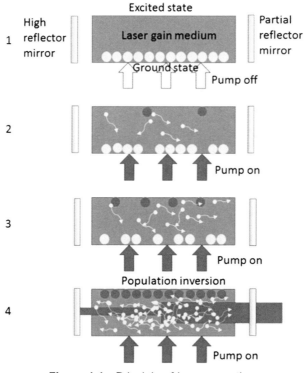

Figure 1.1 Principle of laser operation.

pulses of light that last only a few attoseconds (10^{-18} s). In fact, the shortest controlled laser pulse achieved by researchers was a pulse of 12 attoseconds.[3] The temporal coherence can be important to PBM because it allows the creation of lasers capable of matching the exact absorption peak of a predetermined photoreceptor or photoacceptor. The first lasers were based on crystals (ruby) or gases (helium-neon or argon) as the lasing medium. Since the early days, the vast majority of PBM lasers have been based on semiconductors such as gallium arsenide (GaAS) and gallium-aluminum-arsenide (GaAlAs).

A LED consists of a semiconducting material doped with some impurities to create a gap of energy between the valence and conduction bands of the electrons (called a bandgap). When the LED is switched on, a voltage is applied to bring the electrons in the conduction band close to the holes from the valence band, making them recombine and release energy in the form of photons. This phenomenon is known as electroluminescence. The color of the emitted photon (wavelength of the LED) is determined by the energy bandgap, and the intensity (brightness) of the LED depends exponentially on the applied voltage, assuming it is kept below a limit that would damage the device. Although the phenomenon of electroluminescence has been known since 1907, it was only in 1962 that the first practical LEDs were developed that emitted either infrared or red light. Today, LEDs can be made with a variety of inorganic semiconductor materials, and thus they can emit many different colors, from the ultraviolet ($\lambda < 400$ nm) to infrared ($\lambda > 750$ nm), or else different semiconductors can be combined to emit white light. A common value for the spectral bandwidth (full width at half maximum, FWHM) is approximately 30 nm, and the area of each LED emitting surface is usually smaller than 1 mm^2. A recent advancement is the OLED, which uses small organic molecules as the electroluminescent material. Among other advantages, OLEDs can emit from a large (>1 cm^2) and flexible surface; they are also more efficient and have a narrower bandwidth than standard LEDs.

1.3 Physics and Tissue Optics

The electromagnetic spectrum of radiation ranges from gamma rays ($\lambda < 10^{-12}$ m) to radio waves (λ between 10^{-1} and 10^8 m). The light visible to humans is a small portion of the spectrum (Fig. 1.2) between 400–750 nm that, along with ultraviolet (100–400 nm) and infrared (750 nm to 1 mm) light, composes the optical region of the entire spectrum. Electromagnetic waves are created by the perpendicular oscillation of electric and magnetic fields, which are described by Maxwell's equations. Light, interpreted as a waveform, can be characterized by amplitude, wavelength and polarization, which determine the intensity (or brightness), color, and orientation of these

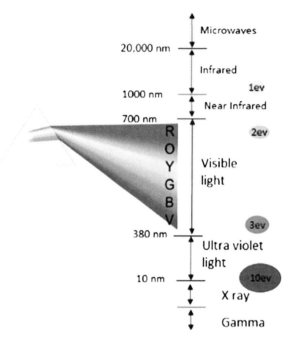

Figure 1.2 Electromagnetic spectrum.

oscillations, respectively. With the advent of quantum theory, the physics of light was better understood and can be interpreted as a particle complementary to the wave interpretation, i.e., light can behave as either waves or particles, depending on the physical situation being studied. These particles of light (photons) are massless packets ("quanta") of energy moving at approximately 3×10^8 m/s. The wavelength of light is determined by the energy of the single photons, and the number of photons in a single direction determines the intensity in that direction.

Light interacts with biological tissue in two ways, absorption and scattering, as shown Fig. 1.3.[4] Light absorption occurs when a photon interacts with an atom, a bond, or a molecule, and the entire energy of the photon is transferred to the atom or molecule. Light-scattering interactions can change both the direction and energy of photons (inelastic), or only the direction (elastic scattering). Visible and near-IR light interactions with biological tissue mainly produce elastic scattering. The scattering depends on the size, shape, and refractive index of the scattering center and on the wavelength of the incident light. Complete knowledge of the penetration and distribution of light inside biological tissues is difficult to acquire because absorption and scattering depend on wavelength, tissue biochemistry, and anatomy.[5]

The effectiveness of PBM is determined by the amount of light reaching the target tissue depth (penetration). However, in many cases, precise and direct measurement of the exact light distribution and intensity inside the tissue is

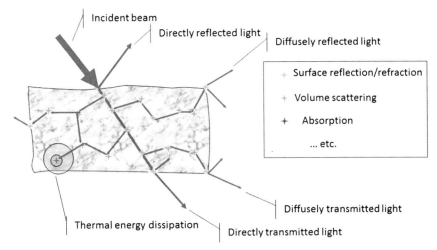

Figure 1.3 Laser–tissue interaction.

not possible. For this reason, the best description of the PBM procedures requires extrapolation from the surface irradiation and dose parameters determined by the output of the device, to the light penetrating to various depths of the tissue (or other biological medium). Overall, PBM dosimetry can be described and divided into two parts: (1) the irradiation parameters, i.e., "the medicine," and (2) how light is delivered, i.e., "the dose." The irradiation parameters, such as wavelength (nm), power (W), beam area (cm^2), and pulse structure, are related to the specific light source. On the other hand, the dose parameters, such as energy (J), energy density (J/cm^2), treatment repetition, and irradiation time (s) and area (cm^2), are operator-controlled. In addition, light dosimetry to some extent depends on the specific characteristics of each patient (e.g., skin color) and of the physiological tissue (e.g., the amount of subcutaneous fat). All of these interrelated considerations and patient-specific factors make PBM dosimetry rather complex, and it may be difficult to optimize in many research and clinical situations.

For PBM to be effective, the various irradiation parameters (wavelength, power, irradiance, and pulse parameters) need to lie within certain ranges and be applied for a suitable amount of time (usually minutes). These therapeutic sessions are typically applied several times (1–10 treatment sessions) at intervals ranging from twice a week to twice a day.

1.4 Irradiation Parameters

In many cases (both experimentally and clinically), it has been found in PBM that more light is not necessarily therapeutically better than less light. This somewhat unexpected relationship has been termed, alternatively, a "biphasic dose response," "Arndt–Schulz," or hormesis. Considering this response, practitioners must determine at what point the amount of light becomes too much.

LLLT can inhibit as well as stimulate, and the techniques and settings for consistently achieving these effects have not always been clearly stated. Many options exist: laser or LED, red or infrared wavelengths, a high- or low-total-power laser (with a small spot size, the latter can produce a high power density), pulses or a continuous wave, treatment twice a day or twice a month.

A systematic review of tendinopathies by Tumilty[6] found that 11 out of 20 studies failed to produce a positive result. The reason identified for the ineffective studies was that either the laser power density was too high or the treatment time was too long. If clinicians want to reduce the risks of using ineffective protocols for their patients and increase their chances of getting the best results, they need to understand the fundamentals about dosimetry. This section reviews the calculation of treatment parameters and dose, followed by the published evidence to see what works.

A biphasic dose response has been frequently observed where low levels of light have an improved ability to stimulate and repair tissues than higher levels of light. Many reports refer to stimulation of biological processes at relatively low levels of energy density or power density; the positive effect diminishes as the dose is increased, and inhibitory effects predominate eventually, which worsens clinical conditions. The so-called Arndt–Schulz curve is frequently used to describe this biphasic dose response.[7]

If the wrong irradiation parameters are used or applied for the wrong irradiation time (dose), then treatment will be ineffective. If the irradiance is too low or the time is too short, then there is likely to be no significant effect; alternatively, if the irradiance is too high or the treatment time is too long, then the benefit is lost and inhibitory effects may occur.[7,8] Many authors of research papers fail to accurately measure or even report some of these parameters. This shortcoming is due in part to a poor appreciation of the relevance of these parameters by authors and reviewers and also because some of these measurements require expensive instruments that need trained operators.[9]

As mentioned earlier, light is composed of packets of energy called photons. These photons sometimes behave like a particle and sometimes like a wave. The color of light is usually expressed by its wavelength (rather than its frequency or photon energy). LEDs and lasers are useful for PBM therapy because they produce just one wavelength or a narrow spectrum of wavelengths ($\sim \pm 1$ nm for diode lasers and up to ± 20 nm for LEDs).

Most PBM research is conducted in the red and near-infrared spectrum (630–980 nm) because these wavelengths penetrate tissue relatively easily, although some penetrate better than others. Coincidentally, these wavelengths exert some action on cytochrome c oxidase, which is usually credited as the main photo-acceptor responsible for most of the effects of PBM therapy.

Other chromophores that absorb light in this range exist (e.g., water at the upper end of this spectrum) that may also contribute to the effects of PBM.

1.5 Penetration Depth

Kendric Smith's 1991 paper[10] on photobiology fundamentals describes an experiment by Karl Norris. Broad-spectrum light was projected through a hand and was measured with a spectrophotometer that showed that red and near-infrared light (630–1100 nm) penetrated particularly well. Many other papers[11–13] have been published comparing the penetration of specific wavelengths, and all are fairly consistent with the original Karl Norris experiment.

Penetration depth is a contentious subject because many PBM product manufacturers like to claim that their system penetrates deeper than others by virtue of extra-high power or "super pulses." This metric does depend on light parameters, such as power, but the term "penetration depth" should be defined as the depth at which there is a sufficient power density to be above the threshold necessary for a therapeutic benefit. For example, the application of a 100-mW laser will deliver higher irradiance at a given depth than a 1-mW laser (assuming all other parameters are equal). The former might generate enough light (threshold) to produce a meaningful therapeutic effect at the required depth in the target tissue, whereas the latter will not, regardless of the length of the illumination time. Therefore, technically speaking, a claim such as "this system penetrates deeper than others by virtue of extra-high power" may be true.

Other factors contribute, such as increased blood perfusion in case of heating at higher average output powers, and at very high temperatures the optical properties of the tissue may change (ablation, carbonization, etc.). This means that the temperature (heating of the tissue) will ultimately be a limiting factor when increasing the power (as a means of increasing penetration depth in the tissue), as will the dose (very high power means very short treatment times to reach the same dose). However, there is some evidence that the treatment time must be longer than a certain minimum value to produce any benefit.

Fairly significant peak powers using short pulses (super pulses) can be applied without heating the tissue while at the same time keeping the average output powers similar to what lower-power continuous wave (cw) instruments would deliver. However, claims of 10-cm effective penetration with pulsed lasers are exaggerated. Different tissue types have slightly different scattering and absorption characteristics, but all of the studies produce broadly similar patterns of results.

One of the best studies on penetration was provided by Tedford et al.[13] in 2015. They performed a light-penetration study on human unfixed cadaver brain tissue at the Uniformed Services University, Bethesda, MD, USA, along with the world's leading authority on light propagation in tissue, Prof. Steve Jacques. They compared 660-nm, 808-nm, and 940-nm laser penetration. 808 nm achieved the best penetration, and they concluded that 808-nm-wavelength light penetrates the scalp, skull, meninges, and brain to a depth of approximately 40 mm. Pulsed light and continuous wave were also compared, and no differences were observed in the effective penetration depth.

The following list defines key terms:

- Wavelength (nm): Light consists of packets of electromagnetic energy that also have a wave-like property. Wavelength is expressed in nanometers (nm) and is visible from approximately 400–750 nm; beyond ~750 nm, the light is invisible. From 750–1500 nm, light is defined as near-infrared. The structure of chromophores and their redox state determine which wavelengths will be absorbed. LLLT devices are typically within the range of 600–1000 nm because there are many absorption peaks for cytochrome c oxidase in that range, they penetrate tissues better than other wavelengths, and many clinical trials have been successful with them (though not in the 700–750-nm range). Wavelengths longer than 900 nm are also absorbed by water and not just by cytochrome c oxidase (CCO). It is speculated that these longer wavelengths are also absorbed in phospholipid bilayers and cause molecular vibration sufficient to perturb ion channels and alter cellular function. If deep penetration is required (>1 cm, up to 5 cm), then wavelengths in the 690–850-nm range penetrate best.[10,14]
- Power (W): Energy (J) per second (s), peak and average when pulsed (see pulsed beam).
- Beam area (cm^2): The beam area must be known to calculate irradiance, but it is difficult to measure and frequently misreported.[9] Diode laser beams are typically not round—more often they are elliptical (unless they are derived from fiber optics), and the beams are usually brighter in the middle and gradually weaker toward the edge (Gaussian distribution). This behavior has been poorly understood by many researchers, and errors are frequently made when reporting the beam area. For example, many assume that the aperture of a device defines the beam size, but it rarely does. The correct way to measure the beam area uses a beam profiler and reports the $1/e^2$ area. This task is more appropriate for a laser engineer or physicist rather than a doctor or therapist.
- Irradiance (power density, W/cm^2): Irradiance is the power (W) divided by the beam area (cm^2). This parameter is frequently misreported because of the difficulty of measuring the beam area. Assuming that the reported parameters can be trusted, studies of beam irradiance report successful tissue repair and anti-inflammatory effects from 5–50 mW/cm^2 at the target tissue depth.[15–17] Analgesia is a different

matter; a systematic review of laboratory studies found that higher irradiances of 300–1730 mW/cm^2 are necessary to inhibit nerve conduction in C fibers and A-delta fibers.[18]

- Pulsed beam: If the beam is pulsed, then the reported power should be the average power, calculated as follows: peak power (W) × pulse width (s) × pulse frequency (Hz) = average power (W). A review[17] concluded that there is some evidence that pulsed light has effects that are different from those of cw light. However, further work is needed to define these effects for different disease conditions and pulse structures. Many laser systems produce a continuous beam only, but some produce a fixed pulse width and fixed pulse frequency. More common is a variable pulse frequency with a fixed duty cycle, e.g., a 10-Hz pulse with a 50% duty cycle has a pulse width of 1/10 × 0.5 = 0.05 s (50 ms) on and a 50-ms off period. If the pulse frequency is increased, then the average power remains constant, so a 100-mW-peak-power laser will deliver a 50-mW average power. Other duty cycles are sometimes used, e.g., 90:10, with 90% on and 10% off, so a 100-mW-peak-power laser will deliver 90 mW on average. Another common format is a fixed pulse width and variable pulse frequency, as in "super-pulsed" lasers. In this format, reducing the pulse frequency reduces the average power. For example, if the pulse is 200 ns and the frequency is 1,000 Hz, then there are 1000 pulses 200 ns long. If the peak power were 10 W, then the average power would be 10 W × 200 ns × 1000 Hz = 2-mW average power. If the pulse frequency were increased to 10,000 Hz, the average power would increase to 20 mW, and so on. Super-pulsed lasers are usually 904- or 905-nm devices. Claims of better penetration from super-pulsed lasers have been discredited.
- Coherence: Coherent light produces laser speckle, which has been postulated to play a role in the PBM interaction with cells and subcellular organelles. The dimensions of speckle patterns coincide with the dimensions of organelles such as mitochondria, and it is speculated that the intensity gradients produced by these speckles may help improve clinical effects particularly in deep tissues where irradiance is low. No definitive trials have been published to date to confirm or refute this claim.[19,20]
- Polarization: Polarized light may have different effects than otherwise identical nonpolarized light (or even 90-deg-rotated polarized light). Polarized light is rapidly scrambled in tissue (probably in the first few hundred micrometers). However, for birefringent protein structures such as collagen, the transmission of plane polarized light will depend on the orientation. Several authors have demonstrated the effects of polarized light on wound healing and burns.[21–23]
- Energy: Calculated as power (W) × time (s) = energy (J). The use of joules as an expression of dosage is potentially unreliable because it

assumes an inverse relationship between power and time, and it ignores irradiance. If a 100-mW laser is applied over two points on an Achilles tendon injury for 80 s, then 8 J has been delivered per point. What this does not indicate is the irradiance of the beam, which could cause the treatment to fail if it is too high. Systematic reviews have established that superficial tendon injuries should have a beam irradiance <100 mW/cm^2.[6,25] Unfortunately, many authors have failed to report irradiance, so the treatment effect is difficult to replicate. A second problem is that of reciprocity. If the power is doubled and the time is halved, the correct energy may be applied with different results.[16,24] To ensure the replication of a successful treatment, the same power, beam area, and time should be used. The use of more powerful lasers as a way of reducing the treatment time is not a reliable strategy.

• Fluence (energy density): Calculated as power (W) × time (s) / beam area = fluence (J/cm^2). The use of fluence as an expression of dosage is also potentially unreliable because it assumes an inverse relationship between power, time, and irradiance. Again, there is no reciprocity. If the power is doubled and the time is halved, the correct energy may be applied with different results.[16,24] If the beam area is halved, the irradiance may remain correct but the total energy applied will be halved and may not cover the whole pathology. To ensure the replication of a successful treatment, the same power, beam area, and time should be used. The use of more powerful lasers as a way of reducing the treatment time is not a reliable strategy.

• Irradiation time (s, min): Given the lack of reciprocity described earlier, the safest way to record and prescribe LLLT defines the irradiation parameters and then defines the irradiation time so as not to rely on energy or fluence parameters. Treatment times vary significantly from a few seconds to many minutes, but they are more often in the range of 30–150 s.[25,26]

• Treatment interval (h, days, weeks): The effects of different treatment intervals is underexplored at this time, although there is sufficient evidence to suggest that this is an important parameter.[17] With the exception of some early treatments of acute injuries, LLLT typically requires two or more treatments a week for several weeks to achieve clinical significance.[17]

1.6 Research in PBM/LLLT

A multidisciplinary approach to a scientific field crosses many disciplinary boundaries to create a holistic and deeper understanding of a specific subject. Photomedicine, and in particular PBM, is an absolutely multidisciplinary and collaborative field of research. In order to achieve new findings in PBM mechanisms, a team of researchers should have some expertise and knowledge about biophysics and biochemistry; new biomedical applications are developed not only by physicians but also scientists and engineers in collaboration. Conversely, the improvement and development of new devices usually has insights from scientists and clinicians. Therefore, in general, laboratory teams researching PBM comprise clinicians, scientists, and engineers from diverse backgrounds. Figure 1.4 shows a graph of the numbers of publications cited in PubMed in the field of PBM/LLLT. The first sizeable increase occurred in 2002, and there was a second notable jump in 2009.

Translational research refers to the "bench-to-bedside" enterprise of moving knowledge from basic scientific discoveries to produce new drugs, better devices, and improved treatment options for patients. Translational research, according to public health authorities, attempts to bring new treatments and research knowledge into practice for patients for whom the treatments are intended.[27] For this reason, contemporary photomedicine research perfectly fits in the paradigm of translational research because it struggles with both objectives. Although considerable efforts have been dedicated to create new devices and treatment options in order to improve PBM, another important task is to make health professionals and patients more knowledgeable about it.

1.7 Present Status

Many clinical trials and laboratory studies have consistently shown good, reproducible results in conditions and diseases where drugs and surgery are failing, but PBM has not been widely adopted by mainstream medicine. The reason for this state of affairs depends on who you ask:

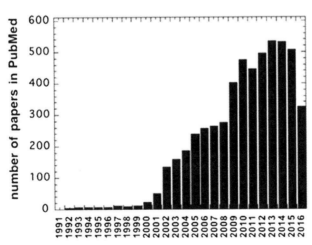

Figure 1.4 Number of PBM publications per year.

- For scientists, it is a lack of mechanism, parameters, and dose evidence;
- For doctors, it is a lack of large, clinical-trial systematic reviews;
- For hospital administrators, it is a lack of reimbursement;
- For insurers, it is a lack of cost/benefit evidence;
- For industry representatives, it is excessive marketing hype and misinformation; and
- For development professionals, it is a lack of a clear path and sufficient funding to achieve clinical approval.

The basic science research of PBM incorporates physics, chemistry, and biology. Physics encompasses light–tissue interactions, tissue optics, and light-source properties; chemistry looks at light absorption, chromophores, photomodulation of reactive oxygen species, and photochemical reactions; and biology covers cell signaling, transcription factors, and proliferation and migration in culture.

The translational research aspects of PBM concentrate on animal models of a broad range of diseases and conditions. Because medical conditions can have strong variations between different patients, it is useful that animal models can create a reproducible controlled environment for researchers. Some examples of conditions studied with animal models and treated with PBM are wound healing, pain, arthritis, inflammation, microbial infections, bone and tendon regeneration, traumatic brain injury (TBI), and some neurological diseases, such as Alzheimer's, Parkinson's, and strokes.

1.8 Clinical and Biomedical Applications of PBM

Light irradiation using a low power density has been reported as a noninvasive, noncarcinogenic, nontraumatic procedure that can provide a therapeutic benefit to many diseases and medical conditions, and that has been reported to have few (if any) side effects. In addition, PBM is used to improve human wellness with aesthetic and cosmetic applications, improvements in sports performance, and has diverse veterinary applications. The biomodulation achieved by PBM allows it to be applied in situations that can be apparently paradoxical because it can sometimes be used to stimulate cells and tissues, and in other situations it can inhibit the same biological effect. For this reason, PBM is referred to by many researchers as a regulator or modulator because it restores the organism to homeostasis. Moreover, there is considerable evidence of the systemic effects of PBM, which means that application to one site of the body can produce an improvement of a condition in another distant body part that did not receive light. Systemic effects can be explained by local effects of light that can be transferred to other sites through the circulating blood, via the lymphatic system, or via the nervous system. Moreover, the blockage of axonal nerve impulses can explain the decrease in pain sensation when PBM is delivered to specific points in the continuously connected nerve pathway from the painful site (periphery) to the central nervous system.

The stimulatory effect of PBM was used for one of the first clinical applications in wound healing because PBM promotes beneficial effects during all four phases of the wound-healing process (coagulation, inflammation, migration,[28] and remodeling[29]). These processes can be regulated by many growth factors and are connected with nitric oxide (NO) signaling. The release and production of NO can be modulated by PBM.[30]

An interesting example of the systemic effect of PBM was provided by Hopkins et al. when they conducted a randomized, triple-blind, placebo-controlled experiment wherein 22 healthy subjects had two standardized 1.27-cm^2 abrasion wounds induced on their anterior forearms. PBM (820 nm, 8 J/cm^2, 125-s duration, 700-Hz pulse rate) was applied on only one of the two randomly chosen wounds.[31] Evidence for a systemic blood (or carried by blood) effect of laser irradiation were obtained in follow-up testing (on days 6, 8, and 10) because it revealed that the laser group had smaller wounds than the sham group for both the treated and for the untreated wounds.[32]

Reduction of inflammation due to light therapy is one of the most well-accepted PBM effects.[33] It is evidenced by a decrease in chemical inflammatory mediators, such as prostaglandin E2,[31,34,35] leucocytes,[36] and tumor necrosis factor (TNFα).[37] PBM can modulate the pro-inflammatory response, increasing both the mRNA expression and the protein concentration of anti-inflammatory mediators, such as IL-10 (related to tendinitis) and heat shock protein-72 (HSP72) (related to rheumatoid arthritis). These anti-inflammatory effects are similar to the ones promoted by treatment with glucocorticoids (anti-inflammatory steroids). The anti-inflammatory and pro-inflammatory effects promoted by PBM are strong evidence that PBM acts as a homeostasis regulator in order to maintain balance between the anti- and pro-inflammatory responses.

There are many ways that PBM can decrease pain, including anti-inflammatory effects, neural blockade, stimulation of lymphatic activity, tissue repair, and reduction of muscle spasm. Each of these mechanisms has been studied in a translational manner from subcellular levels to clinical application. Lasers can relieve nociceptive and neuropathic pain by partially inhibiting nerve conduction and reducing afferent stimulation, mimicking some functions of local anesthetic injections.[29] In addition, PBM can produce a long-lasting pain decrease due to neuroplasticity, which is the capacity of neurons in both the peripheral and central nervous systems, to be modulated by increased or decreased afferent activity from the somatosensory nerves.[38] PBM has been successfully used for decreasing pain in various situations, such as arthritis, crystallopathies, tendinopathies, lateral epicondylitis, post-operative and myofascial pain, as well as muscle-skeletal pain in the neck, back, and shoulder.

Photobiomodulation with red and NIR light has been applied successfully to ameliorate disorders of the cardiovascular and respiratory systems. Oron et al.[39] showed that laser irradiation caused an increase in newly formed blood vessels six days post myocardial infarction in rats. Many functions in vascular walls are regulated by NO, including the suppression of the inflammatory response, vasodilatation, angiogenesis, inhibition of apoptosis, and cell migration.[40] The beneficial effect of PBM on lung function and the reduction of clinical symptoms have been demonstrated by blood irradiation or transcutaneous lung irradiation.[41] Recently, lasers and LED irradiation in the central nervous system have been reported to bring positive outcomes for acute and chronic strokes, traumatic brain injury, memory and mood disorders, and various neurodegenerative diseases, such as Parkinson's, Alzheimer's, and retinal degeneration.[21,22] Importantly, PBM shows no side effects in either animals or humans,[23–25] which is a much desired characteristic for a therapy carried out in the brain and central nervous system. In addition, red and NIR laser irradiation to the spinal cord have been demonstrated for treating spinal cord injuries, the restoration of traumatically injured peripheral nerves,[42] and systemic effects of PBM on crushed sciatic nerves.[43] The application of PBM associated with surgical operative procedures has been rising in importance: pre-surgery application (pre-conditioning[44]) decreases cell death and reduces wound dehiscence; PBM during the operation decreases the inflammatory process; and when used during post-operative care, can reduce the recovery time, especially in the elderly or patients with co-morbidities. These benefits can be observed even in large and complicated surgeries such as saphenectomy in diabetic patients.

Special emphasis must be given to the applications of PBM in dentistry because there is virtually no procedure in that field that will not respond positively to photobiomodulation; using a drill to prepare a restoration or an instrument for mechanical debridement starts an inflammatory response within the tissue and tooth pulp. PBM helps modulate the inflammatory response while reducing pain, making it a useful weapon in every dental practitioner's repertoire that can both ease the job of the practitioner and improve the patient's experience.

Wellness can be provided by PBM for aesthetic applications. The regeneration and stimulation effect of PBM promotes the resurfacing and rejuvenating of the skin. Moreover, it is a very well-established treatment for hair regrowth, and evidence is accumulating for fat reduction.

Sports medicine will benefit from PBM because both professional and amateur athletes can better recover from intense exercise, and the process also aids training regimens. In the near future, sport agencies must deal with "laser doping" by at least openly discussing it because the aforementioned beneficial effects and the pre-conditioning achieved by laser and LED irradiation will highly improve athletic performance.

Not less impressive is the use of PBM in veterinary medicine. PBM has been used for pets (companion animals) with essentially the same applications as mentioned for humans. In addition, it can be used to improve the reproduction of farm animals and prevent extinction of threatened species. Moreover, it is a side-effect-free treatment for injured wild animals.

LLLT/PBM is more than an alternative kind of medical treatment; it is a whole new method to control cellular processes and modulate living organisms by precise alterations in the chemistry of biomolecules. PBM enables the contemporary clinician or therapist who holds a modern and multidisciplinary outlook to fight against diseases and other disorders in both humans and other animals. Moreover, it is a possible way to stimulate or inhibit many different biological processes that occur in most (if not all) different living creatures. It could even be suggested that the photobiomodulation phenomenon is as old as life itself!

References

1. A. Einstein, "Zur Quantentheorie der Strahlung," *Physikalische Zeitschrift* **18**, 121–128 (1917).
2. T. H. Maiman, "Stimulated optical radiation in ruby," *Nature* **187**(4736), 493–494 (1960).
3. S. Koke et al., "Direct frequency comb synthesis with arbitrary offset and shot-noise-limited phase noise," *Nature Photonics* **4**, 462–465 (2010).
4. M. V. Sousa et al., "Laser scattering by transcranial rat brain illumination," *Proc. SPIE* **8427**, 842728 (2012) [doi: 10.1117/12.912616].
5. S. L. Jacques, "Optical properties of biological tissues: a review," *Phys. Med. Biol.* **58**(11), R37–61 (2013).
6. S. Tumilty et al., "Low level laser treatment of tendinopathy: a systematic review with meta-analysis," *Photomed. Laser Surgery* **28**(1), 3–16 (2010).
7. Y. Y. Huang et al., "Biphasic dose response in low level light therapy," *Dose Response* **7**(4), 358–383 (2009).
8. Y. Y. Huang et al., "Biphasic dose response in low level light therapy - an update," *Dose Response* **9**(4), 602–618 (2011).
9. P. A. Jenkins and J. D. Carroll, "How to report low-level laser therapy (LLLT)/photomedicine dose and beam parameters in clinical and laboratory studies," *Photomed. Laser Surgery* **29**(12), 785–787 (2011).
10. K. C. Smith, "The Photobiological Basis of Low Level Laser Radiation Therapy," *Laser Therapy* **3**(1), 6 (1991).
11. K. R. Byrnes et al., "Light promotes regeneration and functional recovery and alters the immune response after spinal cord injury," *Lasers Surgery Med.* **36**(3), 171–185 (2005).
12. D. E. Hudson et al., "Penetration of laser light at 808 and 980 nm in bovine tissue samples," *Photomed. Laser Surgery* **31**(4), 163–168 (2013).

13. C. E. Tedford et al., "Quantitative analysis of transcranial and intraparenchymal light penetration in human cadaver brain tissue," *Lasers Surgery Med.* **47**(4), 312–322 (2015).

14. K. C. Smith, Ed., *The Science of Photobiology*, Plenum Press, New York (1977).

15. A. P. Castano et al., "Low-level laser therapy for zymosan-induced arthritis in rats: Importance of illumination time," *Lasers Surgery Med.* **39**(6), 543–550 (2007).

16. R. J. Lanzafame et al., "Reciprocity of exposure time and irradiance on energy density during photoradiation on wound healing in a murine pressure ulcer model," *Lasers Surgery Med.* **39**(6), 534–542 (2007).

17. J. T. Hashmi et al., "Effect of Pulsing in Low-Level Light Therapy," *Lasers Surgery Med.* **42**(6), 450–466 (2010).

18. R. Chow et al., "Inhibitory effects of laser irradiation on peripheral Mammalian nerves and relevance to analgesic effects: a systematic review," *Photomed. Laser Surgery* **29**(6), 365–381 (2011).

19. A. V. Corazza et al., "Photobiomodulation on the angiogenesis of skin wounds in rats using different light sources," *Photomed. Laser Surgery* **25**(2), 102–106 (2007).

20. Z. Zalevsky and M. Belkin, "Coherence and speckle in photomedicine and photobiology." *Photomed. Laser Surgery* **29**(10), 655–656 (2011).

21. P. Iordanou et al., "Effect of polarized light in the healing process of pressure ulcers," *Int. J. Nurs. Pract.* **8**(1), 49–55 (2002).

22. C. A. Karadag et al., "The efficacy of linear polarized polychromatic light on burn wound healing: an experimental study on rats," *J. Burn Care Res.* **28**(2), 291–298 (2007).

23. A. Durovic et al., "The effects of polarized light therapy in pressure ulcer healing," *Vojnosanit. Pregl.* **65**(12), 906–912 (2008).

24. A. Schindl, B. Rosado-Schlosser, and F. Trautinger, "Reciprocity regulation in photobiology. An overview," *Hautarzt* **52**(9), 779–785 (2001).

25. J. M. Bjordal et al., "A systematic review with procedural assessments and meta-analysis of Low Level Laser Therapy in lateral elbow tendinopathy (tennis elbow)," *BMC Musculoskeletal Disorders* **9**, 75 (2008).

26. R. T. Chow et al., "Efficacy of low-level laser therapy in the management of neck pain: a systematic review and meta-analysis of randomised placebo or active-treatment controlled trials," *Lancet* **374**(9705), 1897–1908 (2009).

27. S. H. Woolf, "The meaning of translational research and why it matters," *JAMA* **299**(2), 211–213 (2008).

28. A. F. Haas et al., "Low-energy helium-neon laser irradiation increases the motility of cultured human keratinocytes," *J. Investigative Dermatol.* **94**(6), 822–826 (1990).

29. R. F. Diegelmann and M.C. Evans, "Wound healing: an overview of acute, fibrotic and delayed healing," *Front Biosci.* **9**(1), 283–289 (2004).

30. Y. Y. Huang et al., "Biphasic dose response in low level light therapy–an update," *Dose Response* **9**(4), 11-009 (2011).

31. J. Bjordal, R. Lopes-Martins, and V. Iversen, "Achilles tendinitis with microdialysis measurement of peritendinous prostaglandin E2 concentrations," *Brit. J. Sports Med.* **40**, 76–80 (2006).

32. J. T. Hopkins et al., "Low-level laser therapy facilitates superficial wound healing in humans: a triple-blind, sham-controlled study," *J. Athletic Training* **39**(3), 223 (2004).

33. R. Lopes-Martins et al., "Low level laser therapy [LLLT] in inflammatory and rheumatic diseases: a review of therapeutic mechanisms," *Current Rheumatol. Rev.* **3**(2), 147–154 (2007).

34. R. C. Pallotta et al., "Infrared (810-nm) low-level laser therapy on rat experimental knee inflammation," *Lasers Med. Sci.* **27**(1), 71–78 (2012).

35. A. P. Castano et al., "Low-level laser therapy for zymosan-induced arthritis in rats: Importance of illumination time," *Lasers Surgery Med.* **39**(6), 543–550 (2007).

36. R. C. Pallotta et al., "Infrared (810-nm) low-level laser therapy on rat experimental knee inflammation," *Lasers Med. Sci.* **27**(1), 71–78 (2012).

37. F. Aimbire et al., "Low-level laser therapy induces dose-dependent reduction of TNFα levels in acute inflammation," *Photomed. Laser Surgery* **24**(1), 33–37 (2006).

38. R. T. Chow et al., "Efficacy of low-level laser therapy in the management of neck pain: a systematic review and meta-analysis of randomised placebo or active-treatment controlled trials," *Lancet* **374**(9705), 1897–1908 (2009).

39. N. Mirsky et al., "Promotion of angiogenesis by low energy laser irradiation," *Antioxidants and Redox Signaling* **4**(5), 785–790 (2002).

40. H. Kimura and H. Esumi, "Reciprocal regulation between nitric oxide and vascular endothelial growth factor in angiogenesis," *ACTA Biochimica Polonica, English Ed.* **50**(1), 49–60 (2003).

41. F. Aimbire et al., "Effect of LLLT Ga–Al–As (685 nm) on LPS-induced inflammation of the airway and lung in the rat," *Lasers Med. Sci.* **20**(1), 11–20 (2005).

42. D. Gigo-Benato, S. Geuna, and S. Rochkind, "Phototherapy for enhancing peripheral nerve repair: a review of the literature," *Muscle and Nerve* **31**(6), 694–701 (2005).

43. S. Rochkind et al., "Systemic effects of low-power laser irradiation on the peripheral and central nervous system, cutaneous wounds, and burns," *Lasers Surgery Med.* **9**(2), 174–182 (1989).

44. T. Agrawal et al., "Pre-conditioning with low-level laser (light) therapy: light before the storm," *Dose Response* **12**(4), 619–649 (2014).

Chapter 2
History of LLLT and Photobiomodulation*

2.1 History of Photomedicine

Tracing the history of what came to be known as low-level laser therapy is an interesting challenge, perhaps because there are two distinct timelines or historical strands to be teased apart, namely, the history of light therapy and the development of the laser. The oldest of these is light therapy or photomedicine, which will be addressed first.

The history of photomedicine goes back over three thousand years to India, where sunlight was employed for therapeutic purposes, as recorded in the sacred Hindu text *Atharva Veda*, dating from 1400 BCE. Sufferers from vitiligo (a patchy depigmentation of the skin then thought to be a form of leprosy) were given certain plant extracts to eat and then exposed to the sun.[1] Starting in the 18th century, sporadic reports began to appear in the medical literature indicating that sunlight could be used to treat a wide variety of different diseases. In 1735, Fiennius[2] described a case in which he cured a cancerous growth on the lip using a sunbath. In 1774, Faure[3] reported that he successfully treated skin ulcers with sunlight, and in 1776, LePeyre and LeConte[4] found that sunlight concentrated through a lens accelerated wound healing and destroyed tumors. There were also reports that sunlight had beneficial effects on internal maladies. In 1782, Harris[2] used sunlight-exposed mollusk shells to improve a case of rickets (fragile bones due to vitamin D deficiency), In 1845, Bonnet[5] first reported that sunlight could be used to treat tuberculous arthritis (a bacterial infection of the joints).

In the second half of the 19th century, the therapeutic application of sunlight, known as heliotherapy, gradually became popular. In 1855, Rikli from Switzerland opened a clinic in Veldes (now called Bled), Slovenia for the provision of heliotherapy.[6] In 1877, Downes and Blunt[7] discovered by chance

---

*Based on material first printed in M. R. Hamblin, M. V. P. de Sousa, and T. Agarwal, Eds., *Handbook of Low-Level Laser Therapy*, Pan Stanford Publishing, Singapore (2016).

that sunlight could kill bacteria. They noted that sugar water placed on a window sill turned cloudy in the shade but remained clear while in the sun. Upon microscopic examination of the two solutions, they realized that bacteria were growing in the shaded solution but not in the one exposed to sunlight.

Theobald Adrian Palm (1848–1928) (Fig. 2.1) discovered the role of sunlight in the prevention of rickets.[8] He had worked as a doctor in Edinburgh, Scotland, where rickets was rife, and also as a missionary in Japan, where rickets was rare. He deduced that the constant pall of smoke that shrouded Edinburgh (a city known colloquially in the British Isles as "Auld Reekie") and effectively blocked the sun from reaching the population was the key difference between the two countries. Many years later, the role of sunlight exposure to the skin, in mediating the biosynthesis of vitamin D, eventually explained these observations.[9]

Nils Ryberg Finsen (1860–1904) (Fig. 2.2) was born in the Faroe Islands and studied medicine at the University of Copenhagen, qualifying in 1890. He suffered from an illness that would later be known as Niemann–Pick's disease, which is characterized by progressive thickening of the connective tissue of the liver, heart, and spleen. His discovery that sun exposure improved his own symptoms encouraged him to treat his patients with light.[10] He had particular success in 1893 when treating smallpox with red light[11] and in 1895 when treating lupus vulgaris (also known as scrofula or cutaneous tuberculosis) with what he thought was ultraviolet light from an arc lamp[12] (but was in fact probably blue light[13]). The Finsen Institute was formed in Copenhagen in 1896 and is still there today (Fig. 2.3), but it now concentrates on cancer

Figure 2.1 Theobald Adrian Palm.

Figure 2.2   Nils Ryberg Finsen.

Figure 2.3   The Finsen Institute at Rigshospitalet in Copenhagen, Denmark.

research rather than photomedicine. Finsen received the Nobel Prize for Physiology or Medicine in 1903,[10] just before his death in 1904.

Two pioneering Swiss physicians, Oskar Bernhard (1861–1939) at St. Moritz and Auguste Rollier (1874–1954) at Leysin, were responsible for extending the use of heliotherapy.[14] Solar therapy as practiced by these practitioners included increasing graduated exposures of parts of the body to sunlight, and the beneficial effects were considered to be enhanced by the fresh and cold mountain air in the Alps.

Bernhard (Fig. 2.4) obtained an impressive initial success treating a large nonhealing abdominal wound (from a knife attack) that had resisted all other accepted healing approaches and which he decided to expose to the sun as a last desperate measure. Thereafter, he treated all nonhealing and infected wounds with sunlight. He then began to treat open tuberculous cavities and, soon after, closed tuberculous foci of the bones, joints, and glands with sunlight. In 1905, Bernhard had established his own small private clinic for sunlight therapy at St. Moritz that could accommodate some 33 patients and had south-facing balconies on two of the upper floors for convenient sun exposure.

Rollier (Fig. 2.5) was born in St. Aubin in the Swiss canton of Neuchatel and graduated in medicine from Zurich and Berne. He became disillusioned with the poor results obtained by surgery for the treatment of skeletal tuberculosis and went into a rural general practice at Leysin, in the Alpes Vaudoises, where, at Bernhard's encouragement, he began to treat non-pulmonary tuberculosis with sunshine and fresh air. Over the next forty years, the technique Rollier devised for exposing the body to sunlight (Rollier's Sunlight Therapy or Heliotherapy) came to be broadly accepted in Europe.[15] His clinic, called "Les Frênes," was the first large, purpose-built sunlight-therapy facility to be constructed in the world (Fig. 2.6).

Figure 2.4 Oskar Bernhard.

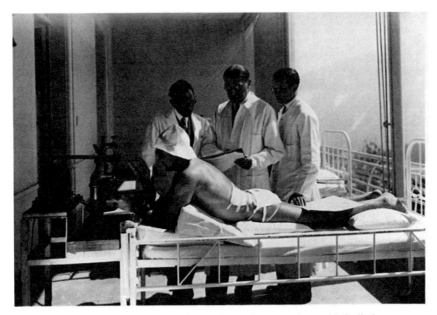

Figure 2.5   Auguste Rollier (center) treating a patient with heliotherapy.

Figure 2.6   Rollier's clinic "Les Frênes" in the Alps at Valais, Switzerland.

2.2 Development of the Laser

H.G. Wells in the *War of the Worlds* (1898) described the use of "rays of light that carry grand and mysterious powers."[16] The end of the 19th century was seen as the age of "rays or waves" with the discovery of radio, x rays, and radioactivity. A whole spectrum of electromagnetic radiation opened up, with wavelengths longer or shorter than visible light, and it was constantly speculated as to what amazing new applications might be discovered for this radiation in medicine, communications, scientific research, or warfare. In 1916, Albert Einstein (1879–1955) (Fig. 2.7), while considering the implications of the newly discovered quantum physics, predicted that electromagnetic rays could stimulate atoms to emit more rays of the same wavelength.[17] However, at that time engineers had no idea how to accomplish this interesting trick, and for decades the idea seemed merely a theoretical curiosity of no practical interest.

The triumphal celebration of the science of physics that came about in the late 1940s, after two ground-breaking advances (the discovery of radar, and the use of two atomic bombs) that had been popularly concluded to have helped the U.S. to win World War II, had a big influence both on scientists and on the general public. As the Cold War against the Soviet Union emerged in the 1950s, the U.S. government made available ever-larger funds for basic and applied physics research. With the possibility of not only military but also civilian applications, corporations and entrepreneurs added their own funds and research personnel to the national effort. Industrial and university laboratories proliferated, and the tantalizing opportunity to make further advances in physics was their main concern.

In the 1930s, before the war, it would have been theoretically possible for scientists to have built a laser because Einstein had provided the theory, and

Figure 2.7 Albert Einstein.

the necessary optical tools were already in existence. However, at that time there was no overriding reason for them to do so. This need only arrived in 1950 from an unexpected direction. Short-wavelength radio waves, called microwaves, had been used to make molecules vibrate in ways that revealed valuable structural information (a technique called microwave spectroscopy). Radar equipment left over from World War II was repurposed to provide the source of radiation.

Charles Hard Townes (1915–2015) (Fig. 2.8), who was working at Columbia University in New York, had studied molecular spectroscopy as a physicist in the 1930s, and during the war he had worked on radar as an electronics engineer. The Office of Naval Research encouraged him and other physicists to devise a way to make powerful beams of microwave radiation at ever shorter wavelengths. In 1951, he found a solution. He reasoned that inside a resonating cavity similar to the devices used to generate radar waves, the right type of atoms or molecules might generate shorter-wavelength radiation if suitably stimulated. Townes gave the problem to Herbert Zeiger, a postdoctoral student, and James P. Gordon, a graduate student. By 1954, they had the device working. Townes called it a maser, i.e., microwave amplification by stimulated emission of radiation (Fig. 2.9). As predicted by theory, the radiation was at a single wavelength, i.e., monochromatic. In Moscow, A. M. Prokhorov and N. G. Basov were working in the same direction, and they built a maser in 1955.

However, the microwaves from masers proved to be only moderately useful, more for scientific research than for military or industrial applications. A few scientists thought an infrared maser might be more important for

Figure 2.8 Charles Hard Townes.

Figure 2.9   The ammonia gas maser demonstrated in New York in 1955. Townes is on the left, and his graduate student James Power Gordon is on the right.

applications and considered how to make one. Infrared rays could not be easily manipulated like radar, and indeed, infrared optical components were largely unavailable.

Townes had been thinking about the problem intensively. In 1957, while studying the equations for amplifying radiation, he realized that much shorter visible wavelengths would be easier to deal with than longer-wavelength infrared waves. He could "skip over" the far-infrared region (which had no available optical components) to the visible region (where well-established optical techniques and components for manipulating light were readily available). Townes discussed the problem with his colleague and brother-in-law Arthur Schawlow, who worked at Bell Labs. Schawlow realized that the key feature was to contain the atoms to be stimulated in a long, narrow cavity with mirrors at each end. The light would bounce back and forth inside so that there would be increasing chances for stimulated atoms to emit more light. One of the mirrors would be only partly silvered so that some of the radiation could escape. This arrangement (a Fabry–Pérot resonator, or etalon) was already familiar to optics researchers.[18]

Figure 2.10 Gordon Gould.

The same key arrangement had also occurred to Gordon Gould (1920–2005) (Fig. 2.10), a graduate student at Columbia University, who had discussed the problem with Townes. For his thesis research with the Nobel laureate Prof. I. I. Rabi, Gould had already been working with "pumping" atoms to higher-energy states so that they would emit light. Gould realized that he was onto something far beyond the much-discussed "infrared maser." In his notebook he confidently named the yet-to-be-invented device a "laser" (light amplification by stimulated emission of radiation). In April 1959, Gould filed patent applications with his employer, the high-tech research firm TRG. Nine months earlier, Schawlow and Townes had applied for a patent on behalf of Bell Labs, which employed Schawlow on staff and Townes as a consultant. When the Bell patent was granted, Gould sued, claiming he was the first to conceive of the device. Legal battles raged for the next thirty years. In 1987, Gould and his backers began to win settlements, and one of the greatest patent wars in history was over.

Although in 1958 Gould, Schawlow, and Townes understood in principle how to build a laser, the actual construction of a working example would require a lot more work to define the correct lasing medium and the best way to pump energy into it. Over the next two years the race to make the first operating laser was in full swing.[19]

Townes at Columbia was working on potassium gas that was theoretically predicted to be an excellent lasing medium, but its corrosive properties attacked the seals, glass, and mirrors. Ali Javan at Bell Labs was trying to use a mixture of helium and neon in a long tube (an electrical discharge would excite the helium that would transfer its energy to the neon). At Westinghouse Research

Labs and at the IBM Thomas J. Watson Research Center, the idea was to use polished crystals as the resonator instead of a tube filled with gas. Peter Sorokin at IBM tried a uranium-doped calcium fluoride crystal polished to have square sides, while Irwin Wieder at Westinghouse tried to pump a synthetic ruby crystal with a tungsten lamp, but concluded "it was impossible to pump sufficient energy into a ruby." However, Theodore Maiman (1927–2007) (Fig. 2.11), working at Hughes Labs, realized that one did not necessarily need to use a continuous-wave pumping source, but instead a bright flash-lamp could have the necessary peak optical power. On May 16, 1960, after assembling a ruby crystal inside a coiled flash-lamp [Figs. 2.12(a) and (b)], the first ever pulses of red laser light were observed.[20] Within two weeks of the press conference that announced Maiman's discovery in July 1960, the groups at Bell Labs and TRG had also obtained flash-lamps like the one shown in Maiman's publicity photograph, and had replicated his device. In November 1960, Sorokin recut his calcium fluoride crystals into cylinders, and after also exciting them with a flash-lamp, he obtained laser light, while in December, Javan also finally succeeded with his HeNe laser. After years of struggle, by the end of 1960 there were suddenly three completely different types of laser systems operating in the U.S.

In the 1960s, the two previously separate themes of (a) photomedicine and (b) the newly discovered lasers gradually came together. In 1961, Leon Goldman (1906–1997) (Fig. 2.13), while working at the University of Cincinnati, started to experiment with the effect that laser beams have on the skin[21] and asked whether they could be used to remove tattoos.[22] He realized that lasers could be used to perform "bloodless surgery" and believed that high-power lasers were superior to cold steel for repairing damaged livers

Figure 2.11   Theodore Harold Maiman.

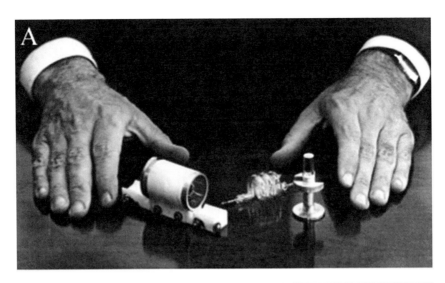

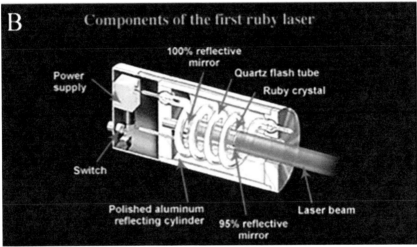

Figure 2.12 (a) Photograph of Maiman's ruby laser, and (b) schematic drawing of Maiman's ruby laser.

and debriding burn wounds.[23] Goldman was officially designated the "father of laser medicine" in 1979 at the Opto-Electronic Conference in Munich, Germany.[24] In the early 1960s, Paul McGuff (1916–2002), while working at Tufts New England Medical Center in Boston,[25] made medical history by using a laser beam to vaporize human cancer cells that had been transplanted into a hamster.[26]

2.3 Discovery of Photobiomodulation

The discovery of PBM can be attributed to Endre Mester (1903–1984) in Hungary, who has been called "the father of photobiomodulation"[27]

Figure 2.13   Leon Goldman.

Figure 2.14   Endre Mester.

(Fig. 2.14). Mester qualified in medicine at the University of Budapest, went on to become full professor and director of the 2nd Department of Surgery at Semmelweis University in Budapest, and was elected as President of the Society of Hungarian Surgeons.[27] In 1965, Mester started laser research and tried to repeat McGuff's experiments by implanting tumor cells beneath the skin of laboratory rats and exposing them to the beam of a customized ruby laser. However, the tumor cells were not destroyed by doses of what was presumed to be high-power laser energy; instead, the skin incisions made to implant the cancer cells appeared to heal faster in laser-treated animals compared to the incisions of control animals that were not treated with light.[28] Moreover, the regrowth of hair on depilated rat skin was observed to be faster after exposure to his ruby laser.[29] After being initially puzzled by these contradictory findings, he realized that his custom-designed ruby laser was much weaker than he originally thought it to be, and instead of being photo-ablative against the tumor tissue, the low-power laser light stimulated the skin to heal faster and caused the hair to regrow. This fortuitous observation (that would not have occurred if Mester had possessed a modern laser power meter) led him to make a series of experiments that showed that treatment with red light indeed produced faster healing of skin wounds. In 1968, he published the first indication of the biphasic dose response, or Arndt–Schulz effect, in a study entitled "Studies on the inhibiting and activating effects of laser beams."[30] Mester continued research into laser biostimulation until 1985 with many papers on wound healing both pre-clinical and clinical,[31–34] regeneration of muscle fibers,[35] and clinical treatment of skin necrosis.[36] In 1971, he was awarded a Scientific Doctorate by the Hungarian Academy of Sciences in recognition of his work. He had several collaborators during his laser research and clinical work, particularly his two sons: Adam Mester, M.D., a radiologist, and Andrew Mester, M.D., an otolaryngologist. They worked and published together,[37] and after Prof. Mester's death, Adam and Andrew continued to conduct laser research and clinical studies.

References

1. T. B. Fitzpatrick and M. A. Pathak, "Historical aspects of methoxsalen and other furocoumarins," *J. Invest. Dermatol.* **32**(2, Part 2), 229–31 (1959).
2. A. C. Giese, "Historical introduction," in *Photophysiology*, A. C. Giese, Editor, Academic Press: New York. 1–18 (1964).
3. E. H. Russell and W. K. Russell, *Ultraviolet Radiation and Actinotherapy*, New York: William Wood (1927).
4. A. Rollier, *Heliotherapy.* London: Oxford Medical Publishers, (1923).
5. A. Bonnet, *Traite des Maladies des Articulations.* Paris: Bailliere (1845).
6. J. Barth and U. Kohler, *Photodermatologie in Dresden-ein historischer Abriss. Festschrift anlasslich des 75. Geburtstages von Prof. Dr. Dr. Dr. h.c. H.-E. Kleine-Natrop (1917–1985).* Dresden (1992).
7. A. Downes and T. P. Blunt, "Researches on the effect of light upon bacteria and other organisms," *Proc. Royal Soc. London* **26**, 488–500 (1877).
8. T. A. Palm, "Letter to the editor," *Br. Med. J.* **2**, 1247 (1888).

9. H. F. DeLuca, "The vitamin D story: a collaborative effort of basic science and clinical medicine," *FASEB J.* **2**(3), 224–36 (1988).

10. N. R. Finsen, *Nobel Lectures, Physiology or Medicine 1901–1921*. Amsterdam: Elsevier Publishing Company (1967).

11. N. R. Finsen, "The Red Light Treatment of Small-Pox," *Br. Med. J.* **2**(1823), 1412–4 (1895).

12. N. R. Finsen, *Om Anvendelse i Medicinen af Koncentrerede Kemiske Lysstraaler*, Copenhagen, Denmark: Gyldendalske Boghandels Forlag (1896).

13. K. I. Moller et al., "How Finsen's light cured lupus vulgaris," *Photodermatol Photoimmunol Photomed* **21**(3), 118–24 (2005).

14. R. A. Hobday, "Sunlight therapy and solar architecture," *Med. Hist.* **41**(4), 455–72 (1997).

15. A. Rollier, *Heliotherapy: with special consideration of surgical tuberculosis*, London: Frowde and Hodder & Stoughton (1923).

16. D. Y. Hughes and H. M. Geduld, *A Critical Edition of The War of the Worlds: H.G. Wells's Scientific Romance*, Indianapolis, IN: Indiana University Press (1993).

17. A. Einstein, "Zur Quantentheorie der Strahlung," *Physikalische Zeitschrift* **18**, 121–128 (1917).

18. C. H. Townes, *How the Laser Happened: Adventures of a Scientist*, Oxford, UK: Oxford University Press (1999).

19. J. Hecht, *Beam: The Race to Make the Laser*, Oxford, UK: Oxford University Press (2005).

20. T. H. Maiman, "Stimulated optical radiation in ruby," *Nature* **187**(4736), 493–494 (1960).

21. L. Goldman et al., "Effect of the laser beam on the skin. Preliminary report," *J. Invest. Dermatol.* **40**, 121–2 (1963).

22. L. Goldman et al., "Radiation from a Q-Switched Ruby Laser. Effect of Repeated Impacts of Power Output of 10 Megawatts on a Tattoo of Man," *J. Invest. Dermatol.* **44**, 69–71 (1965).

23. L. Goldman and R. J. Rockwell, Jr., "Laser systems and their applications in medicine and biology," *Adv. Biomed. Eng. Med. Phys.* **1**, 317–82 (1968).

24. M. L. Geiges, "History of lasers in dermatology," *Curr. Probl. Dermatol.* **42**, 1–6 (2011).

25. P. E. McGuff et al., "Studies of the Surgical Applications of Laser (Light Amplification by Stimulated Emission of Radiation)," *Surg. Forum.* **14**, 143–5 (1963).

26. P. E. McGuff, R. A. Deterling, Jr., and L. S. Gottlieb, "Tumoricidal effect of laser energy on experimental and human malignant tumors," *N. Engl. J. Med.* **273**(9), 490–2 (1965).

27. L. Gaspar, "Professor Endre Mester, the father of photobiomodulation," *J. Laser Dentistry.* **17**, 146–148 (2009).
28. E. Mester et al., "The simulating effect of low power laser rays on biological systems," *Laser Rev.* **1**, 3 (1968).
29. E. Mester, B. Szende, and P. Gartner, "The effect of laser beams on the growth of hair in mice," *Radiobiol Radiother (Berl)* **9**(5), 621–6 (1968).
30. E. Mester et al., "Studies on the inhibiting and activating effects of laser beams," *Langenbecks Arch. Chir.* **322**, 1022–7 (1968).
31. E. Mester et al., "Laser stimulation of wound healing," *Acta. Chir. Acad. Sci. Hung.* **17**(1), 49–55 (1976).
32. I. B. Kovacs, E. Mester, and P. Gorog, "Stimulation of wound healing with laser beam in the rat," *Experientia* **30**(11), 1275–6 (1974).
33. E. Mester, T. Spiry, and B. Szende, "Effect of laser rays on wound healing," *Bull. Soc. Int. Chir.* **32**(2), 169–73 (1973).
34. E. Mester et al., "Stimulation of wound healing by means of laser rays. (Clinical and electron microscopical study)," *Acta. Chir. Acad. Sci. Hung.* **14**(4), 347–56 (1973).
35. E. Mester et al., "The effect of laser irradiation on the regeneration of muscle fibers (preliminary report)," *Z. Exp. Chir.* **8**(4), 258–62 (1975).
36. E. Mester et al., "Laser treatment of coumarin-induced skin necrosis," *Acta. Chir. Acad. Sci. Hung.* **18**(2), 141–8 (1977).
37. E. Mester, A. F. Mester, and A. Mester, "The biomedical effects of laser application," *Lasers Surg. Med.* **5**(1), 31–9 (1985).

Chapter 3
Molecular Mechanisms of LLLT*

3.1 Chromophores

3.1.1 Cytochrome c oxidase

Cytochrome c oxidase (CCO) is the terminal enzyme of the electron transport chain that mediates the electron transfer from cytochrome c to molecular oxygen. Several lines of evidence show that CCO acts as a photoacceptor and transducer of photosignals in the red and NIR regions of the light spectrum.[1] It seems that LLLT increases the availability of electrons for the reduction of molecular oxygen in the catalytic center of CCO, which increases the mitochondrial membrane potential (MMP) and the levels of ATP, cAMP, and ROS, as well.[2]

LLLT increases the activity of complexes I, II, III, and IV, and succinate dehydrogenase in the electron transfer chain. CCO is known as complex IV and, as mentioned before, appears to be the primary photoacceptor. This assumption is supported by the increased oxygen consumption during low-level light irradiation (the majority of the oxygen consumption of a cell occurs at complex IV in the mitochondria) and by the fact that sodium azide, a CCO inhibitor, prevents the beneficial effect of LLLT. Besides ATP and cAMP, the nitric oxide (NO) level is increased, either by being released from metal complexes in CCO (CCO has two heme and two copper centers) or by up-regulation of the activity of CCO as a nitrite reductase.[3]

3.1.2 Retrograde mitochondrial signaling

One of the most accepted mechanisms for light–cell interaction was proposed by Karu,[4] referring to the retrograde mitochondrial signaling that occurs with light activation in the visible and infrared range (Fig. 3.1). According to Karu, the first step is the absorption of a photon with energy $h\nu$ by the chromophore CCO. This interaction increases the mitochondrial membrane potential

---

*Based on material first printed in L. F. de Freitas and M. R. Hamblin, "Proposed mechanisms of photobiomodulation or low-level light therapy," *J. Selected Topics Quant. Electron.* **22**(3), 348–364 (2016).

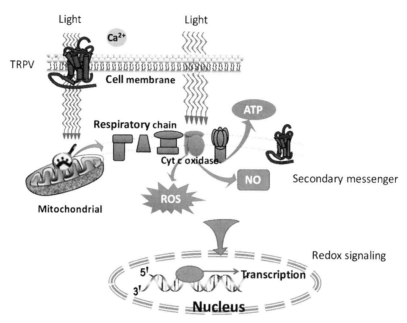

Figure 3.1   Cellular mitochondrial mechanism of PBM.

($\Delta\Psi$m), causing an increase in the synthesis of ATP and changes in the concentrations of reactive oxygen species (ROS) Ca^{2+} and NO. Furthermore, there is a communication between mitochondria and the nucleus, driven by changes in the mitochondria ultrastructure, i.e., changes in the fission–fusion homeostasis in a dynamic mitochondrial network. The alteration in the mitochondrial ultrastructure induces changes in ATP synthesis, in the intracellular redox potential, in the pH, and in cyclic adenosine monophosphate (cAMP) levels. Activator protein-1 (AP1) and NF-κB have their activities altered by changes in membrane permeability and ion flux at the cell membrane. Some complementary routes were also suggested by Karu, such as the direct up-regulation of some genes.[5]

3.1.3 Light-sensitive ion channels

The most well-known ion channels that can be directly gated by light are the channelrhodopsins (ChRs), which are seven-transmembrane-domain proteins that can be naturally found in algae, providing them with light perception. Once activated by light, these cation channels open and depolarize the membrane. They are currently being applied in neuroscientific research in the new discipline of optogenetics.[6]

However, members of another broad group of ion channels are now known to be light sensitive.[7] These channels are called "transient receptor potential" (TRP) channels because they were first discovered in a Drosophila mutant.[7] TRP channels are responsible for vision in insects. There are now known to be at least 50 different TRP isoforms distributed amongst seven subfamilies:[8] the TRPC ("canonical"), TRPV ("vanilloid"), TRPM ("melastatin"), TRPP ("polycystin"), TRPML ("mucolipin"), TRPA ("ankyrin"), and TRPN ("NOMPC") subfamilies (see Fig. 3.2). A wide range of stimuli modulate the activity of different TRPs, such as light, heat, cold, sound, noxious chemicals, mechanical forces, hormones, neurotransmitters, spices, and voltage. TRPs are calcium channels modulated by phosphoinositides.[9] The evidence that light-mediated activation of TRP is responsible for some of the mechanisms of action of LLLT is somewhat sparse at present but slowly mounting.

Mast cells are known to accumulate at the site of skin wounds, and there is some degree of evidence suggesting that these cells play a role in the biological effects of laser irradiation in promoting wound healing. Yang and co-workers demonstrated that after laser irradiation (532 nm), the intracellular $[Ca^{2+}]$ was increased, and, as a consequence, there was a release of histamine. If the TRPV4 inhibitor ruthenium red was used, the histamine release was blocked, indicating the central role of these channels in promoting histamine-dependent wound healing after laser irradiation.[10]

It seems that TRPV1 ion channels are involved in the degranulation of mast cells and laser-induced mast cell activation. It was demonstrated that capsaicin, temperatures above 42°C, and acidic pH could induce the expression of TRPV1 in oocytes, and these ion channels can be activated by green light (532 nm) in a power-dependent manner (although blue and red

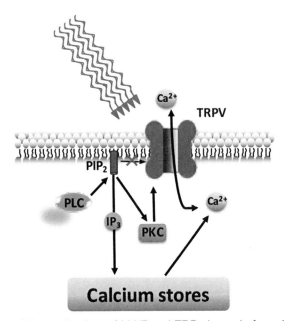

Figure 3.2 Possible mechanism of LLLT and TRP channels for calcium signaling.

light were not able to activate them).[11] Infrared light (2,780 nm) attenuates TRVP1 activation by capsaicin in cultured neurons, decreasing the generation of pain stimuli. TRPV4 is also attenuated by laser light, but the anti-nociceptive effect was less intense; therefore, the anti-nociception in this model is mainly dependent on TRPV1 inhibition.[12] The stimulation of neurons with pulsed infrared light (1,875 nm) can generate laser-evoked neuronal voltage variations, and, in this case, TRPV4 channels were demonstrated to be the primary effectors of the chain reaction activated by the laser,[13] as shown in Fig 3.2.

3.1.4 Direct cell-free light-mediated effects on molecules

There have been some scattered reports that light can have effects on some important molecules in cell-free systems (in addition to the established effect on CCO). The latent form of transforming growth factor beta has been reported to be activated by light exposure.[14] Superoxide dismutase (Cu, Zn) from bovine erythrocytes that had been inactivated by exposure to pH 5.9 was reactivated by exposure to HeNe laser light (632.7 nm).[15] The same treatment also reactivated the heme-containing catalase. Amat et al. showed that irradiation of ATP in solution by 655-nm or 830-nm light appeared to produce changes in its enzyme reactivity, fluorescence, and Mg^{2+} binding capacity.[16] However, other researchers were unable to repeat this somewhat surprising result.[17]

3.2 Signaling Molecules

3.2.1 Adenosine triphosphate

An increase in intracellular ATP is one of the most frequent and significant findings after LLLT both *in vitro* and *in vivo*.[18] The stimulated synthesis of ATP is caused by an increased activity of CCO when activated by light. According to Ferraresi et al.,[19] increased CCO activity is the mechanism of enhanced muscle performance when LLLT is performed before various types of exercises, for example. The authors found increased ATP synthesis after LED (850 ± 20 nm and 630 ± 10 nm) therapy in different muscles (one with a predominantly aerobic metabolism, and the other with mixed aerobic and glycolytic metabolism), unlike some previous data from Hayworth et al.[20]

Extracellular ATP participates in a wide array of signaling pathways, known as purinergic signaling.[21] Originally discovered by Burnstock[22] as a nonadrenergic, noncholinergic neurotransmitter, ATP purinergic signaling is mediated by P2Y G-protein-coupled receptors and P2X ligand-gated ion channels.[23] ATP can be hydrolyzed to adenosine that conducts signals via the P1 G-protein-coupled receptor.[24] At the time of publication, the authors are not aware of any studies that specifically show that extracellular (as opposed to intracellular) ATP or adenosine can be stimulated by LLLT.

3.2.2 Cyclic AMP

Several workers have shown an increase in adenosine-3′,5′-cyclic-monophosphate (cAMP) after LLLT.[25,26] Although it is tempting to suppose that this increase in cAMP is a direct consequence of the rise in ATP caused by light, firm evidence for this connection is lacking. It has been reported that cAMP-elevating agents, i.e., prostaglandin E_2, inhibit the synthesis of TNF and, therefore, down-regulate the inflammatory process. Lima and co-authors investigated the signaling pathways responsible for the anti-inflammatory action of LLLT (660 nm, 4.5 J cm^{-2}) in the lungs and airways. They found reduced TNF levels in the treated tissue, probably because of an increase in cAMP levels. Furthermore, the authors demonstrated that the inflammation caused by LPS or TNF in mice lungs was inhibited by cAMP-elevating agents. Rolipram, a cAMP-elevating agent, acts through inhibition of the enzyme phosphodiesterase, but it does not share this mechanism with low-level light.[25]

cAMP exerts its cellular effects via activation of three different kinds of sensors: cAMP-dependent protein kinase A (PKA), which phosphorylates and activates the cAMP-response element-binding protein (CREB), which then binds to the CRE domain on DNA and in turn activates genes,[27] cyclic nucleotide-gated channels (CNGCs),[28] and exchange proteins directly activated by cAMP (Epac).[29]

3.2.3 Reactive oxygen species

It has been shown that LLLT can produce mitochondrial ROS, leading to activation of the transcription factor nuclear factor kappa B (NF-κB), which can act as a redox-sensor. The fact that the addition of anti-oxidants inhibits the activation of NF-κB by 810-nm light reinforces this assumption.[30]

ROS are one of the classic "Janus-face" mediators: beneficial at low concentrations and brief exposures, but harmful at high concentrations and chronic long-term exposures.[31] ROS are produced at a low level by normal mitochondrial metabolism[32] The concept of mitohormesis was introduced to describe the beneficial of low, controlled amounts of oxidative stress in the mitochondria.[33] However, when the MMP is altered either upward or downward, the amount of ROS is increased. In normal cells, the absorption of light by CCO leads to an increase in MMP, and a short burst of ROS is produced. However, when the MMP is low because of pre-existing oxidative stress,[34] excitotoxicity,[35] or inhibition of electron transport,[34] light absorption leads to an increase in MMP toward normal levels, and the production of ROS is lowered.

There are many different cellular systems that are designed by evolution to detect excessive levels of ROS and activate transcription factors to produce extra levels of antioxidant defenses.[36] Hydrogen peroxide and lipid hydroperoxides[37] are thought to be the ROS most likely to carry out beneficial redox signaling by reversible oxidation of cysteine thiols in the sensor protein.

3.2.4 Calcium

Changes in the mitochondrial ultrastructure may lead to alterations in calcium (Ca^{2+}) concentration. The increment might be a result of Ca^{2+} influx from the extracellular environment and gated by the Ca^{2+} channel TRPV. There is evidence that cytosolic alkalinization can facilitate the opening of TRPV channels, and because laser irradiation can induce cellular alkalinization, LLLT could induce TRPV opening and a consequent Ca^{2+} influx. In mast cells, this Ca^{2+} influx can mediate histamine release.[38] However, it is also possible that light can directly activate TRPV channels as discussed above. LLLT usually leads to an increase in intracellular Ca^{2+}, as shown by fluorescent probes.[39] When intracellular Ca^{2+} levels have been artificially raised (for instance, by causing excitotoxicity with excess glutamate), then LLLT can produce a drop in intracellular calcium and protect the neurons from dying.[35] The increase in calcium seen after LLLT could also be a result of the release of Ca^{2+} from intracellular stores.[40]

Calcium-sensitive signaling pathways are too numerous to cover in detail here, but they include calcium-sensitive enzymes such as protein kinase C (PKC), calcium-calmodulin-dependent kinase II (CamKII) and calcineurin (CaCN),[41] the extracellular calcium-sensing receptor (CaSR),[42] mitochondrial calcium signaling,[43] and calcium-sensitive adenylyl cyclase,[44] among others.

3.2.5 Nitric oxide

As mentioned earlier, NO is often produced after LLLT.[45] NO is a well-known vasodilator that acts via stimulation of soluble guanylate cyclase to form cyclic-GMP (cGMP). cGMP activates protein kinase G, which causes re-uptake of Ca^{2+} and the opening of calcium-activated potassium channels. The fall in concentration of Ca^{2+} prevents myosin light-chain kinase (MLCK) from phosphorylating the myosin molecule, leading to relaxation of the smooth muscle cells in the lining of blood vessels and lymphatic vessels.[46] There are several other mechanisms by which NO could conduct signaling pathways, including the activation of iron-regulatory factor in macrophages,[47] modulation of proteins such as ribonucleotide reductase[48] and aconitase,[49] stimulating the ADP-ribosylation of glyceraldehyde-3-phosphate dehydrogenase,[50] and protein-sulfhydryl-group nitrosylation.[51]

3.3 Activation of Transcription Factors

3.3.1 Nuclear factor kappa B

NF-κB is a transcription factor that regulates the expression of various genes related to many cellular functions, i.e., inflammatory and stress-induced responses and survival. Its activity is regulated by a negative feedback mediated by an inhibitor called IκB, which binds to NF-κB to deactivate it, or it can undergo ubiquitination and undergo proteasomal degradation in order to release NF-κB. The transcription factor, then, can be translocated to the nucleus and promote gene transcription. Several lines of evidence reveal that NF-κB is redox sensitive because ROS can directly activate it, or, alternatively, ROS could be involved in the indirect activation of NF-κB via TNFalpha, interleukin-1 (IL-1), and phorbol esters. LLLT can boost ROS generation, and it was shown that light irradiation can induce NF-κB activation.[30]

The increased NF-κB production after LLLT stimuli leads to enhanced gene transcription that leads to cell proliferation, cell migration,[52] reduced cell death, and enhanced neurological function.

If the total energy density delivered is too high, however, the injury paradoxically tends to be exacerbated by increased oxidative stress and the overabundant activation of NF-κB. The biphasic dose effects of LLLT are thought to occur due to the excessive generation of ROS, excessive production of NO, activation of some cytotoxic pathways, and excessive NFκB activation.[53] In addition, if the tissue is stressed or ischemic, mitochondria can synthesize NO that can displace oxygen from binding to CCO, but this behavior leads to reduced ATP synthesis and increased oxidative stress that can lead to inflammation when NF-κB is activated.[54]

Classical mitochondrial inhibitors such as rotenone are known to decrease mitochondrial ATP levels, produce ROS, and activate NF-κB. Low-level light still produces ROS and activates NF-κB, but in this case it increases ATP levels. Anti-oxidants do not inhibit this ATP increase, suggesting that light augments the electron transport and potentially causes electron leakage (in the absence of anti-oxidants) and superoxide production.[30]

3.3.2 RANKL

Receptor activator of nuclear factor kappa-B ligand (RANKL) is a transmembrane protein member of the TNF superfamily that is involved in bone regeneration and remodeling (acting on osteoclast differentiation and activation). It is also a ligand for osteoprotegerin (OPG). The RANKL/OPG ratio determines whether bone is removed or formed during the remodeling process. The remodeling cycle consists of the increase in the expression of RANKL by osteoblasts and the subsequent binding to the RANK receptor, which is highly expressed on osteoclastic membrane. This behavior causes an expansion of the osteoclast progenitor pool, differentiation into mononucleated progenitor cells, increased survival, fusion into multinucleated osteoclasts, and, finally, their activation. Osteoblasts can modulate this process by expressing OPG, which is a secretory soluble receptor and inhibitor of RANK receptor.

Parenti et al. investigated the RANKL/OPG ratio in osteoblast-like cells that were irradiated with a GaAlAs laser (915 nm) using doses of $1–50\ J\ cm^{-2}$. Although the differences were not statistically significant, there was a trend for a rapid and transitory increase in the RANKL/OPG ratio for all the tested doses. It seems that this ratio after LLLT depends on the tissue and on the parameters used because there is evidence of an increase in the RANKL/OPG ratio in human alveolar-bone-derived cells irradiated with 780-nm light, while the results were the opposite in rat calvarial cells irradiated with 650-nm light.[55]

3.3.3 Hypoxia-inducible factor

Hypoxia-inducible factor (HIF-1α) is a protein involved in cellular adaptation to hypoxia. It is stabilized at low oxygen tensions, but in the presence of higher oxygen concentrations it is rapidly degraded by prolyl hydroxylase enzymes, which are oxygen dependent. HIF-1α activates genes that are important to the cellular response to hypoxic conditions, such as vascular endothelial growth factor (VEGF), VEGF-receptor, glucose carrier (GLUT-1), and phosphoglycerate kinase (PGK) genes. Because there are no significant changes in the gross tissue oxygen concentration during LLLT, HIF-1α activation can be mediated by the mitogen-activated protein kinase (MAPK) and phosphatidylinositol 3-kinase (PI3K)/Akt signaling pathway, by growth factors, or by cytokines.[56] Another possible explanation is that the sudden boost in cellular respiration caused by the light activation of CCO depletes the low amount of oxygen that is present in hypoxic tissues but that is not rapidly consumed because of inhibited electron transport. This sudden oxygen depletion then rapidly activates HIF-1α.

Cury demonstrated the pro-angiogenic effect of LLLT using 660-nm and 780-nm light on skin flaps in rats. He observed that angiogenesis was induced by an increase in HIF-1α and VEGF expression, as well as by a decrease in matrix metalloproteinase 2 (MMP-2) activity.[56] Cury observed that only 660-nm light was able to increase HIF-1α expression, and although VEGF induction occurred in all light doses used, only 40 J cm^{-2} was able to induce angiogenesis, as well as an increase in MMP-2 activity.

3.3.4 Akt/GSK3β/β-catenin pathway

Low-level light may exert a pro-survival effect on cells via the activation of the AKT/GSK3β/β-catenin pathway. Basically, protein kinase B (also known as AKT) can be activated by LLL irradiation and then interact with glycogen synthasekinase 3β (GSK3β), inhibiting its activity. GSK3B is a serine-threoninekinase that mediates various cellular signaling pathways, exerts metabolic control, influences embryogenesis, and is involved in cell death and oncogenesis. There is evidence that this kinase is involved in the pathogenesis of Alzheimer's disease because it promotes hyperphosphorylation of the tau protein and causes the formation of neurofibrillary tangles (NTFs)—both classic hallmarks of this disease.

The decreased activity of GSK3β is due to the fact that LLLT-activated AKT increases the phosphorylation level of its Ser9 residue, which allows the N-terminus of GSK3β to bind with its own binding site. This behavior leads to an accumulation of β-catenin and its translocation to the nucleus, where it can exert its pro-survival action. β-catenin is an important component of the Wnt signaling pathway, responsible for the inhibition of axin-madiated β-cateninphosphorylation by GSK3β. This trait helps to stabilize the under-phosphorylated form of β-catenin and ensure that it is no longer marked for proteasome degradation, so it can accumulate and travel to the nucleus. Once there, the pro-survival action of β-catenin relies on the increased TCF/LEF-dependent transcriptional activity. This pro-survival effect can be useful in the treatment of neurodegenerative diseases, such as Alzheimer's.[57]

One of the most important regulators of apoptosis is Bax, a member of the Bcl-2 family. It is translocated from the cytosol to the mitochondria when a pro-apoptotic stimulus is present, and this translocation is inhibited by LLLT, according to Zhang et al. The authors hypothesized that GSK3β is the mediator between Akt and Bax during the LLLT anti-apoptotic process. The authors found that GSK3β interacts with Bax and activates it, promoting its translocation directly, but LLLT activates Akt, which inhibits the activation of GSK3β and thus inhibits Bax translocation. By using inhibitor compounds such as wortmannin and lithium chloride, there was a significant inhibition of the anti-apoptotic effect observed after LLLT, suggesting that PI3K/Akt pathway (inhibited by wortmannin) and GSK3β translocation (inhibited by lithium chloride) play a key role in the protection against apoptosis caused by low-level light. LiCl, however, was not able to reduce Bax translocation and apoptosis like LLLT, so there must be other upstream regulators of Bax translocation during apoptosis. In conclusion, LLLT exerted a pro-survival action by selectively activating the PI3K/Akt pathway and suppressing the GSK3β/Bax pathway.[58]

3.3.5 Akt/mTOR/CyclinD1 pathway

LLLT has been demonstrated to be useful for stimulating the proliferation of normal cells, but for dysplastic and malignant cells it could be dangerous. Sperandio et al.[59] provided an example of this situation, observing that oral dysplastic cells, considered pre-malignant, had their viability increased after LLLT (660 or 780 nm, 2–6 J cm^{-2}). Moreover, these workers showed higher expression of proteins related to cancer progression and invasion, i.e., Akt, HSP90, pS6$_{ser240/244}$, and Cyclin D1. The data suggest that the Akt/mTOR/Cyclin D1 pathway is important for this phenotype differentiation because the tested oral cancer cells showed higher levels of the signaling mediators that are part of this pathway.

3.3.6 ERK/FOXM1

Fork-head box protein M1 (FOXM1) is a protein involved in the regulation of the transition from the G1 to the S phase of the cell cycle and the progression to mitotic division. Ling et al.[60] investigated the protective effect of LLLT using red light at 632.8 nm against senescence caused by UV light, and reported an activation of the ERK/FOXM1 pathway that caused a reduction in the expression of the p21 protein and G1 phase arrest. Senescence was attenuated by over-expression of FOXM1c with or without LLLT, and if FOXM1 was inhibited by shRNA, the effect of LLLT in reducing cell senescence was abrogated. LLLT promoted the nuclear translocation of extracellular signal-regulated kinase (ERK), increasing FOXM1 accumulation in the nucleus, and the transactivation of c-Myc and p21 expression.

Inhibition of the mitogen-activated kinase (MEK)/ERK pathway with a MEK inhibitor PD98059 prevented the nuclear translocation of FOXM1 after LLLT, suggesting that Raf/MEK/MAPK/ERK signaling is crucial for the anti-cell senescence effect of LLLT mediated by FOXM1.[60]

3.3.7 PPARy

Peroxisome proliferator-activated receptors (PPAR) are mostly present in airway epithelial cells, but also in smooth muscle cells, myofibroblasts, endothelial cells of the pulmonary vasculature and in inflammatory cells such as alveolar macrophages, neutrophils, eosinophils, lymphocytes and mast cells. They are nuclear receptors with transcription factors that regulate gene expression. PPAR-y is involved in the generation of heat shock protein 70 (HSP-70), which is anti-inflammatory, while PPAR-c expression occurs due to an inflammatory response and are associated with massive lung injury and neutrophil infiltration in lungs of mice subjected to endotoxic shock (61).

Lima and co-authors reported a study in which rats were irradiated with 660-nm light (5.4 J) on the skin over the bronchus (chest). They observed a marked rise in the expression of PPAR mRNA after LLLT, as well as increased PPAR-y activity in bronchoalveolar lavage (BALF) cells from animals subjected to laser treatment. In conclusion, Lima proposed that LLLT can work as a homeostatic facilitator, increasing the expression of a transcription factor that is signaling the synthesis of HSP70 and other anti-inflammatory proteins.[61]

3.3.8 RUNX2

Runt-related transcription factor 2 (RUNX-2) is related to osteoblastic differentiation and skeletal morphogenesis, acting as a scaffold for nucleic acids and regulatory factors that are involved in the expression of skeletal-related genes. It regulates the expression of genes related to extracellular matrix components during bone cell proliferation. LLLT can increase the expression of RUNX-2, contributing to a better tissue organization, even in diabetic animals as seen by Patrocínio-Silva.[62]

3.4 Effector Molecules

3.4.1 Transforming growth factor

Transforming growth factor (TGF-β) is a strong stimulator of collagen production, inducing the expression of extracellular matrix components and inhibiting its degradation by inhibiting MMPs. TGF-β expression is elevated during the initial phase of inflammation after an injury and stimulates cellular migration, proliferation, and interactions within the repair zone.[63]

Dang and co-workers[64] suggested that the TGF-β/SMAD signaling pathway might play a role in LLLT used for nonablative rejuvenation. They found that 800-nm diode laser irradiation was able to induce collagen synthesis through the activation of TGF-β/SMAD pathway in a light dose-dependent manner. 40 J cm^{-2} was the most effective light dose in enhancing the gene expression of procollagen type I and IV, compared to 20 and 60 J cm^{-2}. The dermal thickness followed the results for the synthesis of collagen, demonstrating that this process was indeed dose-dependent.[64]

Aliodoust et al.[63] treated rats with 632.8-nm light and observed increased expression of TGF-β1 (one of the three isoforms of TGF-β) mRNA. TGF-β1 is responsible for the initial scar tissue formed at the wound site. It enhances tendon repair during the fibrosis period via the stimulation of cell proliferation and migration, as well as the synthesis of collagen and proteoglycans.

3.4.2 Oxidative stress

The inflammatory process involves an increase in ROS and RNS production, accompanied by a reduction in the activity of antioxidant defenses. This oxidative stress situation can activate NF-κB, as mentioned before, leading to modifications in the expression of genes for pro-inflammatory cytokines, growth factors, chemokines, and adhesion molecules.

Assis et al.[65] investigated the effects of LLLT on muscle injury using 808-nm light (1.4 J), and they observed reduced lipid peroxidation accompanied by a decreased CCO-2 mRNA expression and an increased SOD mRNA expression after irradiation. There was a reduced formation of nitrotyrosine, indicating that iNOS activity was lower, and, consequently, NO and peroxynitrite production was decreased. In conclusion, the inhibition of oxidative and nitrosative stress contributed to a decrease in the deleterious effects observed after muscle injury.[65]

3.4.3 Pro- and anti-inflammatory cytokines

Many cytokines and inflammatory mediators have their levels altered by low-level light irradiation, regardless if they have pro- or anti-inflammatory actions, i.e., TNF, various interleukins, histamine, TGF-β, prostaglandins, and eicosanoids. It seems that when inflammation is present, LLLT exerts an anti-inflammatory action, but in the absence of inflammation, LLLT provides pro-inflammatory mediators that could help with tissue remodeling and mediate cell function. Wu and co-workers[38] investigated the photoacceptor role of CCO and found that the excitation of CCO initiates a photoreaction that results in histamine release *in vitro*. The induced signals from mitochondria to cytosol cause alkalinization of the cytosol, which leads to the opening of TRPV channels. This behavior results in an increment of $[Ca^{2+}]$ and, consequently, an enhanced histamine release.[38] Chen[66] demonstrated in 2014 that an increased calcium influx occurred in mast cells after laser irradiation, which caused histamine release that could help promote wound healing. Furthermore, he found that during short-term muscle remodeling after cryoinjury, cytokine expression is also modulated by LLLT, leading to a decreased expression of TNFalpha and TGF-β.[66]

Although NF-κB activation is known to be pro-inflammatory, LLLT has a pronounced anti-inflammatory activity, even with NF-κB activation. In fact, the anti-inflammatory effects of LLLT could be abrogated if a NF-κB inhibitor is used. This response probably occurs because the initial response to cell stress typical of NF-κB activation triggers another response to lower NF-κB activation after LLLT had its therapeutic effect. Another possibility is that the initial pro-inflammatory response induced by LLLT leads to the expression of eicosanoids that are able to decrease and to end inflammation.[66]

3.4.4 Brain-derived neurotrophic factor

BDNF is part of the family of neurotrophins, molecules that exert actions on nerve cells. BDNF, specifically, seems to modulate the dendritic structure and potentiate synaptic transmission in the CNS. In order to investigate the effects of low-level light on BDNF levels, Meng et al.[67] treated nerve cells with 632.8-nm light (doses from 0.5–4 J cm^{-2}). There was a regulatory role of LLLT in neuroprotection and dendritic morphogenesis. LLLT attenuated the decrease of BDNF, apparently by the ERK/CREB pathway, which could be useful in the treatment of neurodegenerative disorders.[67]

3.4.5 Vascular endothelial growth factor

Angiogenesis is a complex mechanism that requires several cell types, mediators, and signaling pathways. It is initiated by cell migration and the invasion of endothelial cells, subsequent lumen formation, connection of new vascular segments with pre-existing ones, and finally, remodeling of the extracellular matrix. This remodeling is dependent on adequate MMP activity. VEGF and HIF-1α are critical to the angiogenic process.

LLLT has been reported to induce angiogenesis in several experimental models. For example, Cury et al.[56] observed a marked increase in the number of vessels in the skin flap of animals treated with 660- and 780-nm LLLT, alongside a marked increase in VEGF mRNA expression.[56]

3.4.6 Hepatocyte growth factor

HGF is a cytokine that regulates cell proliferation, motility, and morphogenesis, and it exerts anti-apoptotic and anti-inflammatory activity during hepatic regeneration. The activation of its transmembrane tyrosine kinase receptor, called the Met receptor, leads to autophosphorylation of tyrosine residues and phosphorylation of downstream signaling molecules, such as PI3K and MAPK pathway proteins. Araújo and co-workers[68] observed that, after 632.8-nm LLLT, hepatectomized animals showed an increase in the expression of HGF followed by increased phosphorylation of Met and its downstream signaling molecules Akt and ERK. This behavior indicates that LLLT could enhance liver regeneration after hepatectomy.[68]

3.4.7 Basic fibroblast growth factor and keratinocyte growth factor

Growth factors play a key role in the wound-healing process, mediating the transfer of signals between the epithelium and the connective tissue, especially bFGF and KGF. bFGF is known to be a potent mitogen and chemoattractant for endothelial cells and fibroblasts; it also accelerates the formation of granulation tissue and induces re-epithelization. KGF is produced by fibroblasts and exerts a paracrine action on keratinocytes. Therefore, it is responsible for the proliferation and migration of epithelial cells, as well as the maintenance of the epithelium normal structure.

When gingival fibroblasts from a primary culture were irradiated twice with 660- or 780-nm low-level light in a study by Damante et al.,[69] the production of KGF and bFGF was increased. Red light was more effective at stimulating KGF production, but no significant change in bFGF production was produced. NIR light, however, was capable of inducing bFGF release.[69] These results could explain how LLLT can help the wound-healing process.

3.4.8 Heat-shock proteins

Heat-shock protein 27 (HSP27) is an important member of the small HSP family, with an ATP-independent chaperone activity that is produced in response to oxidative stress in order to modulate inflammation and regulate the dynamics of the actin cytoskeleton. When HSP27 is activated, it facilitates the phosphorylation of IκB, causing it to be degraded in the proteasome and increase NF-κB activity. It also contributes to the regulation of NO and ROS production, iNOS expression, and TNF secretion. However, HSP27 plays a negative role in TNF-mediated IκB kinase (IKK) activation. The results of a study performed by Lim and co-workers[70] with HSP27-silenced cells showed that 635-nm light irradiation was not able to decrease ROS generation if

HSP27 was not present, indicating that this chaperone plays an important role in decreasing ROS during inflammation and LLLT.[70]

HSP70 is part of the normal wound-healing process, alongside IL-6 and TGF-β1. Visible (532 nm) and NIR (815 nm) light have been demonstrated to induce HSP70 expression in treated skin cells, which is important for skin-rejuvenating interventions because there is a consequent effect involving the correct folding and transport of newly synthesized collagen.[64]

HSP90 is another chaperone, which assists the maturation of Akt and enables it to perform its downstream actions. Increased activity of chaperones is not desired in cancer, but it could be useful in healing processes. Sperandio et al.[59] found higher levels of HSP90 in laser-treated cells, and an isoform of this chaperone, HSP90N (which has an oncogenic potential), was found in the experimental groups. This isoform is commonly overexpressed in tumoral tissues and is secreted by advanced stages of melanoma.[59]

References

1. T. I. Karu, "Multiple roles of cytochrome c oxidase in mammalian cells under action of red and IR-A radiation," *IUBMB Life* **62**(8), 607–10 (2010).

2. S. Wu, F. Zhou, Y. Wei, W. R. Chen, Q. Chen, and D. Xing, "Cancer phototherapy via selective photoinactivation of respiratory chain oxidase to trigger a fatal superoxide anion burst," *Antioxid Redox Signal* [Internet], **20**(5), 733–46 (2014). Available from: http://www.pubmedcentral.nih.gov/articlerender.fcgi?artid=3910666&tool=pmcentrez&rendertype=abstract

3. R. O. Poyton and K. A. Ball, "Therapeutic photobiomodulation: nitric oxide and a novel function of mitochondrial cytochrome c oxidase," *Discov. Med.* **11**(57), 154–9 (2011).

4. T. I. Karu, "Mitochondrial signaling in mammalian cells activated by red and near-IR radiation," *Photochem. Photobiol.* **84**(5), 1091–9 (2008).

5. T. D. Magrini, "Low-level laser therapy on MCF-7 cells: a micro-Fourier transform infrared spectroscopy study," *J. Biomed. Opt.* **17**(10), 101516 (2012).

6. J. Y. Lin, "A user's guide to channelrhodopsin variants: features, limitations and future developments," *Exp. Physiol.* **96**(1), 19–25 (2011).

7. R. C. Hardie, Photosensitive TRPs, 795–826 (2014). Available from: http://link.springer.com/10.1007/978-3-319-05161-1_4

8. B. Nilius and T. Voets, "TRP channels: A TR(I)P through a world of multifunctional cation channels," *Pflugers. Arch. Eur. J. Physiol.* **451**(1), 1–10 (2005).

9. T. Rohacs, *Phosphoinositide Regulation of TRP Channels*, 1143–76 (2014). Available from: http://link.springer.com/10.1007/978-3-319-05161-1_18

10. W.-Z. Yang, J.-Y. Chen, J.-T. Yu, and L.-W. Zhou, "Effects of low power laser irradiation on intracellular calcium and histamine release in RBL-2H3 mast cells," *Photochem. Photobiol.* **83**(4), 979–84 (2007).

11. Q. Gu, L. Wang, F. Huang, and W. Schwarz, "Stimulation of TRPV1 by green laser light," *Evidence-based Complement Altern. Med.* 2012 (2012).

12. J.-J. Ryu, S. Yoo, K. Y. Kim, J.-S. Park, S. Bang, S. H. Lee et al., "Laser modulation of heat and capsaicin receptor TRPV1 leads to thermal antinociception," *J. Dent. Res.* **89**(12), 1455–60 (2010).

13. E. S. Albert, J. M. Bec, G. Desmadryl, K. Chekroud, C. Travo, S. Gaboyard et al., "TRPV4 channels mediate the infrared laser-evoked response in sensory neurons," *J. Neurophysiol.* **107**(12), 3227–34 (2012).

14. P. R. Arany, A. Cho, T. D. Hunt, G. Sidhu, K. Shin, E. Hahm et al., "Photoactivation of Endogenous Latent Transforming Growth Factor-1 Directs Dental Stem Cell Differentiation for Regeneration," *Sci. Transl. Med.* [Internet], **6**(238), 238ra69–238ra69 (2014 May 28). Available from: http://stm.sciencemag.org/cgi/doi/10.1126/scitranslmed.3008234

15. Y. A. Vladimirov, E. A. Gorbatenkova, N. V. Paramonov, and O. A. Azizova, "Photoreactivation of superoxide dismutase by intensive red (laser) light," *Free. Radic. Biol. Med.* **5**(5–6), 281–6 (1988).

16. A. Amat, J. Rigau, R. W. Waynant, I. K. Ilev, J. Tomas, and J. J. Anders, "Modification of the intrinsic fluorescence and the biochemical behavior of ATP after irradiation with visible and near-infrared laser light," *J. Photochem. Photobiol. B. Biol.* **81**(1), 26–32 (2005).

17. M. Heger, A. A. M. Heemskerk, and G. van der Zwan, "Absence of 633-nm laser irradiation-induced effects on glucose phosphorylation by hexokinase," *J. Photochem. Photobiol. B. Biol.* [Internet], Elsevier B.V.; **98**(3), 216–22 (2010). Available from: 10.1016/j.jphotobiol.2010.01.004

18. S. Farivar, T. Malekshahabi, and R. Shiari, "Biological effects of low level laser therapy," *J. lasers. Med. Sci.* [Internet], **5**(2), 58–62 (2014). Available from: http://www.pubmedcentral.nih.gov/articlerender.fcgi?artid=4291815&tool=pmcentrez&rendertype=abstract

19. C. Ferraresi, M. R. Hamblin, and N. A. Parizotto, "Low-level laser (light) therapy (LLLT) on muscle tissue: Performance, fatigue and repair benefited by the power of light," *Photonics and Lasers in Medicine.* 267–86 (2012).

20. C. Ferraresi, B. Kaippert, P. Avci, Y.-Y. Huang, M. V. P. de Sousa, V. S. Bagnato et al., "Low-level Laser (Light) Therapy Increases Mitochondrial Membrane Potential and ATP Synthesis in C2C12 Myotubes with a Peak Response at 3-6 h," *Photochem. Photobiol.* [Internet], **91**(2), 411–6 (2015). Available from: http://www.pubmedcentral.nih.gov/articlerender.fcgi?artid=4355185&tool=pmcentrez&rendertype=abstract

21. G. R. Dubyak, "Signal transduction by P2-purinergic receptors for extracellular ATP," *American journal of respiratory cell and molecular biology.* 295–300 (1991).

22. G. Burnstock, "Purinergic nerves," *Pharmacol. Rev.* [Internet], **24**(3), 509–81 (1972). Available from: http://www.ncbi.nlm.nih.gov/pubmed/4404211

23. G. Burnstock and A. Verkhratsky, "Evolutionary origins of the purinergic signalling system," *Acta. Physiol.* **195**(4), 415–47 (2009).

24. H. Karmouty-Quintana, Y. Xia, and M. R. Blackburn, "Adenosine signaling during acute and chronic disease states," *J. Mol. Med.* [Internet], **91**(2), 173–81 (2013 Feb). Available from: http://link.springer.com/10. 1007/s00109-013-0997-1

25. F. M. De Lima, L. M. Moreira, A. B. Villaverde, R. Albertini, H. C. Castro-Faria-Neto, and F. Aimbire, "Low-level laser therapy (LLLT) acts as cAMP-elevating agent in acute respiratory distress syndrome," *Lasers Med. Sci.* **26**(3), 389–400 (2011).

26. J. Y. Wu, C. H. Chen, C. Z. Wang, M. L. Ho, M. L. Yeh, and Y. H. Wang, "Low-Power Laser Irradiation Suppresses Inflammatory Response of Human Adipose-Derived Stem Cells by Modulating Intracellular Cyclic AMP Level and NF-κB Activity," *PLoS One.* **8**(1), 1–9 (2013).

27. K. Taskén and E. M. Aandahl, "Localized effects of cAMP mediated by distinct routes of protein kinase A," *Physiol. Rev.* **84**(1), 137–67 (2004).

28. W. N. Zagotta and S. A. Siegelbaum, "Structure and function of cyclic nucleotide-gated channels," *Annu. Rev. Neurosci.* **19**, 235–63 (1996).

29. J. L. Bos, "Epac: a new cAMP target and new avenues in cAMP research," *Nat. Rev. Mol. Cell Biol.* **4**(9), 733–8 (2003).

30. A. C.-H. Chen, P. R. Arany, Y.-Y. Huang, E. M. Tomkinson, S. K. Sharma, G. B. Kharkwal et al., "Low-Level Laser Therapy Activates NF-κB via Generation of Reactive Oxygen Species in Mouse Embryonic Fibroblasts," *PLoS One.* **6**(7), e22453 (2011).

31. A. Popa-wagner, S. Mitran, S. Sivanesan, E. Chang, and A. Buga, "ROS and Brain Diseases : The Good, the Bad, and the Ugly," *Oxid. Med. Cell Longev.* 2013 (Article ID 963520), (2013).

32. M. Ristow and S. Schmeisser, "Extending life span by increasing oxidative stress," *Free Radic. Biol. Med.* [Internet]. Elsevier Inc., **51**(2), 327–36 (2011). Available from: 10.1016/j.freeradbiomed.2011.05.010

33. J. Yun and T. Finkel, "Mitohormesis," *Cell Metabolism.* 757–66 (2014).

34. Y.-Y. Huang, K. Nagata, C. E. Tedford, T. McCarthy, and M. R. Hamblin, "Low-level laser therapy (LLLT) reduces oxidative stress in primary cortical neurons in vitro," *J. Biophotonics* [Internet], **6**(10), 829–38 (2013). Available from: http://www.ncbi.nlm.nih.gov/pubmed/23281261

35. Y. Y. Huang, K. Nagata, C. E. Tedford, and M. R. Hamblin. "Low-level laser therapy (810 nm) protects primary cortical neurons against excitotoxicity in vitro," *J. Biophotonics* **7**(8), 656–64 (2014).

36. A. Bindoli and M. P. Rigobello, "Principles in redox signaling: from chemistry to functional significance," *Antioxid Redox Signal* [Internet], **18**(13), 1557–93 (2013). Available from: http://www.ncbi.nlm.nih.gov/ pubmed/23244515

37. H. J. Forman, F. Ursini, and M. Maiorino, "An overview of mechanisms of redox signaling," *J. Mol. Cell Cardiol.* [Internet]. Elsevier Ltd. **73**, 2–9 (2014). Available from: 10.1016/j.yjmcc.2014.01.018

38. Z. H. Wu, Y. Zhou, J. Y. Chen, and L. W. Zhou, "Mitochondrial signaling for histamine releases in laser-irradiated RBL-2H3 mast cells," *Lasers Surg. Med.* **42**(6), 503–9 (2010).

39. S. K. Sharma, G. B. Kharkwal, M. Sajo, Y. Huang, L. de Taboada, T. Mccarthy et al., "Dose Response Effects of 810 nm Laser Light on Mouse Primary Cortical Neurons," *NIH Public Access.* **43**(8), 851–9 (2012).

40. G. Santulli and A. R. Marks, "Essential roles of intracellular calcium release channels in muscle, brain, metabolism, and aging," *Curr. Mol. Pharmacol.* [Internet], (2015). Available from: http://www.ncbi.nlm.nih.gov/pubmed/25966694

41. M. Kühl, "The WNT/calcium pathway: biochemical mediators, tools and future requirements," *Front Biosci.* **9**, 967–74 (2004).

42. K. Ray, "Calcium-Sensing Receptor: Trafficking, Endocytosis, Recycling, and Importance of Interacting Proteins," *Prog. Mol. Biol. Transl. Sci.* [Internet], **132**, 127–50 (2015). Available from: http://www.ncbi.nlm.nih.gov/pubmed/26055057

43. T. Finkel, S. Menazza, K. M. Holmstrom, R. J. Parks, J. Liu, J. Sun et al., "The Ins and Outs of Mitochondrial Calcium," *Circ. Res.* [Internet], **116**(11), 1810–9 (2015). Available from: http://circres.ahajournals.org/cgi/doi/10.1161/CIRCRESAHA.116.305484

44. V. Krishnan, A. Graham, M. S. Mazei-Robison, D. C. Lagace, K. S. Kim, S. Birnbaum et al., "Calcium-Sensitive Adenylyl Cyclases in Depression and Anxiety: Behavioral and Biochemical Consequences of Isoform Targeting," *Biol. Psychiatry.* **64**(4), 336–43 (2008).

45. T. I. Karu, L. V. Pyatibrat, and N. I. Afanasyeva, "Cellular effects of low power laser therapy can be mediated by nitric oxide," *Lasers Surg. Med.* **36**(4), 307–14 (2005).

46. F. Murad, "Discovery of some of the biological effects of nitric oxide and its role in cell signaling," *Biosci. Rep.* **24**(4-5), 453–74 (2005).

47. J. C. Drapier, H. Hirling, J. Wietzerbin, P. Kaldy, and L. C. Kühn, "Biosynthesis of nitric oxide activates iron regulatory factor in macrophages," *EMBO J.* **12**(9), 3643–9 (1993).

48. M. Lepoivre, F. Fieschi, J. Coves, L. Thelander, and M. Fontecave, "Inactivation of ribonucleotide reductase by nitric oxide," *Biochem. Biophys. Res. Commun.* **179**(1), 442–8 (1991).

49. J. C. Drapier and J. B. Hibbs, "Aconitases: a class of metalloproteins highly sensitive to nitric oxide synthesis," *Methods Enzymol.* **269**, 26–36 (1996).

50. S. Dimmeler, F. Lottspeich, and B. Brune, "Nitric oxide causes ADP-ribosylation and inhibition of glyceraldehyde-3- phosphate dehydrogenase," *J. Biol. Chem.* **267**(24), 16771–4 (1992).

51. J. S. Stamler, D. I. Simon, J. A. Osborne, M. E. Mullins, O. Jaraki, T. Michel et al., "S-nitrosylation of proteins with nitric oxide: synthesis and characterization of biologically active compounds," *Proc. Natl. Acad. Sci. U. S. A.* **89**(1), 444–8 (1992).

52. P. Avci, T. T. Nyame, G. K. Gupta, M. Sadasivam, and M. R. Hamblin, "Low-level laser therapy for fat layer reduction: A comprehensive review," *Lasers Surg. Med.* **45**(6), 349–57 (2013).

53. J. Khuman, J. Zhang, J. Park, J. D. Carroll, C. Donahue, and M. J. Whalen, "Low-Level Laser Light Therapy Improves Cognitive Deficits and Inhibits Microglial Activation after Controlled Cortical Impact in Mice," *J. Neurotrauma.* **29**(2), 408–17 (2012).

54. J. D. Carroll, M. R. Milward, P. R. Cooper, M. Hadis, and W. M. Palin, "Developments in low level light therapy (LLLT) for dentistry," *Dent. Mater.* [Internet]. The Academy of Dental Materials, **30**(5), 465–75 (2014). Available from: 10.1016/j.dental.2014.02.006

55. S. Incerti Parenti, L. Checchi, M. Fini, and M. Tschon, "Different doses of low-level laser irradiation modulate the in vitro response of osteoblast-like cells," *J. Biomed. Opt.* [Internet], **19**(10), 108002 (2014 Oct 3). Available from: http://biomedicaloptics.spiedigitallibrary.org/article.aspx?doi=10.1117/1.JBO.19.10.108002

56. V. Cury, A. I. S. Moretti, L. Assis, P. Bossini, J. De Souza Crusca, C. B. Neto et al., "Low level laser therapy increases angiogenesis in a model of ischemic skin flap in rats mediated by VEGF, HIF-1α and MMP-2," *J. Photochem. Photobiol. B. Biol.* [Internet]. Elsevier B.V.; **125**, 164–70 (2013). Available from: 10.1016/j.jphotobiol.2013.06.004

57. J. Liang, L. Liu, and D. Xing, "Photobiomodulation by low-power laser irradiation attenuates Aβ-induced cell apoptosis through the Akt/GSK3β/β-catenin pathway," *Free Radic. Biol. Med.* [Internet] Elsevier; **53**(7), 1459–67 (2012). Available from: 10.1016/j.freeradbiomed.2012.08.003

58. L. Zhang, Y. Zhang, and D. A. Xing, "LPLI inhibits apoptosis upstream of bax translocation via a GSK-3β-inactivation mechanism," *J. Cell Physiol.* **224**(1), 218–28 (2010).

59. F. F. Sperandio, F. S. Giudice, L. Corrêa, D. S. Pinto, M. R. Hamblin, and SCOM. de Sousa, "Low-level laser therapy can produce increased aggressiveness of dysplastic and oral cancer cell lines by modulation of Akt/mTOR signaling pathway," *J. Biophotonics* [Internet], **29**(6), n/a–n/a (2013 Apr 2). Available from: http://linkinghub.elsevier.com/retrieve/pii/S0734975011001534

60. Q. Ling, C. Meng, Q. Chen, and D. Xing, "Activated ERK/FOXM1 pathway by low-power laser irradiation inhibits UVB-induced senescence

through down-regulating p21 expression," *J. Cell Physiol.* [Internet], n/a–n/a (2013 Jun). Available from: http://doi.wiley.com/10.1002/jcp.24425

61. F. M. de Lima, R. Albertini, Y. Dantas, A. L. Maia-Filho, C. de Loura Santana, H. C. Castro-Faria-Neto et al., "Low-Level Laser Therapy Restores the Oxidative Stress Balance in Acute Lung Injury Induced by Gut Ischemia and Reperfusion," *Photochem. Photobiol.* [Internet], **89**(1), 179–88 (2013 Jan). Available from: http://doi.wiley.com/10.1111/j.1751-1097.2012.01214.x

62. T. L. Patrocínio-Silva, A. M. F. de Souza, R. L. Goulart, C. F. Pegorari, J. R. Oliveira, K. Fernandes et al., "The effects of low-level laser irradiation on bone tissue in diabetic rats," *Lasers Med. Sci.* [Internet], (2013 Aug 29). Available from: http://link.springer.com/10.1007/s10103-013-1418-y

63. M. Aliodoust, M. Bayat, M. R. Jalili, Z. Sharifian, M. Dadpay, M. Akbari et al., "Evaluating the effect of low-level laser therapy on healing of tentomized Achilles tendon in streptozotocin-induced diabetic rats by light microscopical and gene expression examinations," *Lasers Med. Sci.* [Internet], **29**(4), 1495–503 (2014 Jul). Available from: http://link.springer.com/10.1007/s10103-014-1561-0

64. Y. Dang, B. Liu, L. Liu, X. Ye, X. Bi, Y. Zhang et al., "The 800-nm diode laser irradiation induces skin collagen synthesis by stimulating TGF-β/Smad signaling pathway," *Lasers Med. Sci.* **26**(6), 837–43 (2011).

65. L. Assis, A. I. S. Moretti, T. B. Abrahão, V. Cury, H. P. Souza, M. R. Hamblin et al., *NIH Public Access.* **44**(9), 726–35 (2013).

66. C. Chen, C. Wang, Y. Wang, W. Liao, Y. Chen, C. Kuo et al., "Effects of Low-Level Laser Therapy on M1-Related Cytokine Expression in Monocytes via Histone Modification," *Mediators Inflamm. Hindawi Publishing Corporation* **2014**, 1–13 (2014).

67. C. Meng, Z. He, and D. Xing, "Low-level laser therapy rescues dendrite atrophy via upregulating BDNF expression: implications for Alzheimer's disease," *J. Neurosci.* [Internet], **33**(33), 13505–17 (2013). Available from: http://www.ncbi.nlm.nih.gov/pubmed/23946409

68. T. G. Araújo, A. G. de Oliveira, N. Tobar, M. J. A. Saad, L. R. Moreira, E. R. Reis et al., "Liver regeneration following partial hepatectomy is improved by enhancing the HGF/Met axis and Akt and Erk pathways after low-power laser irradiation in rats," *Lasers Med. Sci.* [Internet], **28**(6), 1511–7 (2013 Nov). Available from: http://link.springer.com/10.1007/s10103-013-1264-y

69. C. A. Damante, G. De Micheli, S. P. H. Miyagi, I. S. Feist, and M. M. Marques, "Effect of laser phototherapy on the release of fibroblast growth factors by human gingival fibroblasts," *Lasers Med. Sci.* [Internet], **24**(6),

885–91 (2009 Nov). Available from: http://link.springer.com/10.1007/s10103-008-0582-y

70. W. Lim, J. Kim, S. Kim, S. Karna, J. Won, S. M. Jeon et al., "Modulation of lipopolysaccharide-induced NF-κB signaling pathway by 635 nm irradiation via heat shock protein 27 in human gingival fibroblast cells," *Photochem. Photobiol.* **89**(1), 199–207 (2013).

Chapter 4
Cellular Mechanisms*

4.1 Inflammation

Lim and co-workers found that 635-nm light irradiation at low power can lead to an anti-inflammatory effect by inhibiting prostaglandin E2 (PGE2) production and cyclo-oxygenase 1 and 2 (COX-1 and COX-2) mRNA expression. The light irradiation was able to decrease intracellular ROS, which mediates the expression of calcium-dependent phospholipase A2 (cPLA2), secretory phospholipase A2 (sPLA2), and COX-2, as well as inhibiting the release of PGE2.[1]

PGE2 synthesis is dependent on NF-κB modulation of the cellular signaling mechanism. NF-κB is found in the cytosol in its dimeric form of NF-κB/IκB (the latter is an inhibitory protein). Pro-inflammatory stimuli, such as LPS, can activate the NF-κB upstream signaling regulator IκB kinase (IKK), which is responsible for the phosphorylation and degradation of IκB. The free NF-κB is translocated to the nucleus and induces the expression of pro-inflammatory genes.[8] Lim demonstrated that 635-nm light irradiation suppresses the release of PGE2, possibly through a mechanism related to the inhibition of the NF-κB pathway. It did not affect the phosphorylation of IκB, IKK, and NF-κB in HSP27-silenced human gingival fibroblasts (hGFs), suggesting that NF-κB modulation by 635-nm light through HSP27 is required for the down-regulation of pro-inflammatory gene expression in these fibroblasts.[1]

Macrophages are important antigen-presenting cells that are involved in the induction of primary immunologic response. Interferon gamma (IFN-γ) polarization (either via classical or M1 activation) programs monocytes for increased phagocytic activity, as well as for anti-tumor activity and allergy suppression. Recently, Chen reported that 660-nm LLLT could promote M1 polarization of monocytes and influence the expression of cytokines and

---

*Based on material first printed in L. F. de Freitas and M. R. Hamblin, "Proposed mechanisms of photobiomodulation or low-level light therapy," J. Selected Topics Quant. Electron. 22(3), 348–364 (2016).

chemokines at the level of mRNA and protein expression. The effect was dose-dependent because the optimal light dose was found to be 1 J cm^{-2}, compared to 2 and 3 J cm^{-2}. Furthermore, the author could also clarify the mechanisms of epigenetic regulation by LLLT in immune cells. Modifications on histones, usually performed by histone acetyl- or methyltransferases, could be induced by LLLT: histone H3 and H4 acetylation and H3K4 trimethylation in the TNF gene promoter area, and histone H3 acetylation in the IP-10 gene promoter region. M1-related immunoregulation is important for antiviral immunity, antitumor immunity, and for the pathogenesis of inflammation in autoimmune conditions; therefore, LLLT could help promote anti-viral and anti-tumor immunity but enhance autoimmune and rheumatoid diseases.[2]

4.2 Cytoprotection

Studies have shown that *in vitro* LLLT protects cells at risk from dying due to treatment with various different toxins. Methanol, for instance, generates a toxic metabolite (formic acid) that inhibits cytochrome c oxidase. Because LLLT enhances mitochondrial activity via stimulation of cytochrome c oxidase, it also promotes cell survival during formic acid toxicity. This effect was demonstrated by Eells, who used red light (670 nm) in a rodent model of methanol toxicity and found that the light irradiation induced a significant recovery of cone- and rod-mediated function in the retina of rats after methanol intoxication, as well as protection against histological damage resulting from formic acid.[3]

Cyanide is another toxic compound that can have its effects attenuated by LLLT. Potassium-cyanide-induced apoptosis of neurons was decreased with a pre-treatment of 670-nm light. This result occurs because LLLT decreased the expression of caspase-3 (commonly increased by cyanide) and reversed the cyanide-induced increased expression of Bax, while decreasing the expression of Bcl-2 and inhibiting ROS generation.[4] Wong-Riley and co-workers show that LED pre-treatment could not restore enzymatic activity in cells to control levels after cyanide toxicity, but it successfully reversed the toxic effect of tetrodotoxin, especially with 670- and 830-nm light. These wavelengths correspond to the peaks in the absorption spectrum of cytochrome c oxidase, suggesting that this photobiomodulation depends on the up-regulation of cytochrome c oxidase.[5]

LLLT can be useful in the treatment of Alzheimer's disease because low-power laser irradiation promotes Yes-associated protein (YAP) cytoplasmic translocation and amyloid-β-peptide (Aβ) inhibition. Aβ deposition is a known hallmark of Alzheimer's disease, whereas YAP translocation is involved in the regulation of Aβ-induced apoptosis. Zhang published a study demonstrating that 832.8-nm light irradiation can reduce Aβ-induced toxicity by inhibiting apoptosis through the activation of the Akt/YAP/p73 signaling pathway.[6]

4.3 Proliferation

The proliferation levels of several cell types can have increased by LLLT. Keratinocytes, for example, showed an enhanced proliferation after 660-nm light irradiation, accompanied by an increased expression of Cyclin D1 and a faster maturation of keratinocytes in migration to the wound sites, via the expression of proteins involved in the epithelial proliferation process, i.e., p63, CK10, and CK14. This process is useful for the improvement of epithelial healing.[7] Furthermore, fibroblasts irradiated with 632.8-nm light had their proliferation stimulated and their cell viability increased, demonstrating the stimulatory effect of LLLT and the usefulness of this therapy in the wound-healing process.[8]

Vascular endothelial cells exposed to 635-nm irradiation proliferate faster than non-irradiated cells, showing a decreased VEGF concentration. This result suggests that laser-induced cell proliferation is related to a decrease in VEGF concentration. 830-nm irradiation decreased TGF-β secretion by the endothelial cells.[9]

Amid et al. published a review about the influence of LLLT on the proliferation of osteoblasts. According to the studies reviewed by the authors, wavelengths between 600 nm and 1000 nm have resulted in positive effects on dentistry, the anti-inflammatory process, and osteoblastic proliferation.[10]

4.4 Migration

Tendon healing requires a migration of tenocytes to the injured area, with consequent proliferation and synthesis of extracellular matrix. Tsai and co-workers evaluated the effect of 660-nm light on rat Achilles-tendon-derived tenocytes, and they found that dynamin-2 expression was enhanced and the migration was stimulated *in vitro*. Inhibiting dynamin-2 with dynasore suppressed this stimulatory effect of LLLT, leading to the conclusion that tenocyte migration stimulated by low-level light was mediated by the up-regulation of dynamin-2.[11]

Other cell types are also influenced by light irradiation. Melanocytes, for instance, showed an enhanced viability and proliferation after blue- and red-light irradiation. Melanocyte migration was enhanced by UV, blue and red light in lower doses, but a non-stimulatory effect was observed for higher light doses. Blue light seemed to be more effective compared to UV and red lasers.[12] Human epidermal stem cell migration and proliferation were increased alongside an increased phosphorylation of autocrine extracellular signal-regulated kinase (ERK), which contributed to accelerated wound re-epithelialization.[13] Finally, 780-nm irradiation seemed to accelerate fiber sprouting and neuronal cell migration, at least in embryonic rat brain cultures. Large-size neurons with a dense branched interconnected network of neuronal fibers were also observed after laser irradiation. These results can be seen in

Rochkind's work and may contribute to future treatment modalities for neuronal injuries or diseases.[14]

4.5 Protein Synthesis

As mentioned before, LLLT was able to increase the expression of proteins related to the proliferation and maturation of epithelial cells: p63, CK10, and CK14.[7] In fact, low-level light can increase the expression of several other proteins. A good example is the enhanced collagen I expression by fibroblasts two days after 810-nm light irradiation, as demonstrated by Frozanfar and co-workers in 2013.[15] Moreover, osteoblasts irradiated with 830-nm light increased the expression of proteins and proteoglycans, such as osteoglycin and mimecan. (Osteoglycin is a leucine-rich proteoglycan, previously called a osteoinductive factor, that is easily found in bone matrix, cartilage cells, and connective tissues.) They play a regulatory role in cell proliferation, differentiation, and adhesion of osteoblastic cells; therefore, LLLT applied on the early ploriferation stage of osteoblasts are important for the stimulation of bone formation, in concert with some growth factors and matrix proteins.[16]

4.6 Stem Cells

It appears that stem cells are particularly sensitive to light. LLLT induces stem cell activity shown by increased cell migration, differentiation, proliferation, and viability, as well as by activating protein expression.[17] Mesenchymal stem cells, usually derived from bone marrow, dental pulp, periodontal ligament, and adipose tissue, proliferate more after light irradiation (usually with wavelengths ranging from 600 to 700 nm). Because stem cells in their undifferentiated form show a lower rate of proliferation, this may be a limiting factor for the clinical effectiveness of stem cell therapies. LLLT offers a viable alternative to promote the translation of stem cell research into clinical application.[18]

Min et al. reported that the cell viability of adipose-derived stem cells was found to be increased after irradiation with 830-nm light.[19] Their *in vivo* results also revealed elevated numbers of stem cells compared to the control group. Epidermal stem cells can also be influenced by light, as demonstrated by Liao et al. The authors reveal that 632.8-nm light has photobiological effects on cultured human epidermal stem cells, such as an increase in proliferation and migration *in vitro*.[13] Soares observed a similar effect on human periodontal ligament stem cells irradiated with a 660-nm diode laser.[20]

References

1. W. Lim et al., "Modulation of lipopolysaccharide-induced NF-κB signaling pathway by 635 nm irradiation via heat shock protein 27 in

human gingival fibroblast cells," *Photochem. Photobiol.* **89**(1), 199–207 (2013).

2. C. Chen et al., "Effects of Low-Level Laser Therapy on M1-Related Cytokine Expression in Monocytes via Histone Modification," *Mediators Inflamm.* Hindawi Publishing Corporation, **2014**, 1–13 (2014).

3. J. T. Eells et al., "Therapeutic photobiomodulation for methanol-induced retinal toxicity," *Proc. Natl. Acad. Sci. U S A* **100**(6), 3439–44 (2003).

4. H. L. Liang et al., "Photobiomodulation partially rescues visual cortical neurons from cyanide-induced apoptosis," *Neuroscience* **139**(2), 639–49 (2006).

5. M. T. T. Wong-Riley et al., "Photobiomodulation directly benefits primary neurons functionally inactivated by toxins: Role of cytochrome c oxidase," *J. Biol. Chem.* **280**(6), 4761–71 (2005).

6. H. Zhang, S. Wu, and D. Xing, "Inhibition of Aβ 25-35-induced cell apoptosis by Low-power-laser-irradiation (LPLI) through promoting Akt-dependent YAP cytoplasmic translocation," *Cell Signal* [Internet]. Elsevier Inc., **24**(1), 224–32 (2012). Available from: 10.1016/j.cellsig.2011.09.004

7. F. F. Sperandio, A. Simões, L. Corrêa, A. C. C. Aranha, F. S. Giudice, M. R. Hamblin et al., "Low-level laser irradiation promotes the proliferation and maturation of keratinocytes during epithelial wound repair," *J. Biophotonics* [Internet], **9999**(9999), (2014). Available from: http://www.ncbi.nlm.nih.gov/pubmed/25411997

8. M. Esmaeelinejad, M. Bayat, H. Darbandi, M. Bayat, and N. Mosaffa, "The effects of low-level laser irradiation on cellular viability and proliferation of human skin fibroblasts cultured in high glucose mediums," *Lasers Med. Sci.* **29**(1), 121–9 (2014).

9. J. Szymanska, K. Goralczyk, J. J. Klawe, M. Lukowicz, M. Michalska, B. Goralczyk et al., "Phototherapy with low-level laser influences the proliferation of endothelial cells and vascular endothelial growth factor and transforming growth factor-beta secretion," *J. Physiol. Pharmacol.* **64**(3), 387–91 (2013).

10. R. Amid, M. Kadkhodazadeh, M. G. Ahsaie, and A. Hakakzadeh, "Effect of Low Level Laser Therapy on Proliferation and Differentiation of the Cells Contributing in Bone Regeneration," **5**(4), 163–70 (2014).

11. W. C. Tsai, C. C. Hsu, J. H. S. Pang, M. S. Lin, Y. H. Chen, and F. C. Liang, "Low-level laser irradiation stimulates tenocyte migration with up-regulation of dynamin II expression," *PLoS One* **7**(5), 1–7 (2012).

12. K. M. AlGhamdi, A. Kumar, A. E. Ashour, and A. A. AlGhamdi, "A comparative study of the effects of different low-level lasers on the proliferation, viability, and migration of human melanocytes in vitro," *Lasers Med. Sci.* [Internet], **30**(5), 1541–51 (2015). Available from: http://link.springer.com/10.1007/s10103-015-1758-x

13. X. Liao, G.-H. Xie, H.-W. Liu, B. Cheng, S.-H. Li, S. Xie et al., "Helium-neon laser irradiation promotes the proliferation and migration of human epidermal stem cells in vitro: proposed mechanism for enhanced wound re-epithelialization," *Photomed Laser Surg.* [Internet], **32**(4), 219–25 (2014). Available from: http://www.ncbi.nlm.nih.gov/pubmed/24661127

14. S. Rochklnd, D. El-Ani, Z. Nevo, and A. Shahar, "Increase of neuronal sprouting and migration using 780 nm laser phototherapy as procedure for cell therapy," *Lasers Surg. Med.* **41**(4), 277–81 (2009).

15. A. Frozanfar, M. Ramezani, A. Rahpeyma, S. Khajehahmadi, and H. R. Arbab, "The effects of low level laser therapy on the expression of collagen type I gene and proliferation of human gingival fibroblasts (HGF3-PI 53): In vitro study," *Iran. J. Basic Med. Sci.* **16**(10), 1071–4 (2013).

16. S. Hamajima, K. Hiratsuka, M. Kiyama-Kishikawa, T. Tagawa, M. Kawahara, M. Ohta et al., "Effect of low-level laser irradiation on osteoglycin gene expression in osteoblasts," *Lasers Med. Sci.* **18**(2), 78–82 (2003).

17. H. Abrahamse, "Regenerative Medicine, Stem Cells, and Low-Level Laser Therapy: Future Directives," *Photomed Laser Surg.* [Internet], **30**(12), 681–2 (2012). Available from: http://online.liebertpub.com/doi/abs/10.1089/pho.2012.9881

18. F. Ginani, D. M. Soares, M. P. E. V. Barreto, and C. A. G. Barboza, "Effect of low-level laser therapy on mesenchymal stem cell proliferation: a systematic review," *Lasers Med. Sci.* [Internet] (2015). Available from: http://link.springer.com/10.1007/s10103-015-1730-9

19. K. H. Min, J. H. Byun, C. Y. Heo, E. H. Kim, H. Y. Choi, and C. S. Pak, "Effect of Low-Level Laser Therapy on Human Adipose-Derived Stem Cells: In Vitro and In Vivo Studies," *Aesthetic Plast Surg.* [Internet], Springer US, (2015). Available from: http://link.springer.com/10.1007/s00266-015-0524-6

20. D. M. Soares, F. Ginani, Á. G. Henriques, and C. A. G. Barboza, "Effects of laser therapy on the proliferation of human periodontal ligament stem cells," *Lasers Med. Sci.* [Internet], **30**(3), 1171–4 (2015 Apr). Available from: http://link.springer.com/10.1007/s10103-013-1436-9

Chapter 5
Tissue Mechanisms*

5.1 Muscles

Previous chapters mentioned the positive results of LLLT in muscle recovery, as reported by Ferraresi et al. The authors concluded that it takes 3–6 h for the LLLT to exert the maximum effect on the muscle physiology, consisting of increased matrix metalloproteinase activity and ATP synthesis. This effect could still be observed 24 h after the laser irradiation.[1]

Rochkind and co-workers have also worked with LLLT applied to muscles, investigating the influence of low-power laser irradiation on creatine kinase (CK) and the amount of acetylcholine receptors (AChRs) present in intact gastrocnemius muscle *in vivo*, as well as the synthesis of DNA and of CK in muscle cells *in vitro*. The authors found that LLLT significantly increased CK activity and AChR levels in one and two months, when compared to control animals. The biochemical changes on muscle cells might be due to a trophic signal for increased activity of CK, which leads to a preservation of a reservoir of high-energy phosphate that is available for rapid ATP synthesis.[2]

5.2 Brain

Regarding the neurological field, LLLT can lead to cognitive benefits and memory enhancement in cases of brain damage caused by a controlled cortical impact (CCI). Khuman and co-workers found that a 500-mW cm^{-2} laser irradiation (60 J cm^{-2}) for two minutes improved spatial learning and memory of mice with CCI, and this was not observed in sham-injured mice. The authors observed a brief increase in the temperature of brain, but it returned to baseline before five minutes of irradiation. They also observed reduction of microgiosis at 48 h. Low-level light can be useful in TBI treatment because sub-optimal light doses affect spatial memory, as assessed by

---

*Based on material first printed in L. F. de Freitas and M. R. Hamblin, "Proposed mechanisms of photobiomodulation or low-level light therapy," J. Selected Topics Quant. Electron. 22(3), 348–364 (2016).

visible platform trials, even in the absence of nonspatial procedural learning, which is hippocampus independent.[3]

Near-infrared (NIR) light exerts a protective effect on neurons, but the mechanisms are not fully understood. However, two mechanisms may be involved, one of which is the direct action of NIR light on the cells, improving mitochondrial function, reducing inflammation, and helping the brain to repair itself. Xuan et al. reported that transcranial NIR light could stimulate the process of neurogenesis in the hippocampus and subventricular zone (SVZ) in mice with CCI TBIs.[4] These newly formed neuroprogenitor cells could travel to the injured region of the cortex to help in the repair of the damaged region. In another study, the same group showed that brain-derived neurotrophic factor (BDNF) was increased in the hippocampus and SVZ at one week post-TBI, and that at four weeks post-TBI there as an increase in synaptogenesis in the cortex, showing that new connections between existing brain cells could be stimulated by light.[5]

The second mechanism is based on the hypothesis that NIR can trigger a systemic response, this time not so directly, suggesting the involvement of one or more circulating molecules or cell types. This assumption is based on studies reporting the remote effects on tissues after irradiation of NIR light on specific sites, such as skin wounds. Another study reported brain protection in mice after remote irradiation with NIR light to the dorsum of the animals, without any direct irradiation on the head. One possibility to explain these remote effects is the stimulation of mast cells and macrophages, which could help to protect cells in the brain, as well as the modulation of inflammatory mediators, such as the down-regulation of pro-inflammatory cytokines and up-regulation of anti-inflammatory cytokines. Another possibility is the involvement of bone-marrow-derived stem cells because NIR light can increase the proliferation of c-kit-positive cells located in the bone marrow of the skull, which are then recruited to damaged tissues, especially the myocardial infarct site. These progenitor cells can, along with immune cells, secrete trophic and pro-survival factors such as nerve growth factor (NGF) and vascular endothelial growth factor (VEGF). Finally, mitochondria might be secreting an unidentified extracellular signal, called a "mitokine" by Durieux et al., which is then transmitted to remotely located cells.[3]

5.3 Nerves (Repair and Pain)

Some clinical studies have demonstrated the efficacy of laser-induced analgesia,[6,7] usually with a low-power red or NIR laser, and it seems that the pain reduction is due to a conduction block of central and peripheral nerve fibers and to the release of endorphins. In this field, for instance, Chan and co-workers used a Nd:YAG pulsed laser (1064 nm) with an average power of 1.2 W and a power density of 0.3–0.45 J cm^{-2} in a randomized, double-blind clinical trial, and demonstrated the efficacy of this treatment on the pulpal analgesia of premolar teeth.[8]

Analgesia mediated by LLLT is due to various effects, such as light absorption by mitochondrial chromophore (mainly Cox) biomodulation, vasodilation, stimulation of cell division, release of NO, increase in cortisol levels and protein synthesis, increase in intracellular calcium concentration, and increased activity of the antioxidant enzyme superoxide dismutase. Serra and Ashmawi investigated if serotonin played a role in LLLT-induced analgesia, but their results indicated that this effect is mediated by peripheral opioid receptors and not by peripheral serotoninergic receptors.[9]

Low-level light therapy can be used for the inhibition of pain and for pathological conditions associated with the nervous system. In 2011, Yan et al. postulated that LLLT could suppress afferent fiber signaling as well as modulate synaptic transmission to dorsal horn neurons, including the inhibition of substance P, which can lead to long-term pain depression.[10] LLLT exerts potent anti-inflammatory effects in the peripheral nervous system, can reduce myocardial infarction, promotes the functional recovery and regeneration of peripheral nerves after injury, and can improve neurological deficits after stroke and TBI.[3]

Light with irradiance higher than 300 mW cm^{-2}, when absorbed by nociceptors, can inhibit Aδ and C pain fibers, which slows the conduction velocity, reduces the compound action potential amplitude, and suppresses neurogenicin inflammation. In the case of LLLT, the light can block the anterograde transport of ATP-rich mitochondria in dorsal root ganglion neurons. This inhibition is completely reversible within 48 h and leads to the formation of varicosities, which are usually associated with the disruption of microtubules (an interruption of the fast axonal flow can reduce ATP availability, which is necessary for the polymerization of microtubules and for the maintenance of the resting potential).[11]

5.4 Healing (Bones, Tendons, and Wounds)

Regarding bones, low-power laser irradiation is not believed to affect osteosynthesis, but it is likely that it creates environmental conditions that accelerate bone healing. LLLT stimulates the proliferation and differentiation of osteoblasts *in vivo* and *in vitro*, leading to increased bone formation accompanied by an increase in the activity of alkaline phosphatase (ALP) and in osteocalcin expression. This behavior indicates that laser irradiation can directly stimulate bone formation; according to Fujimoto et al., this effect can be attributed to an increased expression of the insulin-like growth factor (IGF), although other differentiation factors might be involved as well, such as bone morphogenetic proteins (BMPs). BMP-2, -4, -6, and -7 are members of the TGF-β superfamily and potent promoters of osteoblastic differentiation and of bone formation (promoting the change of mesenchymal cells into chondroblasts and osteoblasts).[12]

According to Fujimoto, BMP-2 might be most involved in the effects of LLLT on bone. LLLT stimulated mineralization *in vitro* via increased gene and protein expression of BMPs and Runx-2, as well as the differentiation of osteoblasts into MC3T3-E1 cells. Because BMPs are one of the most important and potent bone-inductive mediators and are expressed in skeletal tissues, it is possible that the bone nodules formed after LLLT are mediated in part by BMP-2 expression.[12]

The balance between oxidants and antioxidants is directly related to the length and quality of the wound-healing process.[13] This process can be divided into four overlapping phases: hemostasis, inflammation, proliferation, and remodeling or resolution. Hemostasis is initiated as soon as the blood vessels are damaged, and consists of the adherence of platelets to the extracellular matrix and further release of growth factors [mostly platelet-derived growth factor (PDGF) and TGF-β], culminating in the production of thrombin, which acts on fibrinogen to produce a fibrin clot. Thrombin also acts as a chemotactic agent and proliferating agent on monocytes, keratinocytes, fibroblasts, and endothelial cells; therefore, defective thrombin activity can delay the wound-healing process. Hoffman reported that LLLT could be beneficial in promoting healing when there is a defect in the hemostasis process.[14]

5.5 Hair

Different mechanisms have been proposed to explain the reason for the first light-mediated effect observed by Mester in 1968 (hypertrichosis in mice)[15] and now widely used clinically to restore hair growth in adult humans.[16] Some researchers have hypothesized that this effect was due to the polycystic ovarian syndrome present in 5 out of 49 female patients under laser treatment for facial hirsutism; others suggested that even if the heat generated by LLLT was not able to ablate cells from the hair follicle, the small amount of heat supposedly produced could induce follicular stem cells to proliferate and differentiate due to the increased level of heat-shock proteins. Another possibility supposes that the release of certain factors could affect the cell cycle and induce angiogenesis.[16] The exact mechanism still needs clarification, but the effects of LLLT on hair growth are already well described.

Hair growth is divided into three basic phases: anagen, catagen, and telogen. Anagen is the growth phase and can last from two to six years. The catagen phase lasts from one to two weeks and consists of club hair transitions upwards toward the skin pore, while the dermal papilla separates from the follicle. During the telogen phase, the dermal papillae fully separate from the hair follicle; it lasts from five to six weeks, until the papillae move upward to meet the hair follicles again and the hair matrix begins to form new hair, returning to the anagen phase. It has been observed that LLLT can stimulate telogen hair follicles to enter the anagen phase, as well as prolong the duration of the anagen phase itself. LLLT can also increase the rate of proliferation of the anagen hair follicles and prevent premature catagen phases. These results might be due to induced protein synthesis caused by the transcription factors activated by LLLT, followed by cell migration and proliferation, alteration in cytokines levels, growth factors, and inflammatory mediators. NO is also augmented in LLL-treated tissues, usually dissociated from Cox, and because it is a well-known vasodilator, it is likely that there is a vasodilation effect on hair follicles after LLLT that could help hair growth. Some inflammatory mediators also have their expression inhibited by LLLT (such as IFN-γ, IL-1a, IL-1b, TNF, and Fas-antigen) and, considering that inflammation is highly disruptive for hair follicles, the anti-inflammatory effect of LLLT could be useful in the treatment of hair conditions such as alopecia areata.[16]

5.6 Skin

LED light has been used for nonthermal, nonablative skin rejuvenation as an alternative for classical abrasive methods, and it has demonstrated promising results for wrinkles and skin laxity.[34–40] This behavior is due to the effects of LLLT on collagen production. Abergel and coworkers, as well as Yu et al., for instance, found an increased production of pro-collagen, collagen, and basic fibroblast growth factor (bFGF), and increased fibroblast proliferation *in vivo* and *in vitro*.[17,18] Other authors reported increased microcirculation and altered levels of platelet-derived growth factor (PDGF) and transforming growth factor beta 1 (TGF-β1), as well as apoptosis inhibition after exposure to low-level light.[19–21] Other biomodulators were found to be increased after LLLT, such as IL-1β, TNF, and ICAM-1, while the ratio between matrix metalloproteinases (MMPs) and their tissue inhibitors (TIMPs) showed to be altered. Increased IL-1β and TNF can possibly induce MMPs in the early response to low-level light, clearing the photodamaged collagen fragments and thus enabling the biosynthesis of new collagen fibers. In the future, TIMPs could protect newly synthesized collagen from proteolytic degradation by MMPs.[22]

Besides skin rejuvenation, low-level light can have applications for the treatment of acne vulgaris, with fewer side effects than the classic treatments.[23] Red light, for example, can change the behavior of keratinocytes and affect the sebum secretion by sebaceous glands,[24] which also alters the levels of cytokines and the phagocytic activity of macrophages in order to decrease inflammation.[23,24] Several authors have demonstrated the positive effects of blue and red light on acne vulgaris, with different application methods.[24–28] LLLT also induces repigmentation responses in patients with segmental-type vitiligo.[29] In this type of vitiligo, a decrease in NGF and bFGF levels seems to play an important role on the pathogenesis, and LLLT induces the release of those mediators *in vitro*.[30] Furthermore, low-level light can induce the proliferation of melanocytes through the enhanced expression of the cAMP response element-binding (CREB) protein.[31]

Another application of LLLT involves the treatment of keloids and benign skin tumors, characterized mainly by the accumulation of collagen and an excessive proliferation of fibroblasts,[32] caused by the poor regulation of IL-6 signaling pathways and TGF-β1 expression.[33–37] Since LLLT acts modulating IL-6, IL-13, IL-15, PDGF, TGF-β1 and MMPs, it was considered an alternative treatment for these conditions (38).

5.7 Fat

The fat-liberating effects of LLLT on adipocytes have been attributed to its ability to induce transitioning micropores, which were visualized with the help of SEM. Furthermore, it has been postulated that these pores stimulated the release of intracellular lipids from the adipocytes. Based on this, it was suggested that up to 99% of the fat stored within the adipocytes could be released and subsequently removed with the help of LLLT (635 nm, 10-mW intensity, 6-minute irradiation time).[39] However, another study demonstrated that cultured adipocytes, when treated with LLLT, exhibited a tendency to attain their native cellular conformation following treatment, which was confirmed using a live–dead assay to assess the viability of these adipocytes following irradiation.[40] An increase in ROS following LLLT has been proposed to bring about lipid peroxidation within the cell membranes of adipocytes and may be responsible for membrane injury, which could present itself as transitory pores.[41–43] However, when Brown et al. attempted to replicate the Neira group's findings, they failed to see any transitory micropores via SEM.[44] No further SEM studies have documented these pores, but findings have been reported that indirectly support the transitory micropore formation theory.

Another proposed mechanism that explains the release of intracellular lipids from adipocytes suggests that the activation of the compliment cascade, which is responsible for the induction of adipocyte apoptosis, results in the subsequent release of intracellular lipid components.[40] To test the feasibility of this theory, a group of researchers exposed differentiated human adipocytes to blood plasma and treated one group of cells to a laser (experimental), whereas the control group received no laser intervention. No differences were noticed regarding the complementary system components in either group, and it was concluded that LLLT did not act through the activation of the complement cascade.[40]

Other evidence suggests that LLLT is capable of inducing an increase in cAMP levels.[45,46] cAMP is responsible for the activation of certain protein kinases, which further activate certain enzymes such as hormone sensitive lipase, which is responsible for the breakdown of triglycerides into fatty acids and glycerol (both of which can traverse the adipocyte membrane and reach the bloodstream).[47,48] However, the findings obtained from cell cultures of human adipocytes treated with LLLT (635–680 nm for ten minutes) did not exhibit any increases in glycerol and fatty acid levels, suggesting that fat liberation from adipocytes in response to LLLT is not due to the lypolytic breakdown of the adipose tissue. As the cellular components were being examined, the presence of triglycerides in the supernatant of extracted samples seemed to support the theory of transient micropore formation in adipocytes (40). Although these mechanisms have been worked out independently, the mechanism by which triglycerides could traverse the adipocyte lipid membrane remains uncertain.

5.8 High-Fluence Low-Power Laser Irradiation

Just like LLLT using low fluences of light, high-fluence low-power laser irradiation (HF-LPLI) stimulates mitochondrial chromophores, but it over-stimulates them, which activates the mitochondrial apoptosis pathway, alters the cell cycle, inhibits cell proliferation, and causes cell death. HF-LPLI induces apoptosis by activating caspase-3, and a mitochondrial permeability transition after HF-LPLI is the main mechanism of mitochondrial injury. In 2010, Sun et al. reported that the signal transducer and activator of transcription 3 (Stat3) was involved in HF-LPLI-induced apoptosis *in vitro*, and this effect is time- and dose-dependent. Steroid receptor coactivator (Src) seems to be the main upstream kinase of Stat3 activation, and the increased ROS generation plays a key role in this process.[49]

Recently, Wu et al. found that HF-LPLI, using light at 633 nm and 120 J cm^{-2}, could ablate tumors via the activation of the mitochondrial apoptotic pathway after ROS generation. The evidence is based on the inactivation of caspase-8, activation of caspase-9, and release of cytochrome c. When this high dose is used, light deactivates Cox (instead of activating Cox), inducing a superoxide burst in the electron transport chain and, finally, producing oxidative damage against cancer cells.[50] Chu and co-workers already observed that LLLT could induce a mitochondrial permeability pore transition when higher levels of ROS are produced. As a consequence, the decrease of mitochondrial transmembrane potential causes the permeabiliza-tion of the mitochondrial outer membrane and, subsequently, the release of cytochrome c and caspase cascade reaction.[51]

Cho also observed the interference that a protein, called survivin, could affect the outcomes of HF-LPLI. Light treatment can activate survivin by inducing an increase in its phosphorylation levels. The activated survivin can inhibit the permeabilization of the mitochondrial outer membrane and therefore prevent the release of cytochrome c and the activation of Bax and caspase-9. Cho then concluded that survivin mediates the self-protection of tumor cells against HF-LPLI-induced apoptosis, through the ROS/cdc25c/CDK1 signaling pathway.[51]

References

1. C. Ferraresi, B. Kaippert, P. Avci, Y.-Y. Huang, M. V. P. de Sousa, V. S. Bagnato et al., "Low-level Laser (Light) Therapy Increases Mitochondrial Membrane Potential and ATP Synthesis in C2C12 Myotubes with a Peak Response at 3-6 h," *Photochem Photobiol.* [Internet], **91**(2), 411–6 (2015). Available from: http://www.pubmedcentral.nih.gov/articlerender.fcgi?artid=4355185&tool=pmcentrez&rendertype=abstract

2. S. Rochkind, S. Geuna, and A. Shainberg, "Phototherapy and Nerve Injury," [Internet]. 1st ed. Tissue Engineering of the Peripheral Nerve: Elsevier Inc., 99–109 (2013). Available from: http://linkinghub.elsevier.com/retrieve/pii/B9780124200456000043

3. J. Khuman, J. Zhang, J. Park, J. D. Carroll, C. Donahue, and M. J. Whalen, "Low-Level Laser Light Therapy Improves Cognitive Deficits and Inhibits Microglial Activation after Controlled Cortical Impact in Mice," *J Neurotrauma.* **29**(2), 408–17 (2012).

4. S. Bouvet-Gerbettaz, E. Merigo, J.-P. Rocca, G. F. Carle, and N. Rochet, "Effects of low-level laser therapy on proliferation and differentiation of murine bone marrow cells into osteoblasts and osteoclasts," *Lasers Surg. Med.* **41**(4), 291–7 (2009).

5. W. Xuan, T. Agrawal, L. Huang, G. K. Gupta, and M. R. Hamblin, "Low-level laser therapy for traumatic brain injury in mice increases brain derived neurotrophic factor (BDNF) and synaptogenesis," *J. Biophotonics.* [Internet], **8**(6), 502–11 (2015). Available from: http://www.ncbi.nlm.nih.gov/pubmed/25196192

6. A. B. Marković and L. Todorović, "Postoperative analgesia after lower third molar surgery: contribution of the use of long-acting local anesthetics, low-power laser, and diclofenac," *Oral Surgery, Oral Med Oral Pathol Oral Radiol Endodontology.* **102**(5) (2006).

7. I. Tanboga, F. Eren, B. Altinok, S. Peker, and F. Ertugral, "The effect of low level laser therapy on pain during dental tooth-cavity preparation in children," *Eur. Arch. Paediatr. Dent.* **12**(2), 93–5 (2011).

8. A. Chan, P. Armati, and A. P. Moorthy, "Pulsed Nd: YAG Laser Induces Pulpal Analgesia: A Randomized Clinical Trial," *J. Dent. Res.* **91**(7 Suppl), S79–84 (2012).

9. A. Peres e Serra and H. A. Ashmawi, "Influence of naloxone and methysergide on the analgesic effects of low-level laser in an experimental pain model," *Rev. Bras. Anestesiol.* [Internet]. Elsevier, **60**(3), 302–10 (2010). Available from: 10.1016/S0034-7094(10)70037-4

10. W. Yan, R. Chow, and P. J. Armati, "Inhibitory effects of visible 650-nm and infrared 808-nm laser irradiation on somatosensory and compound muscle action potentials in rat sciatic nerve: Implications for laser-induced analgesia," *J. Peripher. Nerv. Syst.* **16**(2), 130–5 (2011).

11. J. D. Carroll, M. R. Milward, P. R. Cooper, M. Hadis, and W. M. Palin, "Developments in low level light therapy (LLLT) for dentistry," *Dent. Mater.* [Internet]. The Academy of Dental Materials, **30**(5), 465–75 (2014). Available from: 10.1016/j.dental.2014.02.006

12. K. Fujimoto, T. Kiyosaki, N. Mitsui, K. Mayahara, S. Omasa, N. Suzuki et al., "Low-intensity laser irradiation stimulates mineralization via increased BMPs in MC3T3-E1 cells," *Lasers Surg. Med.* **42**(6), 519–26 (2010).

13. R. V. Gonçalves, R. D. Novaes, M. Do Carmo Cupertino, B. Moraes, J. P. V. Leite, M. Do Carmo Gouveia Peluzio et al., "Time-dependent effects of low-level laser therapy on the morphology and oxidative response in the skin wound healing in rats," *Lasers Med. Sci.* **28**(2), 383–90 (2013).

14. M. Hoffman and D. M. Monroe, "Low intensity laser therapy speeds wound healing in hemophilia by enhancing platelet procoagulant activity," *Wound Repair Regen.* **20**(5), 770–7 (2012).

15. E. Mester, B. Szende, and P. Gärtner, "The effect of laser beams on the growth of hair in mice," *Radiobiol Radiother (Berl).* **9**(5), 621–6 (1968).

16. P. Avci, G. K. Gupta, J. Clark, N. Wikonkal, and M. R. Hamblin, "Low-level laser (light) therapy (LLLT) for treatment of hair loss," *Lasers Surg. Med.* **46**(2), 144–51 (2014).

17. R. P. Abergel, R. F. Lyons, J. C. Castel, R. M. Dwyer, and J. Uitto, "Biostimulation of wound healing by lasers: experimental approaches in animal models and in fibroblast cultures," *J. Dermatol. Surg. Oncol.* [Internet], **13**(2), 127–33 (1987 Feb). Available from: http://www.ncbi.nlm.nih.gov/pubmed/3805475

18. W. Yu, J. O. Naim, and R. J. Lanzafame, "The effect of laser irradiation on the release of bFGF from 3T3 fibroblasts," *Photochem. Photobiol.* [Internet], **59**(2), 167–70 (1994 Feb). Available from: http://www.ncbi.nlm.nih.gov/pubmed/8165235

19. H. Chung, T. Dai, S. K. Sharma, Y.-Y. Huang, J. D. Carroll, and M. R. Hamblin, "The nuts and bolts of low-level laser (light) therapy," *Ann. Biomed. Eng.* [Internet], **40**(2), 516–33 (2012 Feb). Available from: http://www.ncbi.nlm.nih.gov/pubmed/22045511

20. A. Schindl, G. Heinze, M. Schindl, H. Pernerstorfer-Schön, and L. Schindl, "Systemic effects of low-intensity laser irradiation on skin microcirculation in patients with diabetic microangiopathy," *Microvasc. Res.* [Internet], **64**(2), 240–6 (2002 Sep). Available from: http://www.ncbi.nlm.nih.gov/pubmed/12204648

21. N. Ben-Dov, G. Shefer, A. Irintchev, A. Wernig, U. Oron, O. Halevy et al., "Low-energy laser irradiation affects satellite cell proliferation and differentiation in vitro," *Biochim. Biophys. Acta.* [Internet], **1448**(3), 372–80

(1999 Jan 11). Available from: http://www.ncbi.nlm.nih.gov/pubmed/9990289

22. S. Y. Lee, K.-H. Park, J.-W. Choi, J.-K. Kwon, D. R. Lee, M. S. Shin et al., "A prospective, randomized, placebo-controlled, double-blinded, and split-face clinical study on LED phototherapy for skin rejuvenation: clinical, profilometric, histologic, ultrastructural, and biochemical evaluations and comparison of three different tre," *J. Photochem. Photobiol. B.* [Internet], **88**(1), 51–67 (2007 Jul 27). Available from: http://www.ncbi.nlm.nih.gov/pubmed/17566756

23. A. M. Rotunda, A. R. Bhupathy, and T. E. Rohrer, "The new age of acne therapy: light, lasers, and radiofrequency," *J. Cosmet. Laser. Ther.* [Internet], **6**(4), 191–200 (2004 Dec). Available from: http://www.ncbi.nlm.nih.gov/pubmed/16020203

24. N. S. Sadick, "Handheld LED array device in the treatment of acne vulgaris," *J. Drugs. Dermatol.* [Internet], **7**(4), 347–50 (2008 Apr). Available from: http://www.ncbi.nlm.nih.gov/pubmed/18459515

25. S. Y. Lee, C. E. You, and M. Y. Park, "Blue and red light combination LED phototherapy for acne vulgaris in patients with skin phototype IV," *Lasers Surg. Med.* [Internet], **39**(2), 180–8 (2007 Feb). Available from: http://www.ncbi.nlm.nih.gov/pubmed/17111415

26. M. H. Aziz-Jalali, S. M. Tabaie, and G. E. Djavid, "Comparison of Red and Infrared Low-level Laser Therapy in the Treatment of Acne Vulgaris," *Indian J. Dermatol.* [Internet], **57**(2), 128–30 (2012 Mar). Available from: http://www.ncbi.nlm.nih.gov/pubmed/22615511

27. D. J. Goldberg and B. A. Russell, "Combination blue (415 nm) and red (633 nm) LED phototherapy in the treatment of mild to severe acne vulgaris," *J. Cosmet. Laser Ther.* [Internet], **8**(2), 71–5 (2006 Jun). Available from: http://www.ncbi.nlm.nih.gov/pubmed/16766484

28. P. Papageorgiou, A. Katsambas, and A. Chu, "Phototherapy with blue (415 nm) and red (660 nm) light in the treatment of acne vulgaris," *Br. J. Dermatol.* [Internet], **142**(5), 973–8 (2000 May). Available from: http://www.ncbi.nlm.nih.gov/pubmed/10809858

29. A. S. Mandel', "Skin repigmentation after laser therapy," *Vestn Dermatol Venerol.* [Internet], (9), 26–9 (1984 Sep). Available from: http://www.ncbi.nlm.nih.gov/pubmed/6524045

30. H.-S. Yu, C.-S. Wu, C.-L. Yu, Y.-H. Kao, and M.-H. Chiou, "Helium-neon laser irradiation stimulates migration and proliferation in melanocytes and induces repigmentation in segmental-type vitiligo," *J. Invest. Dermatol.* [Internet], **120**(1), 56–64 (2003 Jan). Available from: http://www.ncbi.nlm.nih.gov/pubmed/12535198

31. C-CE. Lan, C.-S. Wu, M.-H. Chiou, T.-Y. Chiang, and H.-S. Yu, "Low-energy helium-neon laser induces melanocyte proliferation via interaction with type IV collagen: visible light as a therapeutic option for vitiligo,"

Br. J. Dermatol. [Internet], **161**(2), 273–80 (2009 Aug). Available from: http://www.ncbi.nlm.nih.gov/pubmed/19438447

32. J. Uitto and D. Kouba, "Cytokine modulation of extracellular matrix gene expression: relevance to fibrotic skin diseases," *J. Dermatol. Sci.* [Internet], **24**(Suppl 1), S60–9 (2000 Dec). Available from: http://www.ncbi.nlm.nih.gov/pubmed/11137398

33. D. Wolfram, A. Tzankov, P. Pülzl, and H. Piza-Katzer, "Hypertrophic scars and keloids–a review of their pathophysiology, risk factors, and therapeutic management," *Dermatol. Surg.* [Internet], **35**(2), 171–81 (2009 Feb). Available from: http://www.ncbi.nlm.nih.gov/pubmed/19215252

34. N. Bouzari, S. C. Davis, and K. Nouri, "Laser treatment of keloids and hypertrophic scars," *Int. J. Dermatol.* [Internet], **46**(1), 80–8 (2007 Jan). Available from: http://www.ncbi.nlm.nih.gov/pubmed/17214728

35. M. Ghazizadeh, M. Tosa, H. Shimizu, H. Hyakusoku, and O. Kawanami, "Functional implications of the IL-6 signaling pathway in keloid pathogenesis," *J. Invest. Dermatol.* [Internet], **127**(1), 98–105 (2007 Jan). Available from: http://www.ncbi.nlm.nih.gov/pubmed/17024100

36. J. Uitto, "IL-6 signaling pathway in keloids: a target for pharmacologic intervention?," *J. Invest. Dermatol.* [Internet], **127**(1), 6–8 (2007 Jan). Available from: http://www.ncbi.nlm.nih.gov/pubmed/17170717

37. W. Liu, D. R. Wang, and Y. L. Cao, "TGF-beta: a fibrotic factor in wound scarring and a potential target for anti-scarring gene therapy," *Curr. Gene. Ther.* [Internet], **4**(1), 123–36 (2004 Mar). Available from: http://www.ncbi.nlm.nih.gov/pubmed/15032619

38. D. Barolet and A. Boucher, "Prophylactic low-level light therapy for the treatment of hypertrophic scars and keloids: a case series," *Lasers Surg. Med.* [Internet], **42**(6), 597–601 (2010 Aug). Available from: http://www.ncbi.nlm.nih.gov/pubmed/20662038

39. R. Neira, J. Arroyave, H. Ramirez, C. L. Ortiz, E. Solarte, F. Sequeda et al., "Fat liquefaction: effect of low-level laser energy on adipose tissue," *Plast. Reconstr. Surg.* [Internet], **110**(3), 912–22; discussion 923–5 (2002 Sep 1). Available from: http://www.ncbi.nlm.nih.gov/pubmed/12172159

40. M. K. Caruso-Davis, T. S. Guillot, V. K. Podichetty, N. Mashtalir, N. V. Dhurandhar, O. Dubuisson et al., "Efficacy of low-level laser therapy for body contouring and spot fat reduction," *Obes. Surg.* **21**(6), 722–9 (2011).

41. H. Chen, F. Ji, V. Olman, C. K. Mobley, Y. Liu, Y. Zhou et al., "Optimal mutation sites for PRE data collection and membrane protein structure prediction," *Structure.* [Internet], **19**(4), 484–95 (2011 Apr 13). Available from: http://www.ncbi.nlm.nih.gov/pubmed/21481772

42. T. I. Karu, "Mitochondrial signaling in mammalian cells activated by red and near-IR radiation," *Photochem. Photobiol.* **84**(5), 1091–9 (2008).

43. J. Tafur and P. J. Mills, "Low-intensity light therapy: exploring the role of redox mechanisms," *Photomed Laser Surg.* [Internet], **26**(4), 323–8 (2008 Aug). Available from: http://www.ncbi.nlm.nih.gov/pubmed/18665762

44. S. A. Brown, R. J. Rohrich, J. Kenkel, V. L. Young, J. Hoopman, and M. Coimbra, "Effect of Low-Level Laser Therapy on Abdominal Adipocytes before Lipoplasty Procedures," *Plast. Reconstr. Surg.* [Internet], **113**(6), 1796–804 (2004 May). Available from: http://content.wkhealth.com/linkback/openurl?sid=WKPTLP:landingpage&an=00006534-200405000-00037

45. T. I. Karu and V. S. Letokhov, "Biological Action of Low-Intensity Monochromatic Light in the Visible Range," *Laser Photobiology and Photomedicine* [Internet]. Boston, MA: Springer US; 57–66 (1985). Available from: http://link.springer.com/10.1007/978-1-4613-2461-4_4

46. T. Karu, "Primary and secondary mechanisms of action of visible to near-IR radiation on cells," *J. Photochem. Photobiol. B Biol.* [Internet], **49**(1), 1–17 (1999 Mar). Available from: http://linkinghub.elsevier.com/retrieve/pii/S101113449800219X

47. R. C. Honnor, G. S. Dhillon, and C. Londos, "cAMP-dependent protein kinase and lipolysis in rat adipocytes," *I. Cell preparation, manipulation, and predictability in behavior. J. Biol. Chem.* [Internet], **260**(28), 15122–9 (1985 Dec 5). Available from: http://www.ncbi.nlm.nih.gov/pubmed/2415513

48. M. S. Nestor, M. B. Zarraga, and H. Park, "Effect of 635nm Low-level Laser Therapy on Upper Arm Circumference Reduction: A Double-blind, Randomized, Sham-controlled Trial," *J. Clin. Aesthet. Dermatol.* [Internet], **5**(2), 42–8 (2012 Feb). Available from: http://www.ncbi.nlm.nih.gov/pubmed/22468172

49. X. Sun, S. Wu, and D. Xing, "The reactive oxygen species-Src-Stat3 pathway provokes negative feedback inhibition of apoptosis induced by high-fluence low-power laser irradiation," *FEBS J.* **277**(22), 4789–802 (2010).

50. S. Wu, F. Zhou, Y. Wei, W. R. Chen, Q. Chen, and D. Xing, "Cancer phototherapy via selective photoinactivation of respiratory chain oxidase to trigger a fatal superoxide anion burst," *Antioxid. Redox. Signal.* [Internet], **20**(5), 733–46 (2014). Available from: http://www.pubmedcentral.nih.gov/articlerender.fcgi?artid=3910666&tool=pmcentrez&rendertype=abstract

51. J. Chu, S. Wu, and D. Xing, "Survivin mediates self-protection through ROS/cdc25c/CDK1 signaling pathway during tumor cell apoptosis induced by high fluence low-power laser irradiation," *Cancer Lett.* [Internet]. Elsevier Ireland Ltd; **297**(2), 207–19 (2010). Available from: 10.1016/j.canlet.2010.05.013

Chapter 6
Biphasic Dose Response*

6.1 Dose Dependence and Dose Rate Effects: The Biphasic Curve

A biphasic response has been demonstrated many times in LLLT research,[1,2] and the Arndt–Schulz law is frequently quoted as a suitable model to describe the dose-dependent effects of LLLT.[3–7] The concept of the law dates from the end of the nineteenth century, when H. Schulz published a series of papers that examined the activity of various kinds of poisons (iodine, bromine, mercuric chloride, arsenious acid, etc.) on yeast, showing that almost all of these agents have a slightly stimulatory effect on the yeast metabolism in low doses.[8,9] He and psychiatrist R. Arndt developed a principle that later became known as the Arndt–Schulz law, stating that weak stimuli slightly accelerate vital activity, stronger stimuli raise it further until a peak is reached, and even stronger stimuli suppress it until a negative response is finally achieved.[10] In 1960, Townsend and Luckey surveyed the field of classic medical pharmacology and published a list of 100 substances capable of causing inhibition at high concentrations and stimulation at low concentrations, and they termed the phenomenon "hormoligosis."[11] The modern term "hormesis" was first used by Stebbing in 1982[12] and has been thoroughly reviewed by Calabrese.[13–17]

In the context of LLLT, the increasing "stimulus" may be irradiation time or increased irradiance. This nonlinear effect contradicts the Bunsen–Roscoe rule of reciprocity (originally formulated for the visual detection of light by photoreceptors[18]), which predicts that if the products of the exposure time in seconds and irradiance in mW/cm^2 are equal, i.e., the energy density is the same, then the changes in the biological endpoint will be equal. This inverse linear relationship between irradiance and time has frequently failed in LLLT research.[7,19]

---

*Based on material first printed in Y. Y. Huang, A. C. Chen, J. D. Carroll, and M. R. Hamblin, "Biphasic dose response in low-level light therapy," *Dose Response* **7**, 358–383 (2009).

A "biphasic" curve can be used to illustrate the expected dose response to light at a subcellular, cellular, tissue, or clinical level. Simply put, it suggests that if insufficient energy is applied, there will be no response (because the minimum threshold has not been met), and if more energy is applied, then a threshold is crossed and biostimulation is achieved. However, when too much energy is applied, then the stimulation disappears and is replaced by bioinhibition. An idealized illustration (Fig. 6.1) similar to that suggested by Sommer[4] helps clarify the concept.

6.2 Biphasic Response: Irradiance

As early as 1978, Endre Mester observed a "threshold phenomenon" after laser irradiation of lymphocytes *in vitro*.[20] In 1991, Peter Bolton irradiated macrophages with two different irradiances (W/cm^2) but the same energy density (J/cm^2) and recorded different results.[21] Karu et al.[19] found that the stimulation of the DNA synthesis rate depends on the light intensity at a constant energy density of 0.1 J/cm^2 with a clear maximum at 0.8 mW/cm^2. In another study,[22] the same group found no less than seven maxima in the dose versus the biological effect curves using a pulsed 810-nm diode laser. Four different biological models were used: luminol-amplified chemiluminescence measured in nucleated cells of murine spleen (splenocytes), bone marrow (karyocytes), and murine blood and adhesion of HeLa cells cultivated *in vitro*. The peaks coincided for all four models. Anders conducted the widest ranging *in vitro* study (on normal human neural progenitor cells) with four different energy density groups; each group tested across a range of six different irradiance parameters,[23] as shown in Table 6.1.

In 1979, Ginsbach found that laser stimulation of wound closure had "no reciprocity relation." His controlled experiments on rats with a He-Ne laser at an energy density of 4 J/cm^2 produced stimulation at an irradiance of 45 mW/cm^2 but not at 12.4 mW/cm^2.[24] Uri Oron[1] showed different reductions of infarct

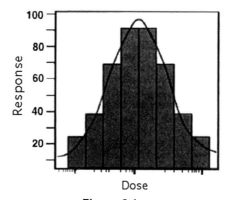

Figure 6.1

Table 6.1 Irradiances and fluences of a 810-nm laser for the differentiation of normal human neural progenitor cells. Cells received light once a day for three days, and neurite outgrowth was measured. NS: no statistical difference; S: group significantly greater than factor group. One-way ANOVA *$p < 0.01$, **$p < 0.001$. (Anders et al., 2007.)

	Average Summed Neurite-Length Parameters					
	1 mW/cm^2	5 mW/cm^2	15 mW/cm^2	19 mW/cm^2	25 mW/cm^2	50 mW/cm^2
0.01 J/cm^2	NS	NS	—	NS	—	—
0.05 J/cm^2	NS	NS	NS	S	S	NS
0.2 J/cm^2	NS	NS	NS	S	S	S
1 J/cm^2	NS	NS	NS	NS	NS	S

size after induced heart attacks in rats. While keeping the energy density constant and varying the irradiance, he found that the beneficial effects were maximal at 5 mW/cm^2 and significantly less effective at lower irradiances (2.5 mW/cm^2) and also at higher irradiances (25 mW/cm^2). Lanzafame et al.[2] conducted a study varying the irradiance and interval of laser-induced healing applied to pressure ulcers in mice. The energy density (5 J/cm^2) was fixed, but four different irradiance (0.7–40 mW/cm^2) parameters were tested, with a significant improvement only occurring for 8 mW/cm^2.

Only one human clinical trial varied irradiance but kept the treatment time the same, and so the energy density (J/cm^2) did not remain the same. This randomized controlled trial (RCT) by Hashimoto et al. treated the stellate ganglion to reduce pain in patients with post-herpetic neuralgia of the facial type. This study compared the effects of 830-nm lasers (delivering 60 mW and 150 mW) and a placebo, each applied for three minutes to the anterior aspect of the lateral process of the seventh cervical vertebrae. Each patient had three treatments (one treatment, three consecutive days), and each treatment was performed with a different laser or placebo. The study was properly blinded and randomized. There was a significant difference in skin temperature of the forehead and in recorded pain scores. The greatest improvements were produced by the 150-mW laser.[25]

There have been several systematic reviews and meta-analyses of RCTs, and these have revealed some irradiance-dependent effects: Bjordal published a review of LLLT for chronic joint disorders and identified 14 RCTs of suitable methodological quality, four of which failed to report a significant effect because the irradiance was either too high or too low and/or delivered insufficient energy. The remaining eight studies produced positive effects.[26] Tumilty et al.[27] reviewed 25 LLLT RCTs of tendinopathies, 13 of which (55%) failed to produce a positive outcome; all of these negative or inconclusive studies that recorded irradiance (or could subsequently be established) had delivered an irradiance in excess of the guidelines set by the World Association for Laser Therapy.[28]

6.3 Biphasic Response: Time or Energy Density

Peter Bolton's study, introduced in Section 3.2, had an energy-density aspect that showed a different response for each of the irradiances used. In the 400-mW/cm^2 study, he found that increasing the energy density from 2.4 J/cm^2 to 7.2 J/cm^2 increased fibroblast proliferation, whereas in the 800-mW/cm^2 group the same process decreased fibroblast proliferation.[21] Anders' study (also mentioned in Section 3.2) looked at four energy-density groups, and for the irradiance parameters that produced significant results, an increasing energy density also increased the neurite length, as shown in Table 6.1.[23] Yamaura and colleagues found a biphasic dose response in MTT activity in rheumatoid arthritis synoviocytes after exposure to an 810-nm laser with a peak at 8 J/cm^2 and a lesser effect at lower and higher fluences.[29] Loevschall measured human oral-mucosal fibroblast cell proliferation by incorporating tritiated thymidine after varying the fluences of an 812-nm laser delivered at 4.5 mW/cm^2; they found a biphasic dose response with a distinct peak at 0.45 J/cm^2.[30] Another study[31] looked at the proliferation of Chinese hamster ovaries and human fibroblasts after various fluences of a He-Ne laser were delivered at a constant irradiance of 1.25 mW/cm^2. They found a clear biphasic dose response with a peak at 0.18 J/cm^2. Zhang et al.[32] found a biphasic dose response in human fibroblast cell numbers after treatment with varying fluences of 628-nm light, with a maximum increase of 30% after 0.88 J/cm^2 and an actual reduction at 9 J/cm^2. Brondon and colleagues[33] found that two treatments per day caused a bigger increase than one or four treatments per day by measuring the proliferation index in human HEP-2 and murine L-929 cell lines. They used a 670-nm LED device with an irradiance of 10 mW/cm^2 and each single treatment was 5 J/cm^2, and the course was stopped after 50 J/cm^2 (at 10, 5, or 2.5 days).

Lopes-Martins found a biphasic response to LLLT based on the number of mononuclear cells that accumulate in the pleural cavity after carrageenan injection. The results included neutrophil influx mice treated with three different laser fluencies (1, 2.5, and 5 J/cm^2), with 2.5 J/cm^2 producing the greatest effect.[34]

As stated in Section 3.2, Hashimoto reported on the laser treatment of the stellate ganglion to reduce pain in patients with post-herpetic neuralgia of the facial type. The study compared the effects of 830-nm lasers delivering 60 mW and 150 mW, and a placebo. The greatest improvements were produced by the 150-mW laser.[25] There have been several systematic reviews and meta-analyses of RCTs that revealed some energy-density-dependent effects.[26,27]

6.4 Beam Measurement Reporting Errors

One notable aspect of the dose-rate (W/cm^2) studies is the wide variation of "optimal" irradiances of *in vitro* studies as they range from 1 to 800 mW/cm^2

in just the few papers referenced in this review. If the primary photoacceptor is cytochrome c oxidase, as postulated here, then why would so many authors arrive at different conclusions for optimal parameters *in vitro*? Should it not be the same for all of them?

Possible explanations include the slightly different wavelengths used or the sensitivity due to the redox state of the mitochondia in the target cells,[35] but the greater contributor might be laser-beam measurement problems. It may be a surprise to nonphysicists that diode laser beams are not inherently round, and even if circularizing lenses are used to correct this fact, then the beam-intensity distribution is not homogeneous. Laser beams are brighter (higher irradiance) in the middle and weaker towards the edge. Cells in the center of a culture well will be exposed to considerably higher irradiances than those on the periphery. Because the edge of a laser beam is hard to define and find, irradiance calculations are significantly different between research centers. Agreement on beam measurement and reporting of intensity distribution is needed to reduce these inconsistencies. This is important not only for *in vitro* studies but also *in vivo* and clinical trials because the reporting of irradiance is just as important, although tissue scattering can diffuse the beam and make nonhomogenous sources less critical to clinical effectiveness.

6.5 Biphasic LLLT Dose Response Studies

6.5.1 *in vitro* activation of NF-kB

Chen et al.[36] hypothesized that NIR light (810-nm laser) would activate the transcription factor NF-kB by generating reactive oxygen species from the mitochondria (see Section 2.5). This hypothesis was tested in mouse embryonic fibroblasts that had been genetically engineered to synthesize luciferase in response to NF-kB activation.[36] A wide range (four orders of magnitude) of delivered fluences was used by adjusting the laser power so that the illumination time was kept constant at five minutes. As shown in Fig. 6.2, there was a biphasic dose-dependent activation of NF-kB as measured by luciferase assay 10 h after the illumination was completed. There was no significant increase at 0.003 J/cm^2 compared to the dark control, a small increase at 0.03 J/cm^2, and the maximum activation was observed at 0.3 J/cm^2. However, at 3 J/cm^2 and especially at 30 J/cm^2, there was a decrease in NF-kB activation, but the level was still higher than that found at 0.03 J/cm^2. The level of luciferase expression was also measured in the presence of cycloheximide (CHI) as a control. CHI is a protein-synthesis inhibitor that removes even the background level of luciferase seen in dark control cells, as well as all of the increases produced by different fluences of 810-nm light.

We tested the hypothesis that the activation of NF-kB by LLLT was mediated by the generation of ROS because NF-kB is known to be a redox-sensitive transcription factor[37] and, moreover, ROS have previously

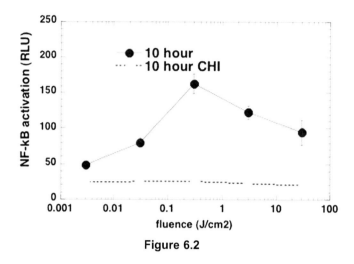

Figure 6.2

been shown to be generated during LLLT.[38–40] Dichlorodihydrofluorescein diacetate (DCHF-DA) was used, which is taken up into cells, hydrolyzed, and then oxidized to a fluorescent form by most species of ROS, probably via lipid peroxides.[41] As can be seen in Fig. 6.3, even the low fluence of 0.003 J/cm^2 produced detectable levels of ROS, more at 0.03 J/cm^2, and the maximum at 0.3 J/cm^2, with a slight decrease observed at 3 J/cm^2. The maximum level observed at 0.3 J/cm^2 was only slightly less than that observed inside the cells after the addition of hydrogen peroxide to the extracellular medium.

6.5.2 Mouse wound healing

An *in vivo* study[42] used a set of fluences of 635-nm ($\pm$15 nm) light delivered from a filtered lamp. The model was a full-thickness dorsal excisional wound in BALB/c mice treated with a single exposure to light 30 minutes after

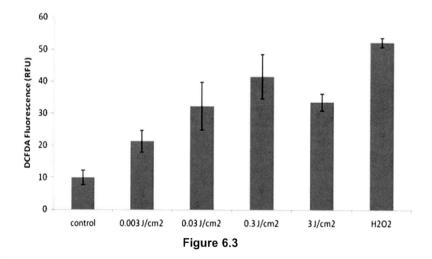

Figure 6.3

wounding. These fluences were 1, 2, 10, and 50 J/cm^2 delivered at a constant fluence rate of 100 mW/cm^2 for 10, 20, 100, and 500 seconds, respectively. The untreated wound in this model tends to expand for 2–3 days after it was made, but even a brief exposure to light soon after wounding reduces or stops the expansion of the wound, and the integrated time course of the wound size can therefore be significantly reduced. The hypothesis is that fibroblasts along the edge of the wounded dermis can be transformed into myofibroblasts, and the contractile nature of these cells with their smooth-muscle actin fibers prevents the wound from expanding. The fibroblast–myofibroblast transition can be mediated by NF-kB activation.[43] As shown in Fig. 6.4, a biphasic dose response with positive effects (difference in the integrated area under the curve of the time course of the wound size compared to no treatment control) appears in low doses with a clear maximum seen at 2 J/cm^2, and the high dose of 50 J/cm^2 worsened the wound-healing time curve, i.e., there was a greater expansion of the wound compared with untreated controls.

6.5.3 Rat arthritis

Another *in vivo* study[44] investigated whether LLLT using an 810-nm laser could have a therapeutic effect in a rat model of inflammatory arthritis caused by zymosan injected into their knee joints. In this model, the severity of the arthritis is quantified by measuring the diameter of the swollen joint every day and plotting a time course for each joint. A comparison was made of illumination regimens consisting of a high and low fluence (3 and 30 J/cm^2), delivered at high and low irradiance (5 and 50 mW/cm^2) using 810-nm laser

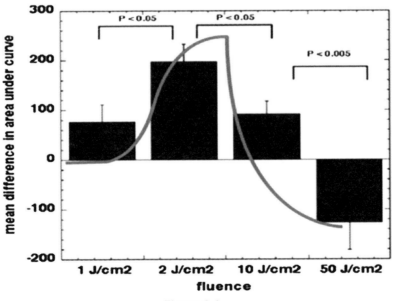

Figure 6.4

light daily for five days, with positive control provided by conventional corticosteroid (dexamethasone) therapy.

Three of the illumination regimens were effective in reducing the mean integrated knee swelling almost as much as the positive control of the powerful steroid, dexamathasone; these regimens were 3 J/cm^2 delivered at 5 mW/cm^2 and 30 J/cm^2 delivered at 50 mW/cm^2 (both of which took 10 minutes), and 30 J/cm^2 delivered at 5 mW/cm^2 (which took 100 minutes). The only ineffective dose regimen was 3 J/cm^2 delivered at 50 mW/cm^2, which took the comparatively short time of one minute to deliver. This observation suggested that the illumination time was an important parameter in some LLLT applications.

6.6 Possible Explanations for Biphasic Dose Response in LLLT

The repeated observations that have been made regarding the biphasic dose response phenomenon in LLLT require some explanation. The natural assumption is that if a small dose of red or near-infrared light produces a significant therapeutic effect, then a larger dose should produce an even more beneficial effect. However, this assumption is frequently not true. This section proposes three possible explanations for the existence of the biphasic dose response based upon the mechanistic considerations outlined in Section 6.2.

6.6.1 Excessive ROS

As discussed in Section 2.5, the light-mediated generation of reactive oxygen species has been observed in many *in vitro* studies and has been proposed to account for the cellular changes observed after LLLT via the activation of redox-sensitive transcription factors.[36] The evidence of ROS-mediated activation of NF-kB in MEF cells presented in Section 4.1 provides additional support for this hypothesis.[36] ROS can have both beneficial and harmful effects;[45] hydrogen peroxide is often used to kill cells *in vitro*.[46] Other examples of ROS, such as singlet oxygen[47] and hydroxyl radicals,[48] are thought to be harmful even at low concentrations. The concept of a biphasic dose response is well established in the field of oxidative stress.[49] If the generation of ROS can be shown to be dose dependent on the delivered energy fluence, it may explain the stimulation and inhibition observed with low and high light fluences.

6.6.2 Excessive NO

The other mechanistic hypothesis that is suggested to explain the cellular effects of LLLT relates to the photolysis of nitrosylated proteins that releases free NO (see Section 2.6). The literature has many papers that discuss the so-called two-faced or "Janus" molecule NO.[50,51] NO can be either protective or harmful, depending on the dose and particularly on the cell or tissue type where it is generated.[52]

6.6.3 Activation of a cytotoxic pathway

The third hypothesis to explain the biphasic dose response of LLLT is the idea that the protective and stimulatory effects of light occur at low doses, but there is an additional pathway that produces damaging effects that only exists at high doses and effectively overwhelms the beneficial effects of low doses of light. Work from South China Normal University provides some support for this hypothesis. Low doses of LLLT were found to phosphorylate the hepatocyte growth factor receptor (c-Met) and initiate signaling via cyclic AMP and Jun kinase and Src.[53] In contrast, high-dose LLLT was found to induce apoptosis via a mitochondrial caspase-3 pathway, and cytochrome c release was attributed to the opening of the mitochondrial permeability transition pore caused by high-level intracellular ROS generation.[54] A secondary signaling pathway through Bax activation was also observed.[54]

6.7 Summary and Conclusion

LLLT delivered at low doses tends to work better than the same wavelength delivered at high levels, which illustrates the basic concept of biphasic dose response or hormesis.[13] In general, fluences of red or NIR as low as 3 or 5 J/cm^2 will be beneficial *in vivo*, but a large dose, e.g., 50 or 100 J/cm^2 will lose the beneficial effect and may even become detrimental. The molecular and cellular mechanisms of LLLT suggest that photons are absorbed by the mitochondria; they stimulate more ATP production and low levels of ROS, which then activates transcription factors, such as NF-kB, to induce many gene transcript products responsible for the beneficial effects of LLLT. ROS are well known to stimulate cellular proliferation at low levels but inhibit proliferation and kill cells at high levels. Nitric oxide is also involved in LLLT and may be photo-released from its binding sites in the respiratory chain and elsewhere. It is possible that NO release in low amounts by low-dose light may be beneficial, while high levels released by high-dose LLLT may be damaging. The third possibility is that LLLT may activate transcription factors, upregulating protective proteins which are anti-apoptotic, and generally promote cell survival. In contrast, it is entirely possible that different transcription factors and cell-signaling pathways, that promote apoptosis, could be activated after higher light exposure. We believe that further advances in the mechanistic understanding of LLLT will continue to be made in the near future. These advances will lead to greater acceptance of LLLT in mainstream medicine and may lead to LLLT being used for serious diseases such as stroke, heart attack, and degenerative brain diseases. Nevertheless, the concept of biphasic dose response or LLLT hormesis (low levels of light are good for you, whereas high levels are bad for you) will remain.

References

1. U. Oron, T. Yaakobi, A. Oron, G. Hayam, L. Gepstein, O. Rubin et al., "Attenuation of infarct size in rats and dogs after myocardial infarction by low-energy laser irradiation," *Lasers Surg. Med.* **28**(3), 204–11 (2001).

2. R. J. Lanzafame, I. Stadler, A. F. Kurtz, R. Connelly, T. A. Peter, Sr., P. Brondon et al., "Reciprocity of exposure time and irradiance on energy density during photoradiation on wound healing in a murine pressure ulcer model," *Lasers Surg. Med.* **39**(6), 534–42 (2007).

3. R. T. Chow, G. Z. Heller, and L. Barnsley, "The effect of 300 mW, 830 nm laser on chronic neck pain: a double-blind, randomized, placebo-controlled study," *Pain.* **124**(1–2), 201–10 (2006).

4. A. P. Sommer, A. L. Pinheiro, A. R. Mester, R. P. Franke, and H. T. Whelan, "Biostimulatory windows in low-intensity laser activation: lasers, scanners, and NASA's light-emitting diode array system," *J. Clin. Laser Med. Surg.* **19**(1), 29–33 (2001).

5. D. Hawkins and H. Abrahamse, "Effect of multiple exposures of low-level laser therapy on the cellular responses of wounded human skin fibroblasts," *Photomed. Laser Surg.* **24**(6), 705–14 (2006).

6. D. H. Hawkins and H. Abrahamse, "The role of laser fluence in cell viability, proliferation, and membrane integrity of wounded human skin fibroblasts following helium-neon laser irradiation," *Lasers Surg. Med.* **38**(1), 74–83 (2006).

7. R. Lubart, R. Lavi, H. Friedmann, and S. Rochkind, "Photochemistry and photobiology of light absorption by living cells," *Photomed. Laser Surg.* **24**(2), 179–85 (2006).

8. H. Schulz, "Uber die Theorie der Arzneimittelwirkung," *Virchows Archiv.* **108**, 423–34 (1877).

9. H. Schulz, "Uber Hefegiste," *Pflügers. Archiv. Gesammte. Physiologie.* **42**, 517–41 (1888).

10. F. Martius, "Das Amdt-Schulz Grandgesetz," *Munch. Med. Wschr.* **70**, 1005–6 (1923).

11. J. F. Townsend and T. D. Luckey, "Hormoligosis in pharmacology," *J. Am. Med. Assoc.* **173**, 44–8 (1960).

12. A. R. Stebbing, "Hormesis; the stimulation of growth by low levels of inhibitors," *Sci. Tot. Environ.* **22**, 213–34 (1982).

13. E. J. Calabrese, "The future of hormesis: where do we go from here?," *Crit. Rev. Toxicol.* **31**(4-5), 637–48 (2001).

14. E. J. Calabrese, "Hormesis: changing view of the dose-response, a personal account of the history and current status," *Mutat. Res.* **511**(3), 181–9 (2002).

15. E. J. Calabrese, "Hormesis: a revolution in toxicology, risk assessment and medicine," *EMBO Rep.* **5**, Spec No: S37–40 (2004).

16. E. J. Calabrese, "Hormesis: from marginalization to mainstream: a case for hormesis as the default dose-response model in risk assessment," *Toxicol. Appl. Pharmacol.* **197**(2), 125–36 (2004).

17. E. J. Calabrese, "Hormetic dose-response relationships in immunology: occurrence, quantitative features of the dose response, mechanistic foundations, and clinical implications," *Crit. Rev. Toxicol.* **35**(2-3), 89–295 (2005).

18. G. S. Brindley, "The Bunsen-Roscoe law for the human eye at very short durations," *J. Physiol.* **118**, 135–9 (1952).

19. T. I. Karu and S. F. Kolyakov, "Exact action spectra for cellular responses relevant to phototherapy," *Photomed. Laser Surg.* **23**(4), 355–61 (2005).

20. E. Mester, S. Nagylucskay, W. Waidelich, S. Tisza, P. Greguss, D. Haina et al., "Effects of direct laser radiation on human lymphocytes," *Arch. Dermatol. Res.* **263**(3), 241–5 (1978).

21. P. Bolton, S. Young, and M. Dyson, "Macrophage responsiveness to light therapy with varying power and energy densities," *Laser Ther.* **3**, 6–9 (1991).

22. T. I. Karu, L. V. Pyatibrat, and T. P. Ryabykh, "Nonmonotonic behavior of the dose dependence of the radiation effect on cells in vitro exposed to pulsed laser radiation at lambda = 820 nm," *Lasers Surg. Med.* **21**(5), 485–92 (1997).

23. J. Anders, T. Romanczyk, H. Moges, I. Ilev, R. Waynant, and L. Longo, Light Interaction With Human Central Nervous System Progenitor Cells. NAALT conference proceedings 2007. (2007).

24. G. Ginsbach, "Laser induced stimulation of woundhealing in bad healing wounds," *Proc. Laser '79 Opto. Elektronics Conf. Munich IPC Science and Technology Press Guildford UK* **5**, (1979).

25. K. Hashimoto, O. Kemmotsu, H. Otsuka, R. Numazawa, and Y. Ohta, "Efficacy of laser irradiation on the area near the stellate ganglion is dose-dependent: a double-blind crossover placebo-controlled study," *Laser Therapy.* **7**, 5 (1997).

26. J. M. Bjordal, C. Couppe, R. T. Chow, J. Tuner, and E. A. Ljunggren, "A systematic review of low level laser therapy with location-specific doses for pain from chronic joint disorders," *Aust. J. Physiother.* **49**(2), 107–16 (2003).

27. S. Tumilty, J. Munn, S. McDonough, D. A. Hurley, J. R. Basford, and G. D. Baxter, Low Level Laser Treatment of Tendinopathy: A Systematic Review with Meta-analysis Photomed Laser Surg.; Ahead of print. (2009)

28. J. M. Bjordal, "Low level laser therapy (LLLT) and World Association for Laser Therapy (WALT) dosage recommendations," *Photomedicine and laser surgery* **30**(2), 61–2 (2012).

29. M. Yamaura, M. Yao, I. Yaroslavsky, R. Cohen, M. Smotrich, and I. E. Kochevar, "Low level light effects on inflammatory cytokine production by rheumatoid arthritis synoviocytes," *Lasers Surg. Med.* **41**(4), 282–90 (2009).

30. H. Loevschall and D. Arenholt-Bindslev, "Effect of low level diode laser irradiation of human oral mucosa fibroblasts in vitro," *Lasers Surg. Med.* **14**(4), 347–54 (1994).

31. F. A. al-Watban and B. L. Andres, "The effect of He-Ne laser (632.8 nm) and Solcoseryl in vitro," *Lasers Med. Sci.* **16**(4), 267–75 (2001).

32. Y. Zhang, S. Song, C. C. Fong, C. H. Tsang, Z. Yang, and M. Yang, "cDNA microarray analysis of gene expression profiles in human fibroblast cells irradiated with red light," *J. Invest. Dermatol.* **120**(5), 849–57 (2003).

33. P. Brondon, I. Stadler, and R. J. Lanzafame, "A study of the effects of phototherapy dose interval on photobiomodulation of cell cultures," *Lasers Surg. Med.* **36**(5), 409–13 (2005).

34. R. A. Lopes-Martins, R. Albertini, P. S. Martins, J. M. Bjordal, and H. C. Faria Neto, "Spontaneous effects of low-level laser therapy (650 nm) in acute inflammatory mouse pleurisy induced by Carrageenan," *Photomed. Laser Surg.* **23**(4), 377–81 (2005).

35. J. Tafur and P. J. Mills, "Low-intensity light therapy: exploring the role of redox mechanisms," *Photomed. Laser Surg.* **26**(4), 323–8 (2008).

36. A. C.-H. Chen, P. R. Arany, Y.-Y. Huang, E. M. Tomkinson, T. Saleem, F. E. Yull et al., editors. "Low level laser therapy activates NF-kB via generation of reactive oxygen species in mouse embryonic fibroblasts," *Mechanisms for Low-Light Therapy IV*; San Jose: The International Society for Optical Engineering, Bellingham, WA (2009).

37. R. Schreck, K. Albermann, and P. A. Baeuerle, "Nuclear factor kappa B: an oxidative stress-responsive transcription factor of eukaryotic cells (a review)," *Free Radic. Res. Commun.* **17**(4), 221–37 (1992).

38. E. Alexandratou, D. Yova, P. Handris, D. Kletsas, and S. Loukas, "Human fibroblast alterations induced by low power laser irradiation at the single cell level using confocal microscopy," *Photochem. Photobiol. Sci.* **1**(8), 547–52 (2002).

39. R. Lubart, M. Eichler, R. Lavi, H. Friedman, and A. Shainberg, "Low-energy laser irradiation promotes cellular redox activity," *Photomed. Laser Surg.* **23**(1), 3–9 (2005).

40. G. Pal, A. Dutta, K. Mitra, M. S. Grace, T. B. Romanczyk, X. Wu et al., "Effect of low intensity laser interaction with human skin fibroblast cells using fiber-optic nano-probes," *J. Photochem. Photobiol. B* **86**(3), 252–61 (2007).

41. G. Diaz, S. Liu, R. Isola, A. Diana, and A. M. Falchi, "Mitochondrial localization of reactive oxygen species by dihydrofluorescein probes," *Histochem. Cell. Biol.* **120**(4), 319–25 (2003).

42. T. N. Demidova-Rice, E. V. Salomatina, A. N. Yaroslavsky, I. M. Herman, and M. R. Hamblin, "Low-level light stimulates excisional wound healing in mice," *Lasers Surg. Med.* **39**(9), 706–15 (2007).

43. M. R. Watson, K. Wallace, R. G. Gieling, D. M. Manas, E. Jaffray, R. T. Hay et al., "NF-kappaB is a critical regulator of the survival of rodent and human hepatic myofibroblasts," *J. Hepatol.* **48**(4), 589–97 (2008).

44. A. P. Castano, T. Dai, I. Yaroslavsky, R. Cohen, W. A. Apruzzese, M. H. Smotrich et al., "Low-level laser therapy for zymosan-induced arthritis in rats: Importance of illumination time," *Lasers Surg. Med.* **39**(6), 543–50 (2007).

45. S. S. Huang and R. L. Zheng, "Biphasic regulation of angiogenesis by reactive oxygen species," *Pharmazie.* **61**(3), 223–9 (2006).

46. J. A. Imlay, "Cellular defenses against superoxide and hydrogen peroxide," *Annu Rev. Biochem.* **77**, 755–76 (2008).

47. L. O. Klotz, K. D. Kroncke, and H. Sies, "Singlet oxygen-induced signaling effects in mammalian cells," *Photochem. Photobiol. Sci.* **2**(2), 88–94 (2003).

48. W. A. Pryor, K. N. Houk, C. S. Foote, J. M. Fukuto, L. J. Ignarro, G. L. Squadrito et al., "Free radical biology and medicine: it's a gas, man!," *Am J. Physiol. Regul. Integr. Comp. Physiol.* **291**(3), R491–511 (2006).

49. R. M. Day and Y. J. Suzuki, "Cell proliferation, reactive oxygen and cellular glutathione," *Dose Response.* **3**(3), 425–42 (2005).

50. E. Anggard, "Nitric oxide: mediator, murderer, and medicine," *Lancet.* **343**(8907), 1199–206 (1994).

51. P. Lane and S. S. Gross, "Cell signaling by nitric oxide," *Semin. Nephrol.* **19**(3), 215–29 (1999).

52. E. J. Calabrese, "Nitric oxide: biphasic dose responses," *Crit. Rev. Toxicol.* **31**(4–5), 489–501 (2001).

53. X. Gao and D. Xing, "Molecular mechanisms of cell proliferation induced by low power laser irradiation," *J. Biomed. Sci.* **16**, 4 2009.

54. S. Wu, D. Xing, X. Gao, and W. R. Chen, "High fluence low-power laser irradiation induces mitochondrial permeability transition mediated by reactive oxygen species," *J. Cell. Physiol.* **218**(3), 603–11 (2009).

Chapter 7
Pre-conditioning*

7.1 Introduction

Many diseases and traumatic events involving tissue damage are injurious because of ischemia, a sudden or more gradual process characterized by the deprivation of life-sustaining oxygen. Ischemic heart disease and ischemic stroke account for the largest cause of mortality and morbidity in modern life. The term "pre-conditioning" (PC) was first applied to a regimen in which repetitive short episodes of ischemia and reperfusion could lead the myocardium to develop resistance to a subsequent ischemic insult, i.e., heart attack.[1] A novel treatment strategy to counter ischemic cardiac disease and stroke has been developed, termed ischemic pre-conditioning (IPC).[2] IPC is based on the premise that brief durations of ischemia induce intrinsic cellular defense systems and lead to the tolerance of vital organs to subsequent, more-severe ischemia. During direct pre-conditioning, for example, brief occlusions of a coronary or carotid artery protect the heart or the brain from longer durations of ischemia and reduce the resulting infarct volumes after heart attack or stroke. In remote IPC, brief ischemia is deliberately induced in one organ, typically an easily accessible tissue such as a limb, and subsequently protects a distant organ (typically the brain or the heart) from more-severe ischemia. This concept was originally discovered using a rabbit heart-attack model, when an initial episode of mild ischemia followed by reperfusion made the heart more resistant to a subsequent lethal ischemic insult.[3] Since then, IPC has become a powerful experimental technique to combat ischemic insults in most organs and has been extensively studied in many laboratories around the world.[4]

In the brain, IPC responses are found to occur in specific time windows consisting of an early and a late phase. The early phase, if the duration between the initial pre-conditioning and the final insult is around one hour, has the maximum protective effect.[4] During the second (late) phase, the combination of released factors and activated pathways results in delayed

*Based on material first printed in T. Agrawal et al., "Pre-conditioning with low-level laser (light) therapy: light before the storm," *Dose Response* **12**, 619–649 (2014).

pre-conditioning. If this late phase is extended to several days after the pre-conditioning insult, it may provide more robust and longer lasting neuroprotection than the early phase.

7.2 Mechanisms of IPC

It was previously believed that the mechanism of IPC was mediated by increased flow through the coronary collateral circulation. However, this theory was abandoned after a study by Murray et al.[3] in which they measured tissue radioactivity after injecting radiolabeled microspheres into the left atrial chamber of a dog heart and found no difference in the collateral blood flow between pre-conditioned dogs and controls.[3] IPC represents a complex molecular process that is rapidly generated and multifactorial in nature and then transduced into an intracellular message and amplified to produce the final effector mechanism.[5] In response to a brief duration of sublethal ischemic insults, the receptors of the triggering factors may activate, signaling pathways that consist of a well-organized series of events (see Fig. 7.1). These delayed PC-activated signaling pathways govern gene expression that results in cells expressing a phenotype that is highly resistant to ischemic insults. Locally released agonists, such as adenosine, bradykinin, catecholamines, and opioids, activate the protective response through various G-protein coupled receptors that, when stimulated, increase the activity of phospholipases C and D.[6] Kinases, such as protein kinase C tyrosine kinase p38 MAPKinase, contribute to the signaling pathway. Ytrehus et al. demonstrated inhibition of the protection obtained after IPC by administering PKC inhibitors in the rabbit heart model.[7] It has also been shown that among the PKC isozymes, the PKC-ε isoenzyme specifically provides cardioprotection against ischemia/

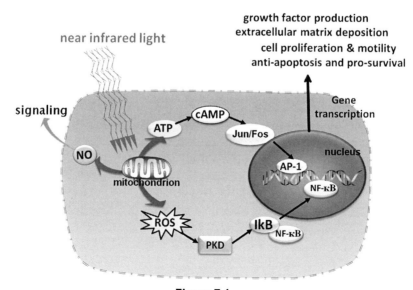

Figure 7.1

reperfusion damage.[8,9] Consistently, in all of the animal models tested—including mice, rats, rabbits, and pigs—the PKC-ε-selective activating peptide protected hearts, and inhibitors of PKC-ε inhibited ischemic/hypoxic or pharmacologic pre-conditioning.[6] On the other hand, the deletion of cardiac PKC-ε resulted in a failure to decrease the infarct size in mice, suggesting a major role of PKC-ε activation in IPC.[10] Another hypothesis for the underlying mechanism of IPC involves the production of an inducible 70-kD stress or heat shock protein (HSP70i).[11] A variety of stimuli (including hemodynamic overload, myocyte stretch, hypertension, ischemia, exercise, and oxidative stress) lead to an increase in the synthesis of HSP70i. After 24 h of IPC, it has been shown that the levels of HSP70i were increased, and, notably, overexpression of the HSP70i gene in transgenic mice decreased the infarct size and improved myocardial recovery.[12,13] The mechanism of cardioprotection in IPC by HSP70i could be due to the identification of damaged proteins and the synthesis of new proteins under myocardial stress.[14]

Another primary mediator in IPC could be the activation of hypoxia inducible factor 1α (HIF-1α), which is the means by which tissue and cells can sense hypoxia. An autonomous adaptive response by the cell to chronic hypoxia regulated by HIF-1 is decreased mitochondrial mass and/or metabolism. Fibroblasts deficient in HIF-1, when exposed to chronic hypoxia, generate high levels of ROS and lead to cell death.[15] The HIF-1α gene has been shown to produce cardioprotective effects during PC by stimulating the secretion of the hormone erythropoietin (EPO) in the kidney.[16] HIF-1α knockout (KO) mice exposed to alternating cycles of ambient hypoxia and re-oxygenation failed to develop protective cardiac PC as compared to the wild-type mice.[17] The direct administration of EPO to the perfused hearts of HIF-1α KO mice resulted in acute protection from ischemia-reperfusion injury.[18] The levels of adenosine increased in the hearts subjected to IPC, and the blocking of the adenosine receptor inhibited the protective effects of IPC, whereas adenosine receptor agonists protected the heart.[19,20] The HIF-1 gene induced CD73, the enzyme that produces adenosine, thus indirectly helping with IPC. On the other hand, HIF-1 regulates mitochondrial metabolism and thus contributes to the protective effects of IPC.[20] Increased plasma IL-10 levels and decreased myocardial infarct size are observed in remote IPC wild-type mice but could not be demonstrated in HIF-1α KO mice. Injecting the active form of HIF-1α into the mouse hind limb muscle significantly increased plasma IL-10 levels and decreased the myocardial infarct size. In conclusion, HIF-1 plays a major role in IPC and thus protecting the myocardium.[21]

7.3 Other Modalities for Pre-conditioning

In addition to ischemic pre-conditioning, other effective PC stimuli and regimens have been reported. These are both numerous and diverse,[22] including hypothermia, hyperthermia, physical exercise, hyperbaric oxygen, exposure to neurotoxins and pharmacological agents (such as resveratrol, volatile anesthetics, and xenon), and even the mild inflammation produced by an endotoxin.

In aged animals, there is a decrease in ischemic tolerance, which leads to the impairment of the cardioprotective effect of IPC. Heat pre-conditioning (HP) protects against myocardial injuries induced by eight weeks of overload training. HP enables one to adjust the activities of creatine kinase (CK), catalase (CAT), and superoxide dismutase (SOD); and it regulates the expressions of apoptosis-related genes (Bcl-2, Bax, caspase-3, caspase-9) and adhesion molecules (ICAM-1, VCAM-1, and PECAM-1), resulting in enhanced capacity against overload-training-induced injuries and reduced damage to the myocardium.[23] Hypothermic preconditioning is induced by rapid cycles of cooling and warming which produces sub-lethal stress to the brain's microenvironment leading to the protection of the CNS from successive insults such as cerebral ischemia.[24] Exercise pre-conditioning lessens the harmful effect of ischemia/reperfusion injury by increasing the expression of neurotrophic factors, the extracellular matrix (ECM) proteins, integrins, angiogenic factors, and heat-shock proteins (Hsp-70) and by decreasing the expression of matrix metalloproteinase (MMP-9) and Toll-like receptor-4. Chronic exercise pre-conditioning increases cerebral metabolism following periods of hypoxia by increasing the neuronal response by increasing ATP production.[25,26]

Pre-conditioning with hyperbaric oxygen reduces the number of apoptotic neural cells and promotes nervous functional recovery in rats after spinal cord injury.[27] Additionally, pre-conditioning coronary-artery-disease patients with hyperbaric oxygen prior to an on-pump cardiopulmonary bypass or coronary artery bypass graft (CABG) surgery can improve left ventricular function and result in reduced myocardial injury, less intraoperative blood loss, shorter length of stay in intensive care, fewer post-operative complications, and reduced patient costs, post-CABG.[28] Lifelong caloric restriction has been found to modify the physiological and pathophysiological changes induced by aging and also increase life expectancy. In aged rats, short-term caloric restriction was found to provide cardioprotection by improving ischemic tolerance.[29] Pre-treatment with perivascular or intramuscular neurotoxins, such as botulinum toxin A (Btx-A), has a potential role in the ischemic pre-conditioning of muscle flaps, which is believed to be achieved through the release of substance P, calcitonin gene-related peptide (CGRP), and vascular endothelial growth factor (VEGF).[30] Pre-conditioning with resveratrol has been found to induce brain tolerance against ischemia by suppressing the inflammatory response via regulation of NF-κB, COX-2, and iNOS.[31] The administration of volatile anesthetics before a prolonged ischemic episode is known as anesthetic pre-conditioning, which has been developed as a cardioprotective modality in both animal and human coronary-disease models.[32] Moreover, pre-conditioning with anesthetics, such as xenon gas, can also exert neuroprotective and cardioprotective effects in different models, suggesting the use of xenon pre-conditioning as an alternative strategy for the prevention of various neurological and cardiovascular diseases.[33] Studies have shown that lipopolysaccharide (LPS) from Gram-negative bacteria used in pre-conditioning provides neuroprotection against successive cerebral ischemic injury. LPS activates Toll-like receptors and causes systemic inflammation. After stroke, mice pre-conditioned with LPS had a significant decrease in the levels of TNF-alpha, neuronal TNF-receptor 1 (TNFR1), and TNFR-associated death domain (TRADD). Additionally, to establish LPS-induced tolerance before ischemia, it was necessary to show up-regulation of TNF-alpha, whereas if LPS was given during ischemia, then suppression of TNF-alpha signaling was associated with neuroprotection after LPS pre-conditioning.[34]

7.4 Similarities between IPC and LLLT

Part of the aim of this review is to draw comparisons between the hypothesized mechanisms of IPC and those of LLLT when used during pre-conditioning or post-injury. A remarkable number of similarities can be found between the two modalities, although there are also some differences. One of the unifying mechanisms is hypothesized to exist at the level of mitochondria.[36]

7.5 Skeletal Muscle Pre-conditioning through Light

In acute conditions, skeletal muscle fatigue impairs the strength of the muscle, its motor coordination, and its capacity to perform work.[37] Overall fatigue decreases the muscle function, which is thought to be a result of metabolic changes such as the depletion of ATP and glycogen, oxidative stress, tissue hypoxia, and blood acidification. Phototherapy has been shown to improve muscle fatigue and exhaustion.[38] Studies have shown that pre-treatment with specific doses of phototherapy decreases inflammatory biomarkers and lactate levels in blood after strenuous upper- and lower-extremity exercise.[39] On the basis of these studies, it can be inferred that pre-conditioning the muscle with phototherapy increases the contractile function, decreases exercise-induced muscle fatigue, and improves post-exercise recovery.

There are two different phases of exercise-induced damage; one is primary and the other is secondary. The primary phase of muscle damage results from direct exercise-induced mechanical stress, and secondary muscle damage is due to the inflammatory response that follows after mechanical stress.[40] Pre-conditioning with phototherapy protects the muscle from both primary and secondary damage, whereas phototherapy administered after injury protects cells from secondary damage only. *In vivo* studies have shown that applying pre-conditioning phototherapy to injured muscles produces anti-inflammatory and antioxidant effects, thus protecting the muscle from secondary damage.[41]

In order for the muscle to receive the optimum irradiation, the irradiation points should be designed to cover the largest area and to better distribute the energy applied over the muscles.[42] Figures 7.2 and 7.3 illustrate some examples of the number and distribution of the irradiation points on femoral quadriceps using LLLT or LEDT.[42]

Studies support the hypothesis that the ergogenic effects of phototherapy on muscles are due to increases in intramuscular micro-circulation,[43] decreases in lactic acid production,[44–46] improved mitochondrial function, improved antioxidant ability of the exercising muscles, enhanced contractile function, prevention of exercise-induced cell damage, and improved post-exercise recovery

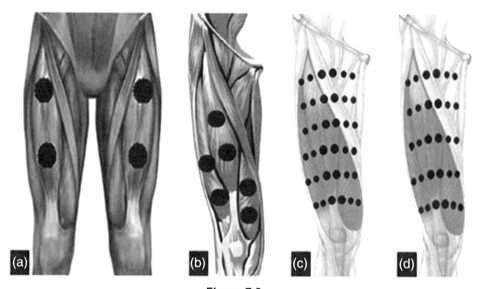

Figure 7.2

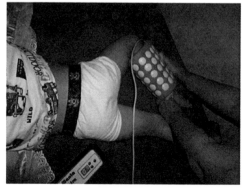

Figure 7.3

of strength and function.[47–49] Borsa et al. critically evaluated these studies that address the ability of phototherapeutic devices, such as lasers and LEDs, to improve skeletal muscle contractile function, decrease exercise-induced muscle fatigue, and enable post-exercise recovery.[49] The main outcome measures included total lapsed time to fatigue, number of repetitions to fatigue, overall work performed, maximal voluntary isometric contraction (strength), electromyographic activity, and post-exercise biomarker levels. Ten of the randomized controlled trials met the inclusion criteria including 32 data sets. In all of the studies, Borsa et al. consistently found that phototherapy administered before resistance exercise provided ergogenic and prophylactic benefits to skeletal muscle.[49]

A randomized double-blind study using 22 untrained male volunteers was performed by Marchi et al. The subjects were pre-conditioned with LLLT for 30 seconds on a lower limb before a standardized exercise protocol on a treadmill until they were exhausted. Figures 7.4 and 7.5 show the pre- and post-exercise activity markers of muscle-damage lactate dehydrogenase (LDH) and CK. Marchi et al. observed that pre-conditioning with LLLT before exercise also decreased the post-exercise improvement in the activities of CK and LDH compared to the placebo group, demonstrating that pre-treatment with LLLT can protect skeletal muscle against exercise-induced damage in long-duration exercises.[50] In a similar study, male volleyball players were pre-conditioned with

1. an active LEDT cluster-probe (660 nm = 10 mW, 850 nm = 30 mW),
2. a placebo cluster probe with no output, and
3. a single-diode 810-nm, 200-mW laser on the rectus femoris muscle and followed by three Wingate cycle tests.

Post-exercise CK levels were significantly lower in the active LEDT cluster group compared to the placebo cluster or single-diode group (Fig. 7.6).[45]

Conversely, pre-conditioning with LEDT in healthy male volunteers did not improve maximal knee extensor muscle isokinetic voluntary contractions (pre-MVC) performed before the isokinetic fatigue test as compared to the placebo group. However, higher torque values were observed in post-MVC subjects pre-conditioned with LEDT compared to the placebo group (Fig. 7.7). Pre-treatment with LEDT increased the exercise performance by producing higher isometric torque after high-intensity concentric isokinetic exercise.[43]

Leal-Junior et al. performed a meta-analysis to explore the effects of phototherapy applied before, during, and after exercise. Data from 13 randomized control trials was assessed based on the number of repetitions and time until exhaustion for muscle performance and the CK activity to assess the risk for exercise-induced muscle damage. The meta-analysis concluded that pre-conditioning skeletal muscles with phototherapy (lasers and LEDs) improves muscular performance and accelerates recovery.[51]

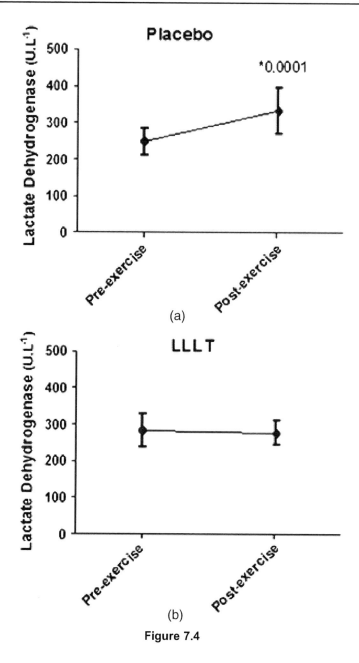

Figure 7.4

7.6 Improving Inflammation and the Analgesic Effect

In temporomandibular joint (TMJ) disorders, pain is usually a very common finding. Barretto et al. studied the effect of LLLT on the pain and inflammation of rat TMJs.[52] In order to assess the nociceptive response, formalin and carrageenan was injected to induce inflammation into the rat TMJ. Nociceptive responses were quantified by assessing behavioral responses categorized by

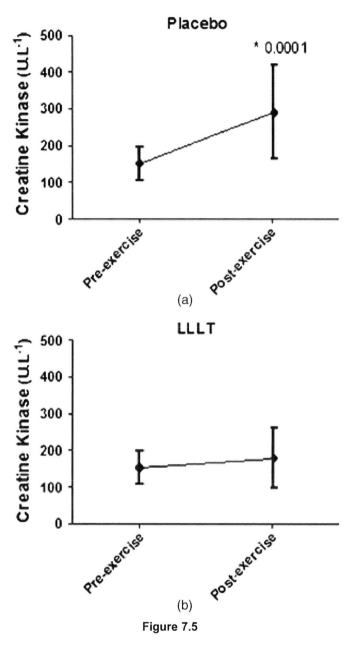

Figure 7.5

rubbing the orofacial region and flinching the head quickly. Baretto et al. observed that rats pre-treated with diclofenac sodium (10 mg/kg i.p.) and LLLT infrared (LST group, 780 nm, 70 mW, 30 s, 2.1 J, 52.5 J/cm^2 GaAlAs) had a significantly reduced formalin nociceptive response. The inflammatory response was assessed by the presence of infiltrate rich in neutrophils, and the presence of liquefactive necrosis and interstitial edema, hemorrhagic areas, or enlargement of the joint space in the region during histomorphological analysis. The rats

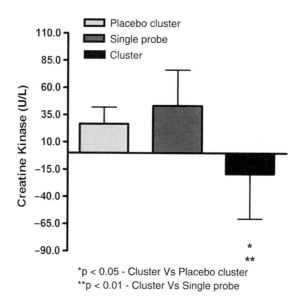

*p < 0.05 - Cluster Vs Placebo cluster
**p < 0.01 - Cluster Vs Single probe

Figure 7.6

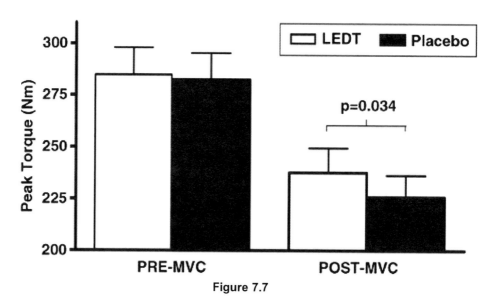

Figure 7.7

pre-treated with LLLT displayed a significantly reduced inflammatory response and exuberant granulation tissue with higher vascularization and the formation of new collagen fibers. The study established that the pre-conditioning LLLT had an anti-nociceptive and anti-inflammatory effect on the inflammation induced in the TMJ of rodents.[52]

A similar study, revealing the effect of infrared LLLT in modulating the inflammatory processes and immunological responses, was performed on mouse hind paws. Carrageenan inoculation (CGN) was used to induce edema into the plantar surface of the left hind paw of male mice. The animals were distributed into five groups: CGN (control), no treatment; Diclo, sodium diclofenac; Paw, LLLT on the paw; Ly, LLLT on the inguinal lymph nodes; and Paw+Ly, LLLT on both paw and lymph nodes. They were also subdivided by time of irradiation: A, 1 h and 2 h before CGN; B, 1 h and immediately before CGN; C, 1 and 2 h after CGN; and D, 3.5 and 4.5 h after CGN. Figure 7.8 shows the average of the volume of edema at time A. The mice were pre-conditioned with irradiation 2 h and 1 h before edema induction. The study showed that by the second hour there was a steady decrease in the edema of Paw+Ly group, and it was lower than all irradiated groups by the fourth hour, suggesting that the Paw+Ly group was the best irradiation option when pre-conditioned 2 h and 1 h before edema induction. Figure 7.9 shows the average of the volume of edema at time B, where pre-conditioning was performed 1 h and immediately before the edema induction. The Ly group was the best group to prevent edema 1 h and immediately before the induction, and the edema reduction was 44.9% compared with the CGN group. These results suggest that LLLT pre-conditioning produced both anti-inflammatory and pro-inflammatory effects, depending on the site and timing of irradiation.[53]

LLLT has been implicated in reducing neuropathic pain by releasing local neurotransmitters such as serotonin,[54] stimulating the release of endorphins, and reducing inflammatory cells.[55–57] As a mode of peripheral endogenous opioid analgesia, the opioid-containing immune cells migrate to inflamed sites and release endorphins to inhibit pain. Pre-conditioning of blood by LLLT via peripheral endogenous opioid analgesia in a rat model of inflamed paw tissue induces analgesia that was transiently antagonized by naloxone. Up-regulation

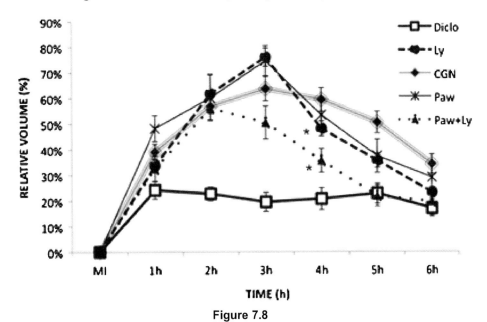

Figure 7.8

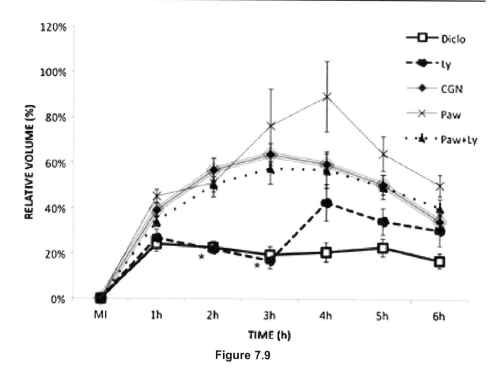

Figure 7.9

in the expression of an peripheral opioid precursor, including endorphin precursors, pro-opiomelanocortin, and corticotrophin-releasing factor in blood cells suggests that direct induction by LLLT can mediate analgesia.[55]

Another study exploring the effect of pre-conditioning with light to reduce pain in rats was performed by Yang et al.[58] They pre-treated with a 650-nm laser and moxibustion in a visceral traction pain model of rats. The differences in the pain score, systolic pressure, activity of acetylcholinesterase (AChE), leu-enkephaline (LEK), and the positive index of c-Fos protein and glial fibrillary acidic protein (GFAP) were assessed. The study determined that the pre-conditioned group that received both laser light and moxibustion could inhibit visceral traction pain by a mechanism that might be due to decreasing the activity of AChE and increasing the activity of LEK, thereby decreasing the expression of c-Fos protein and GFAP.[58]

The aforementioned studies suggest that pre-conditioning with photo-therapy might reduce pain and inflammation. Although the mechanism needs to be further explored, this gives us hope in clinical practice for various pain syndromes.

7.7 Reducing Damage after Heart Attack

The beneficial effect of LLLT has been revealed in the infarcted heart model of rat and dogs, which showed a reduction of 50–70% of infarct size in

4–6 weeks post-infarction.[59–61] A study by Oron et al. irradiated a heart with LLLT in both intact and post-infarction rats. Myocardial infarction (MI) was induced by occlusion of the left anterior descending artery.[62] The myocardium was irradiated for two minutes at an energy density of 5 and 12 mW/cm^2 and pre-conditioned with LLLT; after seven days, myocardial infarction was induced, and the rats were euthanized 21 days post- infarction. Figure 7.10 shows the effect of pre-conditioning with LLLT before MI, following the development of infarct post-MI. Tuby et al. observed that laser-irradiated pre-conditioned hearts with a power density of 5 mW/cm^2 had 64% smaller infarct size, and with a power density of 12 mW/cm^2 they had a 69% smaller infarct size compared to those that were not pre-conditioned with laser irradiation prior to MI-induction. The expression of genes [iNOS and vascular endothelial growth factor (VEGF)] responsible for angiogenesis and cardio-protection was analyzed. Pre-conditioning the heart with laser treatment before infarction induction resulted in increased levels of VEGF and iNOS in the rat hearts and a significant reduction in the infarct size.[62]

Another study by Zhang et al. studied the effect of pre-conditioning the infarcted myocardium with LLLT prior to cell transplantation.[63] Cell transplantation has emerged as a promising method to regenerate the injured myocardium. Myocardium infarction was induced by ligating the left anterior descending artery of rats. Pre-conditioning to the myocardium was performed by irradiating with a 635-nm, 5-mW diode laser and energy density of 0.96 J/cm^2 for 150 seconds. After three weeks, bone marrow mesenchymal stem cells (BMSCs) were injected into rats with or without LLLT pre-treatment. After LLLT pre-conditioning, there was increased protein and mRNA expression of VEGF, glucose-regulated protein 78 (GRP78), as well as increased superoxide dismutase (SOD) activity and reduced

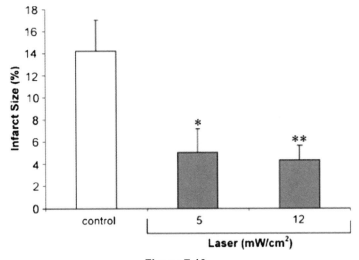

Figure 7.10

malondialdehyde (MDA) in the infarcted myocardium. LLLT pre-conditioning increased the cell-survival rate, decreased apoptotic percentage of implanted BMSCs and increased angiogenesis. The study established that LLLT pre-conditioning is a unique noninvasive approach for cell transplantation given intraoperatively to augment cell survival and therapeutic prospects.[63]

7.8 Protecting Cells from Toxins

In mammalian tissues, the major photoacceptor molecules that absorb light in NIR range are hemoglobin, myoglobin, and cytochrome c oxidase.[64] Among these, only cytochrome c oxidase (EC 1.9.3.1) has been implicated in the production of energy. Cytochrome c oxidase, a photoacceptor in the NIR range, plays an important role in therapeutic photobiomodulation.[64] In primary neuronal cultures, a 670-nm LED in the NIR range was able to reverse the effect of tetrodotoxin (TTX, a voltage-dependent sodium channel blocker), which impedes neuronal impulse activity, decreases ATP demand, and down-regulates cytochrome c oxidase activity. The treatment with a 670-nm LED not only brought the cytochrome c oxidase back to control levels but also up-regulated enzyme activity of normal neurons above control levels.[64] LED treatments improved the retinal function in rats intoxicated with methanol by removing the inhibition of formic acid on cytochrome c oxidase,[65] and thus they play a significant role in the therapeutic process of photobiomodulation. Based on these findings, Wong-Riley et al. studied the effect of the cytochrome c oxidase inhibitor, potassium cyanide (KCN), on primary cultured neurons and whether KCN could reduce the beneficial effect of LED treatment.[66] They observed that LED treatment partially restored cytochrome c oxidase activity which had been blocked by KCN (10–100 μm) and significantly reduced neuronal cell death (induced by KCN at 300 μm) from 83.6% to 43.5%. Pre-conditioning of the primary neuronal cells enhanced the protective action of LED during KCN exposure (10–100 μm). LED pre-treatment for 10 minutes using a total energy density of 30 J/cm^2 effectively reduced the number of neurons exhibiting cell death after 300 μm KCN by 48%. Thus, pre-conditioning of neuronal cells by photobiomodulation up-regulated cytochrome c oxidase, which led to increased energy metabolism in neurons and promoted wound healing and reversed intoxication by various toxins that deactivate cytochrome c oxidase *in vitro*.[66]

Liang et al. investigated the effect of NIR-LED pre-conditioning on primary neuronal cultures to test if it could inhibit apoptotic cell death induced by KCN.[67] The primary neuronal cells were cultured from postnatal rat visual cortex and were pre-treated with a LED for 10 minutes at a total energy density of 30 J/cm^2 and were then exposed to potassium cyanide (100–300 μm) for 28 h. The neural cell death via apoptosis was confirmed by an electron microscope (Hoechst 33258), single-stranded DNA, Bax, and active caspase-3. LED pre-conditioning, applied to the primary neuronal cells, significantly reduced apoptosis, representing a 50.3% (100-μm KCN) and 32.8% (300-μm KCN) reduction. LED pre-treatment significantly decreased the expression of KCN-induced caspase-3, reversed the increased expression of Bax, and decreased the expression of Bcl-2 to control levels. The study concluded that pre-conditioning with light partly protected the neuronal cells from cyanide by a mechanism most likely involving a decrease of ROS production, down-regulation of pro-apoptotic proteins, activation of anti-apoptotic proteins, and an increase in the energy metabolism in the neurons.[67]

7.9 Wound Healing

The penetration of NIR is deeper than UV or visible light and is harmless to living tissue. Therapeutic devices using NIR have successfully treated various injuries, chiefly infected, ischemic, and hypoxic wounds.[68–70] Studies have shown that NIR promotes wound healing, but the mechanisms are poorly understood.

Wound healing is a complex process consisting of multiple physiologic events that are controlled by an infinite array of signaling mechanisms.[71] Any dysregulation in the process of wound healing leads to abnormal scarring and might lead to the development of keloids and hypertrophic cells. Treatment of these abnormal scars is challenging for clinicians and is associated with low self-esteem and impaired quality of life in affected individuals. Recent studies have implicated a major role of transforming growth factor beta-I (TGF-β1) in the formation of hypertrophic scars and keloids. A higher expression or dysregulation of TGF-β1 is associated with fibroblastic proliferation and excess collagen deposition.[72,73] LLLT with red light and NIR has been shown to promote wound healing, including modulation of TGF-β1, making it useful in scar treatment. A study by Barolet et al. used LED pre-conditioning with NIR irradiation (805 nm at 30 mW/cm^2) for 30 days in three patients prone to developing hypertrophic scars or keloids after surgery. They found a significant improvement in the NIR-treated areas compared to the control scars. The enhancement of the wound-healing process might be due to the modulation of proteins involved in the regulation of wound repair, such as TGF-β1 platelet-derived growth factor (PDGF), interleukins (IL-6, -13, -15), and matrix metalloproteinases (MMPs) by LLLT. However, large patient samples are needed to evaluate this promising technique.[71]

7.10 Central Nervous System

The function of the brain is highly dependent on cerebral blood flow (CBF).[74,75] In diseases with reduced CBF, such as traumatic brain injury or degenerative diseases such as Parkinson's disease and Alzheimer's disease, improving the CBF has shown to not only prevent these diseases but also increase the response to treatment.[76,77] The photobiostimulation effects of NIR laser irradiation have been known for a long time. It has also been shown that NIR laser irradiation is very efficient for reducing cerebral ischemia both *in vivo* and clinically. The NIR laser irradiation produces vasodilatory effects that might be mediated by NO.[78] Uozumi et al. studied the effect of 808-nm laser irradiation at three different power densities (0.8, 1.6, and 3.2 W/cm^2) on CBF in mice, and they directly measured NO in brain tissue during NIR laser irradiation using an amperometric NO-selective electrode. They also observed the influence of NO and a neurotransmitter, glutamate, to the regulation of CBF by using a nitric oxide synthase (NOS) inhibitor, nitro-L-arginine methyl ester hydrochloride (L-NAME), and an N-methyl-D-aspartate (NMDA) receptor blocker, MK-801, respectively. The protective effect of NIR laser irradiation on transient cerebral ischemia using a model of transient bilateral common carotid artery occlusion (BCCAO) in mice was also investigated. As compared to the control mice, the NIR laser irradiation (1.6 W/cm^2 for 15–45 minutes) significantly increased local CBF and cerebral NO concentration. Pre-conditioning the brain with NIR laser irradiation increased the residual CBF by 30% and significantly decreased the number of apoptotic cells in the hippocampus in mice subjected to BCCAO and neuronal damage. These results can be partly explained by the fact that pre-conditioning with NIR laser irradiation led to the alleviation of NO surge after the reperfusion.[77]

Low-level laser irradiation in the far-red to NIR range not only has vasodilatory effects but can also modulate many biological processes[79] by increasing mitochondrial respiration or ATP synthesis[80,81] and promoting cell survival.[82] NIR is believed to accelerate the electron transfer in the respiratory chain and activation of photoacceptors, including cytochrome c oxidase in the mitochondria.[83] Cyanide toxicity has been implicated in cell death by its inhibition of cytochrome oxidase[84] and compromising energy status.[66] Moreover, depending on the concentration[85] or the susceptibility of the brain,[86] cyanide produces neuronal cell death by either apoptosis or necrosis. Exposure to cyanide produces apoptosis in cortical neurons but necrosis in mesencephalic cells.[87]

7.11 Protecting Skin from Ultraviolet Damage

Ultraviolet radiation (UVA, 290–320 nm; UVB, 320–400 nm) exposure damages skin cells, which leads to photoaging and cancer of the skin.[88,89] The mechanisms responsible for the UV damage to the skin could be the breakdown of collagen fibers, free radical formation, DNA damage, and inhibition of the immune system.[90] The effects of UV radiation can be minimized by avoiding sun exposure or the use of sunscreens. Conversely, exposure to sun cannot be avoided in certain occupations, and the use of sunscreen has many limitations, such as compliance, allergy, and possible harmful effects of nanoparticles that are contained in most sunscreens.[91] Recent studies have demonstrated the protective effects of infrared (IR) exposure against the harmful effects of UV irradiation of the skin.[92]

The light in the early morning is predominantly composed of visible and NIR solar wavelengths, and at noon it contains substantial amounts of UVB and UVA radiation, suggesting a natural defense mechanism for mammals that involves pre-conditioning the skin with red/NIR light in the morning to protect against impending damaging UV radiation later in the day.[93] Patients with polymorphous light eruption (PLE) and healthy controls were exposed to LED treatments (660 nm) on the experimental anterior thigh region. Baseline minimal erythema doses (MEDs) were then determined. UV radiation was thereafter performed on both experimental and control areas, and digital pictures of the MED test areas were taken prior to UV exposure and immediately, 24 h, 7 days, and 14 days after. Figures 7.11 and 7.12 show the erythema index at 24 h as a function of MEDs for the LED pre-treated and control sides. There was a significant reduction in UV-B induced erythema reaction in both control and patients suffering from PLE preconditioned with LED. Overall, less redness was observed for each tested MED on the pre-conditioned experimental areas compared to control areas. These results suggest that pre-conditioning with a LED prior to UV exposure provided significant protection against UV-B induced erythema.[93]

Illumination of the skin with noncoherent NIR (700–2000 nm) generated a strong cellular defense mechanism against solar UV cytotoxicity and induced cellular mitosis without increasing the skin temperature. This protection against UV light was long lasting (at least 24 h) and had a cumulative effect.[94]

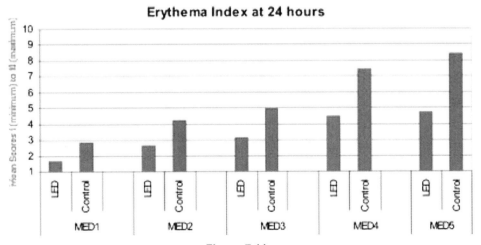

Figure 7.11

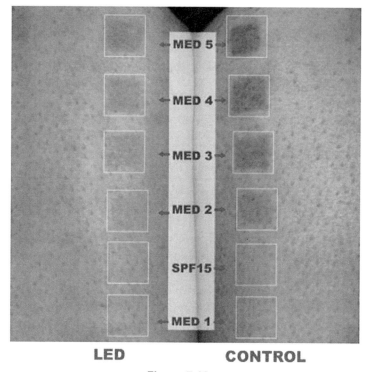

Figure 7.12

Furthermore, another study proposed that pre-conditioning with IR radiation protects human fibroblast cells by inducing resistance to the harmful effects of UV light by affecting the genes of the mitochondrial apoptotic pathway. IR pre-conditioning of human fibroblasts inhibited UVB activation of caspase-9 and -3 and partial release of cytochrome c and Smac/Diablo, decreased proapoptotic proteins (i.e., Bax), and increased anti-apoptotic proteins (i.e., Bcl-2 or Bcl-xL), prompting the cell to resist UVB-triggered apoptosis. This effect could most likely be mediated by the induction of heat-shock protein Hsp27 with IR, which prevents apoptosome assembly.[95]

7.12 Conclusion

Pre-conditioning regimens are receiving more attention in the biomedical arena. The concept that low levels of stress can induce a protective response against all manner of subsequent insults is inherently attractive. One of the problems preventing wider acceptance is that of striking a balance between the degrees of pre-conditioning stress needed, the severity of the possible adverse consequence, and its likelihood of happening. For instance, being subjected to hypoxia, caloric restriction, hypothermia, or hyperthermia might be considered too much of a price to pay to protect oneself against a slim chance of relatively mild extra damage in a heart bypass operation. The same cannot be said about light therapy. LLLT has many advantages in that it is painless, inexpensive if LEDs are employed, and free of potential side effects, making it a "no-brainer" before surgery or potentially hazardous adventures. Moreover, the multiple demonstrations of LLLT's effectiveness for pre-conditioning muscles before exercise suggests that it will soon be taken up by the general public and may have to be regulated by athletic authorities due to a concern over "light-doping."

One topic that is of great interest to all investigators working in the pre-conditioning field looks at the similarities and differences between the molecular and cellular mechanisms that have been proposed to explain the effects of each modality. It is clear that there will not be a single "unified field theory" that will explain every pre-conditioning modality that has been reported. However, it is equally clear that there are an intriguing number of overlaps between the various modalities. Mitochondria, ROS, HIF-1α, and HSF have all been implicated in more than one modality of pre-conditioning, and there may yet be more common pathways left to discover. As pre-conditioning therapy continues to progress into the mainstream of clinical medicine, one can expect more interesting science will be reported.

References

1. M. Das and D. K. Das, "Molecular mechanism of preconditioning," *IUBMB Life* **60**(4), 199–203 (2008).
2. S. Koch, D. Della-Morte, K. R. Dave, R. L. Sacco, and M. A. Perez-Pinzon, "Biomarkers for ischemic preconditioning: finding the responders," *Journal of cerebral blood flow and metabolism: official journal of the International Society of Cerebral Blood Flow and Metabolism* (2014).
3. C. E. Murry, R. B. Jennings, and K. A. Reimer, "Preconditioning with ischemia: a delay of lethal cell injury in ischemic myocardium," *Circulation* **74**(5), 1124–36 (1986).
4. S. V. Narayanan, K. R. Dave, and M. A. Perez-Pinzon, "Ischemic preconditioning and clinical scenarios," *Curr. Opin. Neurol.* **26**(1), 1–7 (2013).
5. A. Hawaleshka and E. Jacobsohn, "Ischaemic preconditioning: mechanisms and potential clinical applications," *Canadian journal of anaesthesia = Journal canadien d'anesthesie* **45**(7), 670–82 (1998).
6. X. Yang, M. V. Cohen, and J. M. Downey, "Mechanism of cardioprotection by early ischemic preconditioning," *Cardiovasc. Drugs Ther.* **24**(3), 225–34 (2010).
7. K. Ytrehus, Y. Liu, and J. M. Downey, "Preconditioning protects ischemic rabbit heart by protein kinase C activation," *The American journal of physiology* **266**(3 Pt 2), H1145–52 (1994).

8. G. W. Dorn, 2nd, M. C. Souroujon, T. Liron, C. H. Chen, M. O. Gray, H. Z. Zhou et al., "Sustained in vivo cardiac protection by a rationally designed peptide that causes epsilon protein kinase C translocation," *Proc. Natl. Acad. Sci. U.S.A* **96**(22), 12798–803 (1999).

9. P. Ping, C. Song, J. Zhang, Y. Guo, X. Cao, R. C. Li et al., "Formation of protein kinase C(epsilon)-Lck signaling modules confers cardioprotection," *J. Clin. Invest.* **109**(4), 499–507 (2002).

10. K. Inagaki, R. Begley, F. Ikeno, and D. Mochly-Rosen, "Cardioprotection by epsilon-protein kinase C activation from ischemia: continuous delivery and antiarrhythmic effect of an epsilon-protein kinase C-activating peptide," *Circulation* **111**(1), 44–50 (2005).

11. R. W. Currie, "Effects of ischemia and perfusion temperature on the synthesis of stress-induced (heat shock) proteins in isolated and perfused rat hearts," *J. Mol. Cell. Cardiol.* **19**(8), 795–808 (1987).

12. D. M. Yellon, E. Pasini, A. Cargnoni, M. S. Marber, D. S. Latchman, and R. Ferrari, "The protective role of heat stress in the ischaemic and reperfused rabbit myocardium," *J. Mol. Cell. Cardiol.* **24**(8), 895–907 (1992).

13. M. S. Marber, R. Mestril, S. H. Chi, M. R. Sayen, D. M. Yellon, and W. H. Dillmann, "Overexpression of the rat inducible 70-kD heat stress protein in a transgenic mouse increases the resistance of the heart to ischemic injury," *The Journal of clinical investigation* **95**(4), 1446–56 (1995).

14. V. Richard, N. Kaeffer, and C. Thuillez, "Delayed protection of the ischemic heart–from pathophysiology to therapeutic applications," *Fundamental & clinical pharmacology* **10**(5), 409–15 (1996).

15. G. L. Semenza, "Hypoxia-inducible factor 1: regulator of mitochondrial metabolism and mediator of ischemic preconditioning," *Biochim. Biophys. Acta.* **1813**(7), 1263–8 (2011).

16. G. L. Wang and G. L. Semenza, "Purification and characterization of hypoxia-inducible factor 1," *J. Biol. Chem.* **270**(3), 1230–7 (1995).

17. Z. Cai, D. J. Manalo, G. Wei, E. R. Rodriguez, K. Fox-Talbot, H. Lu et al., "Hearts from rodents exposed to intermittent hypoxia or erythropoietin are protected against ischemia-reperfusion injury," *Circulation* **108**(1), 79–85 (2003).

18. Z. Cai and G. L. Semenza, "Phosphatidylinositol-3-kinase signaling is required for erythropoietin-mediated acute protection against myocardial ischemia/reperfusion injury," *Circulation* **109**(17), 2050–3 (2004).

19. M. S. Marber, D. S. Latchman, J. M. Walker, and D. M. Yellon, "Cardiac stress protein elevation 24 hours after brief ischemia or heat stress is associated with resistance to myocardial infarction," *Circulation* **88**(3), 1264–72 (1993).

20. J. D. Thornton, G. S. Liu, R. A. Olsson, and J. M. Downey, "Intravenous pretreatment with A1-selective adenosine analogues protects the heart against infarction," *Circulation* **85**(2), 659–65 (1992).

21. Z. Cai, W. Luo, H. Zhan, and G. L. Semenza, "Hypoxia-inducible factor 1 is required for remote ischemic preconditioning of the heart," *Proc. Natl. Acad. Sci. U.S.A* **110**(43), 17462–7 (2013).

22. R. A. Stetler, R. K. Leak, Y. Gan, P. Li, F. Zhang, X. Hu et al., "Preconditioning provides neuroprotection in models of CNS disease: Paradigms and clinical significance," *Progress in neurobiology* **114C**, 58–83 (2014).

23. Y. Yang, Z. Li, H. Liu, W. Shi, and J. Zhang, "Effects of heat preconditioning on overload training induced myocardial injury," *The Journal of sports medicine and physical fitness* **53**(1), 93–100 (2013).

24. L. M. Katz, J. E. Frank, A. Dvorak, A. Finch, A. Szymanowski, and C. J. Gordon, "Independence of brain and trunk temperature during hypothermic preconditioning in rats," *Journal of neuroscience methods* **179**(2), 179–83 (2009).

25. D. Dornbos, 3rd, and Y. Ding, "Mechanisms of neuronal damage and neuroprotection underlying ischemia/reperfusion injury after physical exercise," *Current drug targets* **13**(2), 247–62 (2012).

26. Y. H. Ding, C. N. Young, X. Luan, J. Li, J. A. Rafols, J. C. Clark et al., "Exercise preconditioning ameliorates inflammatory injury in ischemic rats during reperfusion," *Acta. neuropathologica* **109**(3), 237–46 (2005).

27. P. G. Lu, H. Feng, S. J. Yuan, R. W. Zhang, M. Li, R. Hu et al., "Effect of preconditioning with hyperbaric oxygen on neural cell apoptosis after spinal cord injury in rats," *Journal of neurosurgical sciences* **57**(3), 253–8 (2013).

28. J. Z. Yogaratnam, G. Laden, L. Guvendik, M. Cowen, A. Cale, and S. Griffin, "Hyperbaric oxygen preconditioning improves myocardial function, reduces length of intensive care stay, and limits complications post coronary artery bypass graft surgery," *Cardiovascular revascularization medicine: including molecular interventions* **11**(1), 8–19 (2010).

29. K. Shinmura, K. Tamaki, and R. Bolli, "Short-term caloric restriction improves ischemic tolerance independent of opening of ATP-sensitive K+ channels in both young and aged hearts," *J. Mol. Cell. Cardiol.* **39**(2), 285–96 (2005).

30. A. Akcal, K. Z. Sevim, A. Yesilada, V. Kiyak, D. O. Sucu, H. S. Tatlidede et al., "Comparison of perivascular and intramuscular applied botulinum toxin a pretreatment on muscle flap ischemia-reperfusion injury and chemical delay," *The Journal of craniofacial surgery* **24**(1), 278–83 (2013).

31. F. Simao, A. Matte, A. S. Pagnussat, C. A. Netto, and C. G. Salbego, "Resveratrol preconditioning modulates inflammatory response in the rat hippocampus following global cerebral ischemia," *Neurochemistry international* **61**(5), 659–65 (2012).

32. D. M. Muntean, V. Ordodi, R. Ferrera, and D. Angoulvant, "Volatile anaesthetics and cardioprotection: lessons from animal studies," *Fundamental & clinical pharmacology* **27**(1), 21–34 (2013).

33. W. Liu, Y. Liu, H. Chen, K. Liu, H. Tao, and X. Sun, "Xenon preconditioning: molecular mechanisms and biological effects," *Medical gas research* **3**(1), 3 (2013).

34. H. L. Rosenzweig, M. Minami, N. S. Lessov, S. C. Coste, S. L. Stevens, D. C. Henshall et al., "Endotoxin preconditioning protects against the cytotoxic effects of TNFalpha after stroke: a novel role for TNFalpha in LPS-ischemic tolerance," *Journal of cerebral blood flow and metabolism: official journal of the International Society of Cerebral Blood Flow and Metabolism* **27**(10), 1663–74 (2007).

35. Y. Y. Huang, S. K. Sharma, J. Carroll, and M. R. Hamblin, "Biphasic dose response in low level light therapy – an update," *Dose Response* **9**(4), 602–18 (2011).

36. U. Dirnagl and A. Meisel, "Endogenous neuroprotection: mitochondria as gateways to cerebral preconditioning?" *Neuropharmacology* **55**(3), 334–44 (2008).

37. D. G. Allen, G. D. Lamb, and H. Westerblad, "Skeletal muscle fatigue: cellular mechanisms," *Physiological reviews* **88**(1), 287–332 (2008).

38. E. C. Leal Junior, R. A. Lopes-Martins, P. de Almeida, L. Ramos, V. V. Iversen, and J. M. Bjordal, "Effect of low-level laser therapy (GaAs 904 nm) in skeletal muscle fatigue and biochemical markers of muscle damage in rats," *European journal of applied physiology* **108**(6), 1083–8 (2010).

39. R. A. Lopes-Martins, R. L. Marcos, P. S. Leonardo, A. C. Prianti, Jr., M. N. Muscara, F. Aimbire et al., "Effect of low-level laser (Ga-Al-As 655 nm) on skeletal muscle fatigue induced by electrical stimulation in rats," *J. Appl. Physiol. (1985)* **101**(1), 283–8 (2006).

40. M. A. Merrick, "Secondary injury after musculoskeletal trauma: a review and update," *Journal of athletic training* **37**(2), 209–17 (2002).

41. D. Avni, S. Levkovitz, L. Maltz, and U. Oron, "Protection of skeletal muscles from ischemic injury: low-level laser therapy increases antioxidant activity," *Photomedicine and laser surgery* **23**(3), 273–7 (2005).

42. C. Ferraresi, M. R. Hamblin, and N. A. Parizotto, "Low-level laser (light) therapy (LLLT) on muscle tissue: performance, fatigue and repair benefited by the power of light," *Photonics Lasers Med.* **1**(4), 267–86 (2012).

43. B. M. Baroni, E. C. Leal Junior, J. M. Geremia, F. Diefenthaeler, and M. A. Vaz, "Effect of light-emitting diodes therapy (LEDT) on knee extensor muscle fatigue," *Photomedicine and laser surgery* **28**(5), 653–8 (2010).

44. E. C. Leal Junior, R. A. Lopes-Martins, R. P. Rossi, T. De Marchi, B. M. Baroni, V. de Godoi et al., "Effect of cluster multi-diode light emitting diode therapy (LEDT) on exercise-induced skeletal muscle fatigue and skeletal muscle recovery in humans," *Lasers Surg. Med.* **41**(8), 572–7 (2009).

45. E. C. Leal Junior, R. A. Lopes-Martins, B. M. Baroni, T. De Marchi, R. P. Rossi, D. Grosselli et al., "Comparison between single-diode low-level laser therapy (LLLT) and LED multi-diode (cluster) therapy (LEDT) applications before high-intensity exercise," *Photomedicine and laser surgery* **27**(4), 617–23 (2009).

46. E. C. Leal Junior, R. A. Lopes-Martins, B. M. Baroni, T. De Marchi, D. Taufer, D. S. Manfro et al., "Effect of 830 nm low-level laser therapy applied before high-intensity exercises on skeletal muscle recovery in athletes," *Lasers Med. Sci.* **24**(6), 857–63 (2009).

47. E. C. Leal Junior, R. A. Lopes-Martins, L. Frigo, T. De Marchi, R. P. Rossi, V. de Godoi et al., "Effects of low-level laser therapy (LLLT) in the development of exercise-induced skeletal muscle fatigue and changes in biochemical markers related to postexercise recovery," *J. Orthop. Sports Phys. Ther.* **40**(8), 524–32 (2010).

48. E. C. Leal Junior, V. de Godoi, J. L. Mancalossi, R. P. Rossi, T. De Marchi, M. Parente et al., "Comparison between cold water immersion therapy (CWIT) and light emitting diode therapy (LEDT) in short-term skeletal muscle recovery after high-intensity exercise in athletes–preliminary results," *Lasers Med. Sci.* **26**(4), 493–501 (2011).

49. P. A. Borsa, K. A. Larkin, and J. M. True, "Does phototherapy enhance skeletal muscle contractile function and postexercise recovery? A systematic review," *Journal of athletic training* **48**(1), 57–67 (2013).

50. T. De Marchi, E. C. Leal Junior, C. Bortoli, S. S. Tomazoni, R. A. Lopes-Martins, and M. Salvador, "Low-level laser therapy (LLLT) in human progressive-intensity running: effects on exercise performance, skeletal muscle status, and oxidative stress," *Lasers Med. Sci.* **27**(1), 231–6 (2012).

51. E. C. Leal-Junior, A. A. Vanin, E. F. Miranda, P. D. de Carvalho, S. Dal Corso, and J. M. Bjordal, "Effect of phototherapy (low-level laser therapy and light-emitting diode therapy) on exercise performance and markers of exercise recovery: a systematic review with meta-analysis," *Lasers Med. Sci.* (2013).

52. S. R. Barretto, G. C. de Melo, J. C. dos Santos, M. G. de Oliveira, R. N. Pereira-Filho, A. V. Alves et al., "Evaluation of anti-nociceptive and anti-inflammatory activity of low-level laser therapy on temporomandibular

joint inflammation in rodents," *J. Photochem. Photobiol. B.* **129**, 135–42 (2013).

53. D. T. Meneguzzo, L. A. Lopes, R. Pallota, L. Soares-Ferreira, R. A. Lopes-Martins, and M. S. Ribeiro, "Prevention and treatment of mice paw edema by near-infrared low-level laser therapy on lymph nodes," *Lasers Med. Sci.* **28**(3), 973–80 (2013).

54. J. Walker, "Relief from chronic pain by low power laser irradiation," *Neurosci. Lett.* **43**(2-3), 339–44 (1983).

55. S. Hagiwara, H. Iwasaka, A. Hasegawa, and T. Noguchi, "Pre-Irradiation of blood by gallium aluminum arsenide (830 nm) low-level laser enhances peripheral endogenous opioid analgesia in rats," *Anesth. Analg.* **107**(3), 1058–63 (2008).

56. R. Albertini, A. B. Villaverde, F. Aimbire, M. A. Salgado, J. M. Bjordal, L. P. Alves et al., "Anti-inflammatory effects of low-level laser therapy (LLLT) with two different red wavelengths (660 nm and 684 nm) in carrageenan-induced rat paw edema," *J. Photochem. Photobiol. B.* **89**(1), 50–5 (2007).

57. R. A. Lopes-Martins, R. Albertini, P. S. Martins, J. M. Bjordal, and H. C. Faria Neto, "Spontaneous effects of low-level laser therapy (650 nm) in acute inflammatory mouse pleurisy induced by carrageenan," *Photomedicine and laser surgery* **23**(4), 377–81 (2005).

58. H. Y. Yang, T. T. Guo, Y. N. Ma, T. Y. Liu, and M. Gao, "Effects of 650 nm laser and moxibustion pretreatment on enteric nervous system and medullary visceral zone in rats with visceral traction pain," *Zhongguo. Zhen. Jiu.* **30**(9), 745–51 (2010).

59. U. Oron, T. Yaakobi, A. Oron, D. Mordechovitz, R. Shofti, G. Hayam et al., "Low-energy laser irradiation reduces formation of scar tissue after myocardial infarction in rats and dogs," *Circulation* **103**(2), 296–301 (2001).

60. U. Oron, T. Yaakobi, A. Oron, G. Hayam, L. Gepstein, O. Rubin et al., "Attenuation of infarct size in rats and dogs after myocardial infarction by low-energy laser irradiation," *Lasers Surg. Med.* **28**(3), 204–11 (2001).

61. T. Yaakobi, Y. Shoshany, S. Levkovitz, O. Rubin, S. A. Ben Haim, and U. Oron, "Long-term effect of low energy laser irradiation on infarction and reperfusion injury in the rat heart," *J. Appl. Physiol. (1985)* **90**(6), 2411–9 (2001).

62. H. Tuby, L. Maltz, and U. Oron, "Modulations of VEGF and iNOS in the rat heart by low level laser therapy are associated with cardioprotection and enhanced angiogenesis," *Lasers Surg. Med.* **38**(7), 682–8 (2006).

63. H. Zhang, J. F. Hou, Y. Shen, W. Wang, Y. J. Wei, and S. Hu, "Low level laser irradiation precondition to create friendly milieu of infarcted myocardium and enhance early survival of transplanted bone marrow cells," *J. Cell. Mol. Med.* **14**(7), 1975–87 (2010).

64. Y. Y. Liu, M. T. Wong-Riley, H. L. Liu, Y. Jia, X. Y. Jiao, C. T. Wang et al., "Increase in cytochrome oxidase activity in regenerating nerve fibers of hemitransected spinal cord in the rat," *Neuroreport* **12**(15), 3239–42 (2001).

65. J. T. Eells, M. M. Henry, P. Summerfelt, M. T. Wong-Riley, E. V. Buchmann, M. Kane et al., "Therapeutic photobiomodulation for methanol-induced retinal toxicity," *Proc. Natl. Acad. Sci. U.S.A* **100**(6), 3439–44 (2003).

66. M. T. Wong-Riley, H. L. Liang, J. T. Eells, B. Chance, M. M. Henry, E. Buchmann et al., "Photobiomodulation directly benefits primary neurons functionally inactivated by toxins: role of cytochrome c oxidase," *J. Biol. Chem.* **280**(6), 4761–71 (2005).

67. H. L. Liang, H. T. Whelan, J. T. Eells, H. Meng, E. Buchmann, A. Lerch-Gaggl et al., "Photobiomodulation partially rescues visual cortical neurons from cyanide-induced apoptosis," *Neuroscience* **139**(2), 639–49 (2006).

68. M. J. Conlan, J. W. Rapley, and C. M. Cobb, "Biostimulation of wound healing by low-energy laser irradiation," *A review J. Clin. Periodontol.* **23**(5), 492–6 (1996).

69. A. P. Sommer, A. L. Pinheiro, A. R. Mester, R. P. Franke, and H. T. Whelan, "Biostimulatory windows in low-intensity laser activation: lasers, scanners, and NASA's light-emitting diode array system," *J. Clin. Laser Med. Surg.* **19**(1), 29–33 (2001).

70. H. T. Whelan, R. L. Smits, Jr., E. V. Buchman, N. T. Whelan, S. G. Turner, D. A. Margolis et al., "Effect of NASA light-emitting diode irradiation on wound healing," *J. Clin. Laser Med. Surg.* **19**(6), 305–14 (2001).

71. D. Barolet and A. Boucher, "Prophylactic low-level light therapy for the treatment of hypertrophic scars and keloids: a case series," *Lasers Surg. Med.* **42**(6), 597–601 (2010).

72. D. Wolfram, A. Tzankov, P. Pulzl, and H. Piza-Katzer, "Hypertrophic scars and keloids–a review of their pathophysiology, risk factors, and therapeutic management," *Dermatol. Surg.* **35**(2), 171–81 (2009).

73. N. Bouzari, S. C. Davis, and K. Nouri, "Laser treatment of keloids and hypertrophic scars," *Int. J. Dermatol.* **46**(1), 80–8 (2007).

74. G. S. Ling and C. J. Neal, "Maintaining cerebral perfusion pressure is a worthy clinical goal," *Neurocrit. Care* **2**(1), 75–81 (2005).

75. M. Balestreri, M. Czosnyka, P. Hutchinson, L. A. Steiner, M. Hiler, P. Smielewski et al., "Impact of intracranial pressure and cerebral perfusion pressure on severe disability and mortality after head injury," *Neurocrit. Care* **4**(1), 8–13 (2006).

76. L. I. Wolfson, K. L. Leenders, L. L. Brown, and T. Jones, "Alterations of regional cerebral blood flow and oxygen metabolism in Parkinson's disease," *Neurology* **35**(10), 1399–405 (1985).

77. Y. Uozumi, H. Nawashiro, S. Sato, S. Kawauchi, K. Shima, and M. Kikuchi, "Targeted increase in cerebral blood flow by transcranial near-infrared laser irradiation," *Lasers Surg. Med.* **42**(6), 566–76 (2010).

78. M. R. Hamblin, "The role of nitric oxide in low level light therapy," *Proc. SPIE* **6846**, 1–14 (2008).

79. T. Karu, "Primary and secondary mechanisms of action of visible to near-IR radiation on cells," *J. Photochem. Photobiol. B.* **49**(1), 1–17 (1999).

80. S. Passarella, E. Casamassima, S. Molinari, D. Pastore, E. Quagliariello, I. M. Catalano et al., "Increase of proton electrochemical potential and ATP synthesis in rat liver mitochondria irradiated in vitro by helium-neon laser," *FEBS Lett.* **175**(1), 95–9 (1984).

81. T. Karu, L. Pyatibrat, and G. Kalendo, "Irradiation with He-Ne laser increases ATP level in cells cultivated in vitro," *J. Photochem. Photobiol. B.* **27**(3), 219–23 (1995).

82. G. Shefer, T. A. Partridge, L. Heslop, J. G. Gross, U. Oron, and O. Halevy, "Low-energy laser irradiation promotes the survival and cell cycle entry of skeletal muscle satellite cells," *J. Cell. Sci.* **115**(Pt 7), 1461–9 (2002).

83. B. Beauvoit, T. Kitai, and B. Chance, "Contribution of the mitochondrial compartment to the optical properties of the rat liver: a theoretical and practical approach," *Biophys. J.* **67**(6), 2501–10 (1994).

84. R. Bhattacharya and P. V. Lakshmana Rao, "Pharmacological interventions of cyanide-induced cytotoxicity and DNA damage in isolated rat thymocytes and their protective efficacy in vivo," *Toxicol. Lett.* **119**(1), 59–70 (2001).

85. K. Prabhakaran, L. Li, J. L. Borowitz, and G. E. Isom, "Caspase inhibition switches the mode of cell death induced by cyanide by enhancing reactive oxygen species generation and PARP-1 activation," *Toxicol. Appl. Pharmacol.* **195**(2), 194–202 (2004).

86. E. M. Mills, P. G. Gunasekar, L. Li, J. L. Borowitz, and G. E. Isom, "Differential susceptibility of brain areas to cyanide involves different modes of cell death," *Toxicol. Appl. Pharmacol.* **156**(1), 6–16 (1999).

87. K. Prabhakaran, L. Li, J. L. Borowitz, and G. E. Isom, "Cyanide induces different modes of death in cortical and mesencephalon cells," *J. Pharmacol. Exp. Ther.* **303**(2), 510–9 (2002).

88. R. P. Sinha and D. P. Hader, "UV-induced DNA damage and repair: a review," *Photochem. Photobiol. Sci.* **1**(4), 225–36 (2002).

89. C. Calles, M. Schneider, F. Macaluso, T. Benesova, J. Krutmann, and P. Schroeder, "Infrared A radiation influences the skin fibroblast transcriptome: mechanisms and consequences," *J. Invest. Dermatol.* **130**(6), 1524–36 (2010).

90. P. Schroeder, C. Calles, T. Benesova, F. Macaluso, and J. Krutmann, "Photoprotection beyond ultraviolet radiation–effective sun protection

has to include protection against infrared A radiation-induced skin damage," *Skin. Pharmacol. Physiol.* **23**(1), 15–7 (2010).

91. E. Kimura, Y. Kawano, H. Todo, Y. Ikarashi, and K. Sugibayashi, "Measurement of skin permeation/penetration of nanoparticles for their safety evaluation," *Biol. Pharm. Bull.* **35**(9), 1476–86 (2012).

92. P. Avci, A. Gupta, M. Sadasivam, D. Vecchio, Z. Pam, N. Pam et al., "Low-level laser (light) therapy (LLLT) in skin: stimulating, healing, restoring," *Semin. Cutan. Med. Surg.* **32**(1), 41–52 (2013).

93. D. Barolet and A. Boucher, "LED photoprevention: reduced MED response following multiple LED exposures," *Lasers Surg. Med.* **40**(2), 106–12 (2008).

94. S. Menezes, B. Coulomb, C. Lebreton, and L. Dubertret, "Non-coherent near infrared radiation protects normal human dermal fibroblasts from solar ultraviolet toxicity," *J. Invest. Dermatol.* **111**(4), 629–33 (1998).

95. S. Frank, L. Oliver, C. Lebreton-De Coster, C. Moreau, M. T. Lecabellec, L. Michel et al., "Infrared radiation affects the mitochondrial pathway of apoptosis in human fibroblasts," *J. Invest. Dermatol.* **123**(5), 823–31 (2004).

Chapter 8
Low-Level Laser Therapy and Stem Cells

Qi Zhang, Tingting Dong, and Chang Zhou

Adult stem cells are found in many tissues and organs, including the brain, blood, bone, skin, lungs, and liver. They usually stay in a special micro-environment called "stem cell niche." They remain quiescent under normal conditions and become activated when there is a need to repair injury or maintain tissue. Stem cells are a very promising subject for regenerative medicine to treat injury and disease. However, when isolated and cultured *in vitro* or *ex vivo*, the stem cells have limited capacity to proliferate and differentiate, which makes it difficult to grow large quantities of stem cells for medical applications. Low-level laser therapy (LLLT) has been demonstrated to stimulate the proliferation of many kinds of cultured cells, including stem cells. The augmentation of stem-cell-based therapies to modulate the regenerative process through LLLT holds great potential. The mechanisms of action, the effects of LLLT on stem cells, and the potential applications of LLLT on stem-cell-based treatment are discussed in this chapter.

8.1 Effects of LLLT on Stem Cells

8.1.1 Hematopoietic stem cells

In the bone marrow, a small fraction of hematopoietic stem cells (HSCs) could produce heterogeneous populations of actively dividing hematopoietic pro-genitors. They produce approximately 500 billion blood cells per day, including lymphoid lineage (B-cell, T-cell, and NK-cell) and myeloid lineage (red blood cell, platelet, monocyte and macrophage, dendritic cell, neutrophil, eosinophil, and basophil). During the major phases of blood biogenesis, as illustrated in Fig. 8.1, the mitochondrial respiratory chain produces >90% ATP for a cell and plays a vital role. Inadequate mitochondrial respiration can impair HSC differentiation into myeloid lineage-committed progenitors, i.e., GEMM, that

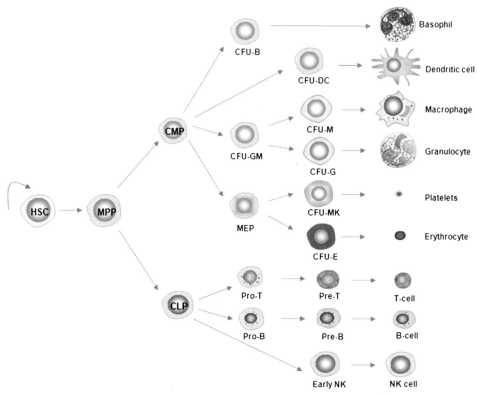

Figure 8.1 The hierarchy of a human hematopoietic stem cell (HSC): MPP, multipotent progenitor; CMP, common myeloid progenitor; CLP, common lymphoid progenitor; MEP, megakaryocyte/erythroid progenitor; and CFU, colony-forming unit.

have the potential to produce granulocytes (G), erythrocytes (E), monocytes (M), and megakaryocytes (M).[42,43] Furthermore, HSCs reside in the most hypoxic niche in the bone marrow and face cell-fate decisions between quiescence, self-renewal, and differentiation.[44] The hypoxic micro-environment of the bone marrow niche highlights the importance of redox signaling in maintaining the HSC function. These reasons reveal the potential effects of LLLT on the modulation of HSC functions.

LLLT has been used in wound healing for 30 years in clinics with a long history of safety, and also widely applied to regenerative medicine and dentistry to enhance healing process. As for its effects on hematopoiesis, Vacek et al. demonstrated that exposure of murine bone marrow cells to LLLT increased their differentiation potential into myeloid progenitors *ex vivo*.[45] LLLT at 685 nm also stimulated stem cell proliferation in *Dugesia tigrina*.[46] Likewise, the growth and differentiation potential of long-term (three years) cryopreserved human peripheral blood progenitors (PBPs) was mostly restored by LLLT.[47] These studies demonstrated the ability of LLLT to enhance HSC differentiation in both humans and mice, provided that the right laser parameter is selected.

8.1.2 Mesenchymal stem cells

Mesenchymal stem cells (MSCs), also known as bone-marrow stromal stem cells, are generally found in bone marrow. They have the potential to differentiate into various cell types, including osteoblasts, chondrocytes, and adipocytes, and are used in cell therapy or tissue engineering. Several studies have shown that LLLT, with different parameters, can directly increase the proliferation of MSCs. Hou et al. reported that irradiation at 0.5 J/cm^2 with a 635-nm diode laser significantly stimulated the proliferation of bone marrow derived mesenchymal stem cells from rats. They also observed that the laser at 5 J/cm^2 increased the production of vascular endothelial growth factor (VEGF) and nerve growth factor (NGF), and dramatically facilitated the myogenic differentiation of the MSCs.[48] Similar results were found in mice: a 635-nm laser increased the proliferation of mice MSCs.[49] The laser energy density seems to be a critical factor to stimulate the MSCs. Lasers with an optimally low energy density could significantly increase cell proliferation, whereas a high energy density produces limited stimulating effects or even inhibiting effects.[50] Using a 660-nm diode laser, Horvát-Karajz et al. found that the proliferation of MSCs was increased by 41% when cells were treated at 1.9 J/cm^2, whereas they were inhibited by 42% at 11.7 J/cm^2.[51] In another study, it was found that an 808-nm laser at 4 J/cm^2 did not enhance the murine MSC proliferation.[52] Leonida et al. reported that irradiation with a Nd:Yag laser at 100 mJ or 150 mJ could increase cell proliferation after seven days post-irradiation; however, there was no significant difference after 14 days between the laser group and control group. Based on previous studies of various laser parameters and cell types, energy-density ranges from 0.5 to 4.0 J/cm^2 and wavelengths from 600 to 700 nm of LLLT are effective at enhancing the proliferation of various cell lines.[53] Oron et al. also showed that LLLT can stimulate bone-marrow MSCs and reduce heart scarring after heart attack.[26,54]

The mechanism by which LLLT stimulates MSC proliferation is not fully understood. Mechanisms at the cellular and molecular levels have been proposed to explain the phenomenon. In a recent study, Wu et al. found that LLLT at 0.5 J/cm^2 could induce the transcription and expression of 119 genes, most of which were involved in cell proliferation and survival.[55] Using microarray analysis, Wang et al. found that microRNA-193 was significantly up-regulated after LLLT treatment. The blockade of miRNA-193 suppressed the enhancing effect of LLLT on MSC proliferation. Moreover, the authors reported that miRNA-193 was involved to regulate the expression of cyclin-dependent kinase 2 (CDK2) and could target the inhibitor of growth family member 5 (ING5). Inhibition of ING5 was found to stimulate MSC proliferation.[56] Giannelli et al. reported that a 635-nm diode laser increased mouse MSC proliferation, which was associated with the activation of the Notch-1 pathway. The MSC proliferation and Notch-1 up-regulation were closely related to the increased membrane conductance through voltage-gated channels. Inhibition of the channels resulted in attenuation of the laser's stimulating effects.[57]

8.1.3 Adipose-derived stem cells

Recently, adipose-derived stem cells (ADSCs) have become an appealing source of stem cells due to the ease of obtaining them from fat tissues. A low-level laser at a wavelength of 636 nm and a fluence of 5 J/cm^2 was found to increase human ADSC cellular viability and proliferation in cell cultures.[58–60] Besides stimulating cell proliferation, Wu et al. reported that LLLT also has an anti-inflammatory effect on ADSCs. The authors found that LLLT at 8 J/cm² markedly inhibited LPS-induced, pro-inflammatory cytokine expression in human ADSCs, including Cox-2, IL-1β, IL-6, and IL-8. The anti-inflammatory effect might be due to the up-regulation of cAMP and down-regulation of the NF-κB pathway induced by laser.[60] It is well known that LLLT has an anti-inflammatory effect on many different cells and tissues. Thus, LLLT may have potential applications for stem-cell therapy under inflammatory conditions.

8.2 Clinical Applications of LLLT for Stem Cells

8.2.1 Stem-cell transplantation

LLLT has potential applications for stem-cell transplantation treatment. Tuby et al. use LLLT-irradiated MSCs to treat infarcted hearts in rats. The MSCs were isolated from the rat bone marrow, irradiated with an 810-nm Ga-Al-As laser, and implanted into infarcted rat hearts. They found that infarcted hearts implanted with irradiated MSCs showed a significant reduction in infarcted size by 53% as compared to hearts implanted with nonirradiated MSCs. Implantation with LLLT-irradiated MSCs resulted in significantly increased cell density and proliferation, and enhanced angiogenesis in the infarcted hearts.[61] In keeping with this study, Zhang et al. found that LLLT pre-treatment could remodel the infarcted myocardium micro-environment to enhance the early survival of transplanted MSCs and improve therapeutic angiogenesis and heart function.[62] The authors used a 635-nm, 5-mW diode laser with an energy density of 0.96 J/cm^2 for 150 s, and they observed increased VEGF, glucose-regulated protein 78 (GRP78), and superoxide dismutase (SOD) production, and decreased malondialdehyde (MDA) production in the infarcted myocardium.

LLLT has also been investigated for stimulating liver regeneration following hepatectomy. Oron et al. applied a diode [Ga-Al-As] laser with a wavelength of 804 nm to irradiate rats after acute hepatectomy, and they found that the laser significantly enhanced liver regeneration by forming new hepatocytes and MSCs, and angiogenesis.[63] In a recent study, Choi et al. explored the feasibility of using ADSCs seeded in a cellular dermal matrix along with LLLT to repair bone defect in athymic nude mice.[64] After the seeded ADSCs were applied, the laser group received light from a 632.8-nm laser at 1 J/cm^2 daily for 56 days, while the control group receive no laser treatment. The authors reported that bone regeneration was observed in LLLT group on day 28, whereas it was observed in the control group on day 56. Moreover, the bone mineral density in the LLLT group significantly increased after seven days, whereas the control group took 14 days. The authors found that LLLT significantly enhanced ADSC proliferation both *in vitro* and *in vivo*, indicating that LLLT combined with ADSCs could promote bone healing.

8.2.2 Wound healing and skin restoring

LLLT is known to stimulate wound healing and skin restoring. Stem cells in skin can be activated to facilitate wound healing. Kim et al. investigated the effect of LLLT on ADSC-induced skin healing using a mouse model. LLLT was found to accelerate the wound-closure and skin-regeneration process compared with the nonlaser group. LLLT increased ADSC survival in the wound bed by inhibiting the apoptosis of ADSCs. In addition, the secretion of growth factors was increased in the LLLT group compared with the nonlaser group.[65] Hawkins et al. reported that LLLT (632.8-nm He-Ne laser) at a dose of 5 J/cm^2 significantly stimulated the proliferation of wounded skin fibroblasts. However, high doses of 10- or 16-J/cm^2 of laser-induced decreased both cell viability and proliferation of damage to the cell membrane and DNA.[66]

8.2.3 Neural regeneration

Studies have shown supportive evidence that LLLT could accelerate the regeneration of peripheral nerve tissue. Akgul et al. used a 650-nm diode laser at 25 mW and 10 J/cm^2 to treat rats with a crushed sciatic nerve, and they found that LLLT could accelerate the recovery of peripheral nerves in this model. Interestingly, they found that a delayed treatment began at seven days post-injury showed better effects than immediate treatment.[67] Besides direct effects on nerve regeneration, LLLT may also be used together with stem cell transplantation to further stimulate the recovery of injured nerve tissue. Yang et al. combined LLLT with MSC transplantation to treat crushed sciatic nerve in rats and found that LLLT plus MSC transplantation groups showed better recovery than either LLLT or MSC treated groups. The MSC-LLLT group also showed fewer inflammatory cells and less vacuole formation than MSC or LLLT single treatment groups, suggesting that LLLT combined with

MSC transplantation may achieve better functional recovery than conventional treatment after nerve crush injury.[68]

Unlike the peripheral nerve system, the regeneration of neurons in the central nervous system (CNS) is not so significant. It was long considered that neurons do not regenerate until recent studies demonstrated that neural stem cells can differentiate into new neurons under certain circumstances. Neuron regeneration in CNS would be beneficial for the treatment of neural degenerative diseases and traumatic brain injury. Using a rat spinal cord injury (SCI) model, Wu et al. reported that LLLT treatment with a 810-nm diode laser at 150 mW/cm^2 and a daily dose of 1589 J/cm^2 significantly promoted axonal regeneration and induced better functional recovery after SCI.[69] Xuan et al. found that LLLT (810 nm, 25 mW/cm^2, and 18 J/cm^2) could improve the neurological performance after traumatic brain injury in mice. The authors found more proliferating cells in the injured sites that were treated by LLLT than in untreated ones, suggesting that LLLT may promote neurogenesis.[70]

8.2.4 Treating hair loss

The mechanisms by which LLLT promotes hair growth or regrowth are not fully understood. It has been proposed that LLLT stimulates mitochondria to produce more ATP and alters the ROS level, resulting in the induction of downstream signaling pathways that further enhance cell proliferation and migration. It is possible that the epidermal stem cells in hair follicles are stimulated by LLLT, and the follicles are shifted into the anagen phase.[71] A double-blind, randomized, and controlled trial showed that 665-nm laser or LED treatment for 16 weeks significantly increased hair counts by 39% in males with androgenetic alopecia, compared with a placebo control group.[72] Another recent study found that a FDA-cleared laser comb was effective for the treatment of male and female pattern hair loss.[73] A total of 128 male and 141 female subjects were enrolled in this trial. After receiving 26 weeks of treatment with either a laser comb or a sham device, there was a significant difference in the increase of terminal hair density between the laser group and sham group, suggesting that LLLT may be an effective method to treat pattern hair loss in both men and women. More *in vitro* and *in vivo* studies are needed to elucidate the detailed mechanisms of LLLT for treating hair loss.

References

1. J. T. Eells, M. T. Wong-Riley, J. VerHoeve, M. Henry, E. V. Buchman, M. P. Kane, L. J. Gould, R. Das, M. Jett, B. D. Hodgson, D. Margolis, and H. T. Whelan, "Mitochondrial signal transduction in accelerated wound and retinal healing by near-infrared light therapy," *Mitochondrion* **4**, 559–567 (2004).

2. T. I. Karu, L. V. Pyatibrat, S. F. Kolyakov, and N. I. Afanasyeva, "Absorption measurements of a cell monolayer relevant to phototherapy: reduction of cytochrome c oxidase under near IR radiation," *J. Photochem. Photobiol. B* **81**, 98–106 (2005).

3. L. Wilden and R. Karthein, "Import of radiation phenomena of electrons and therapeutic low-level laser in regard to the mitochondrial energy transfer," *J. Clin. Laser Med. Surg.* **16**, 159–165 (1998).

4. Q. Zhang, C. Zhou, M. R. Hamblin, and M. X. Wu, "Low-level laser therapy effectively prevents secondary brain injury induced by immediate early responsive gene X-1 deficiency," *J. Cereb. Blood Flow Metab.* **34**, 1391–1401 (2014).

5. K. M. AlGhamdi, A. Kumar, and N. A. Moussa, "Low-level laser therapy: a useful technique for enhancing the proliferation of various cultured cells," *Lasers Med. Sci.* **27**, 237–249 (2012).

6. J. Kujawa, L. Zavodnik, I. Zavodnik, V. Buko, A. Lapshyna, and M. Bryszewska, "Effect of low-intensity (3.75–25 J/cm^2) near-infrared (810 nm) laser radiation on red blood cell ATPase activities and membrane structure," *J. Clin. Laser Med. Surg.* **22**, 111–117 (2004).

7. J. Kujawa, I. B. Zavodnik, A. Lapshina, M. Labieniec, and M. Bryszewska, "Cell survival, DNA, and protein damage in B14 cells under low-intensity near-infrared (810 nm) laser irradiation," *Photomed. Laser Surg.* **22**, 504–508 (2004).

8. T. I. Karu and S. F. Kolyakov, "Exact action spectra for cellular responses relevant to phototherapy," *Photomed. Laser Surg.* **23**, 355–361 (2005).

9. T. Karu, "Primary and secondary mechanisms of action of visible to near-IR radiation on cells," *J. Photochem. Photobiol. B* **49**, 1–17 (1999).

10. Q. Zhang, C. Zhou, M. R. Hamblin, and M. X. Wu, "Low-level laser therapy effectively prevents secondary brain injury induced by immediate early responsive gene X-1 deficiency," *J. Cereb. Blood Flow Metab.* (2014).

11. M. Greco, G. Guida, E. Perlino, E. Marra, and E. Quagliariello, "Increase in RNA and protein synthesis by mitochondria irradiated with helium-neon laser," *Biochem. Biophys. Res. Commun.* **163**, 1428–1434 (1989).

12. S. Passarella, E. Casamassima, S. Molinari, D. Pastore, E. Quagliariello, I. M. Catalano, and A. Cingolani, "Increase of proton electrochemical potential and ATP synthesis in rat liver mitochondria irradiated in vitro by helium-neon laser," *FEBS Lett.* **175**, 95–99 (1984).

13. P. Brondon, I. Stadler, and R. J. Lanzafame, "A study of the effects of phototherapy dose interval on photobiomodulation of cell cultures," *Lasers. Surg. Med.* **36**, 409–413 (2005).

14. J. Zhang, D. Xing, and X. Gao, "Low-power laser irradiation activates Src tyrosine kinase through reactive oxygen species-mediated signaling pathway," *J. Cell. Physiol.* **217**, 518–528 (2008).

15. E. Mester, B. Szende, and P. Gartner, "The effect of laser beams on the growth of hair in mice," *Radiobiol. Radiother. (Berl.)* **9**, 621–626 (1968).

16. G. Jamtvedt, K. T. Dahm, A. Christie, R. H. Moe, E. Haavardsholm, I. Holm, and K. B. Hagen, "Physical therapy interventions for patients with osteoarthritis of the knee: an overview of systematic reviews," *Phys. Ther.* **88**, 123–136 (2008).

17. A. Gur, A. J. Sarac, R. Cevik, O. Altindag, and S. Sarac, "Efficacy of 904 nm gallium arsenide low level laser therapy in the management of chronic myofascial pain in the neck: a double-blind and randomize-controlled trial," *Lasers Surg. Med.* **35**, 229–235 (2004).

18. M. van Middelkoop, S. M. Rubinstein, T. Kuijpers, A. P. Verhagen, R. Ostelo, B. W. Koes, and M. W. van Tulder, "A systematic review on the effectiveness of physical and rehabilitation interventions for chronic non-specific low back pain," *Eur. Spine J.* **20**, 19–39 (2011).

19. S. Tumilty, J. Munn, S. McDonough, D. A. Hurley, J. R. Basford, and G. D. Baxter, "Low level laser treatment of tendinopathy: a systematic review with meta-analysis," *Photomed. Laser Surg.* **28**, 3–16 (2010).

20. P. V. Peplow, T. Y. Chung, and G. D. Baxter, "Laser photobiomodulation of wound healing: a review of experimental studies in mouse and rat animal models," *Photomed. Laser Surg.* **28**, 291–325 (2010).

21. E. C. Leal Junior, R. A. Lopes-Martins, B. M. Baroni, T. De Marchi, D. Taufer, D. S. Manfro, M. Rech, V. Danna, D. Grosselli, R. A. Generosi, R. L. Marcos, L. Ramos, and J. M. Bjordal, "Effect of 830 nm low-level laser therapy applied before high-intensity exercises on skeletal muscle recovery in athletes," *Lasers Med. Sci.* **24**, 857–863 (2009).

22. Y. Lampl, J. A. Zivin, M. Fisher, R. Lew, L. Welin, B. Dahlof, P. Borenstein, B. Andersson, J. Perez, C. Caparo, S. Ilic, and U. Oron, "Infrared laser therapy for ischemic stroke: a new treatment strategy: results of the NeuroThera Effectiveness and Safety Trial-1 (NEST-1)," *Stroke* **38**, 1843–1849 (2007).

23. J. A. Zivin, G. W. Albers, N. Bornstein, T. Chippendale, B. Dahlof, T. Devlin, M. Fisher, W. Hacke, W. Holt, S. Ilic, S. Kasner, R. Lew, M. Nash, J. Perez, M. Rymer, P. Schellinger, D. Schneider, S. Schwab, R. Veltkamp, M. Walker, and J. Streeter, "Effectiveness and safety of transcranial laser therapy for acute ischemic stroke," *Stroke* **40**, 1359–1364 (2009).

24. W. Xuan, F. Vatansever, L. Huang, Q. Wu, Y. Xuan, T. Dai, T. Ando, T. Xu, Y. Y. Huang, and M. R. Hamblin, "Transcranial low-level laser therapy improves neurological performance in traumatic brain injury in mice: effect of treatment repetition regimen," *PLoS One* **8**, e53454 (2013).

25. J. A. Zivin, G. W. Albers, N. Bornstein, T. Chippendale, B. Dahlof, T. Devlin, M. Fisher, W. Hacke, W. Holt, S. Ilic, S. Kasner, R. Lew, M. Nash, J. Perez, M. Rymer, P. Schellinger, D. Schneider, S. Schwab,

R. Veltkamp, M. Walker, and J. Streeter, "Effectiveness and safety of transcranial laser therapy for acute ischemic stroke," *Stroke* **40**, 1359–1364 (2009).

26. H. Tuby, E. Hertzberg, L. Maltz, and U. Oron, "Long-term safety of low-level laser therapy at different power densities and single or multiple applications to the bone marrow in mice," *Photomed. Laser Surg.* **31**, 269–273 (2013).

27. N. Grossman, N. Schneid, H. Reuveni, S. Halevy, and R. Lubart, "780 nm low power diode laser irradiation stimulates proliferation of keratinocyte cultures: involvement of reactive oxygen species," *Lasers Surg. Med.* **22**, 212–218 (1998).

28. P. Moore, T. D. Ridgway, R. G. Higbee, E. W. Howard, and M. D. Lucroy, "Effect of wavelength on low-intensity laser irradiation-stimulated cell proliferation in vitro," *Lasers Surg. Med.* **36**, 8–12 (2005).

29. A. D. Agaiby, L. R. Ghali, R. Wilson, and M. Dyson, "Laser modulation of angiogenic factor production by T-lymphocytes," *Lasers Surg. Med.* **26**, 357–363 (2000).

30. J. M. Bjordal, M. I. Johnson, R. A. Lopes-Martins, B. Bogen, R. Chow, and A. E. Ljunggren, "Short-term efficacy of physical interventions in osteoarthritic knee pain. A systematic review and meta-analysis of randomised placebo-controlled trials," *BMC Musculoskelet. Disord.* **8**, 51 (2007).

31. R. P. Abergel, R. F. Lyons, J. C. Castel, R. M. Dwyer, and J. Uitto, "Biostimulation of wound healing by lasers: experimental approaches in animal models and in fibroblast cultures," *J. Dermatol. Surg. Oncol.* **13**, 127–133 (1987).

32. A. V. Corazza, J. Jorge, C. Kurachi, and V. S. Bagnato, "Photobiomodulation on the angiogenesis of skin wounds in rats using different light sources," *Photomed. Laser Surg.* **25**, 102–106 (2007).

33. A. Schindl, G. Heinze, M. Schindl, H. Pernerstorfer-Schon, and L. Schindl, "Systemic effects of low-intensity laser irradiation on skin microcirculation in patients with diabetic microangiopathy," *Microvasc. Res.* **64**, 240–246 (2002).

34. A. Oron, U. Oron, J. Streeter, L. de Taboada, A. Alexandrovich, V. Trembovler, and E. Shohami, "low-level laser therapy applied transcranially to mice following traumatic brain injury significantly reduces long-term neurological deficits," *J. Neurotrauma.* **24**, 651–656 (2007).

35. V. E. Shaw, S. Spana, K. Ashkan, A. L. Benabid, J. Stone, G. E. Baker, and J. Mitrofanis, "Neuroprotection of midbrain dopaminergic cells in MPTP-treated mice after near-infrared light treatment," *J. Comp. Neurol.* **518**, 25–40 (2010).

36. Y. Lampl, J. A. Zivin, M. Fisher, R. Lew, L. Welin, B. Dahlof, P. Borenstein, B. Andersson, J. Perez, C. Caparo, S. Ilic, and U. Oron,

"Infrared laser therapy for ischemic stroke: a new treatment strategy: results of the NeuroThera Effectiveness and Safety Trial-1 (NEST-1)," *Stroke* **38**, 1843–1849 (2007).

37. M. T. Wong-Riley, X. Bai, E. Buchmann, and H. T. Whelan, "Light-emitting diode treatment reverses the effect of TTX on cytochrome oxidase in neurons," *Neuroreport.* **12**, 3033–3037 (2001).

38. L. I. Fillipin, J. L. Mauriz, K. Vedovelli, A. J. Moreira, C. G. Zettler, O. Lech, N. P. Marroni, and J. Gonzalez-Gallego, "Low-level laser therapy (LLLT) prevents oxidative stress and reduces fibrosis in rat traumatized Achilles tendon," *Lasers Surg. Med.* **37**, 293–300 (2005).

39. G. Morrone, G. A. Guzzardella, P. Torricelli, M. Rocca, D. Tigani, G. B. Brodano, M. Fini, and R. Giardino, "Osteochondral lesion repair of the knee in the rabbit after low-power diode Ga-Al-As laser biostimulation: an experimental study," *Artif. Cells Blood Substit. Immobil. Biotechnol.* **28**, 321–336 (2000).

40. J. B. Weber, A. L. Pinheiro, M. G. de Oliveira, F. A. Oliveira, and L. M. Ramalho, "Laser therapy improves healing of bone defects submitted to autologous bone graft," *Photomed. Laser Surg.* **24**, 38–44 (2006).

41. X. H. Shao, Y. P. Yang, J. Dai, J. F. Wu, and A. H. Bo, "Effects of He-Ne laser irradiation on chronic atrophic gastritis in rats," *World J. Gastroenterol.* **11**, 3958–3961 (2005).

42. S. Inoue, S. Noda, K. Kashima, K. Nakada, J. Hayashi, and H. Miyoshi, "Mitochondrial respiration defects modulate differentiation but not proliferation of hematopoietic stem and progenitor cells," *FEBS Lett.* **584**, 3402–3409 (2010).

43. C. M. Barbosa, C. M. Leon, A. Nogueira-Pedro, F. Wasinsk, R. C. Araujo, A. Miranda, A. T. Ferreira, and E. J. Paredes-Gamero, "Differentiation of hematopoietic stem cell and myeloid populations by ATP is modulated by cytokines," *Cell Death Dis.* **2**, e165 (2011).

44. S. Roy, M. Tripathy, N. Mathur, A. Jain, and A. Mukhopadhyay, "Hypoxia improves expansion potential of human cord blood-derived hematopoietic stem cells and marrow repopulation efficiency," *Eur. J. Haematol.* **88**, 396–405 (2012).

45. A. Vacek, A. Bartonickova, and D. Rotkovska, "Increase in the capacity of bone marrow exposed to He-Ne laser radiation for growth of GM-CFC colonies in vitro," *Folia Biol. (Praha.)* **36**, 65–70 (1990).

46. S. C. de Souza, E. Munin, L. P. Alves, M. A. Salgado, and M. T. Pacheco, "Low power laser radiation at 685 nm stimulates stem-cell proliferation rate in Dugesia tigrina during regeneration," *J. Photochem. Photobiol. B* **80**, 203–207 (2005).

47. R. X. do Nascimento and F. Callera, "Low-level laser therapy at different energy densities (0.1–2.0 J/cm^2) and its effects on the capacity of human

long-term cryopreserved peripheral blood progenitor cells for the growth of colony-forming units," *Photomed. Laser Surg.* **24**, 601–604 (2006).

48. J. F. Hou, H. Zhang, X. Yuan, J. Li, Y. J. Wei, and S. S. Hu, "In vitro effects of low-level laser irradiation for bone marrow mesenchymal stem cells: proliferation, growth factors secretion and myogenic differentiation," *Lasers Surg. Med.* **40**, 726–733 (2008).

49. M. Giannelli, F. Chellini, C. Sassoli, F. Francini, A. Pini, R. Squecco, D. Nosi, D. Bani, S. Zecchi-Orlandini, and L. Formigli, "Photoactivation of bone marrow mesenchymal stromal cells with diode laser: effects and mechanisms of action," *J. Cell Physiol.* **228**, 172–181 (2013).

50. Y. Y. Huang, A. C. Chen, J. D. Carroll, and M. R. Hamblin, "Biphasic dose response in low level light therapy," *Dose Response* **7**, 358–383 (2009).

51. K. Horvat-Karajz, Z. Balogh, V. Kovacs, A. H. Drrernat, L. Sreter, and F. Uher, "In vitro effect of carboplatin, cytarabine, paclitaxel, vincristine, and low-power laser irradiation on murine mesenchymal stem cells," *Lasers Surg. Med.* **41**, 463–469 (2009).

52. S. Bouvet-Gerbettaz, E. Merigo, J. P. Rocca, G. F. Carle, and N. Rochet, "Effects of low-level laser therapy on proliferation and differentiation of murine bone marrow cells into osteoblasts and osteoclasts," *Lasers Surg. Med.* **41**, 291–297 (2009).

53. K. M. AlGhamdi, A. Kumar, and N. A. Moussa, "Low-level laser therapy: a useful technique for enhancing the proliferation of various cultured cells," *Lasers Med. Sci.* **27**, 237–249 (2012).

54. H. Tuby, L. Maltz, and U. Oron, "Induction of autologous mesenchymal stem cells in the bone marrow by low-level laser therapy has profound beneficial effects on the infarcted rat heart," *Lasers Surg. Med.* **43**, 401–409 (2011).

55. Y. H. Wu, J. Wang, D. X. Gong, H. Y. Gu, S. S. Hu, and H. Zhang, "Effects of low-level laser irradiation on mesenchymal stem cell proliferation: a microarray analysis," *Lasers Med. Sci.* **27**, 509–519 (2012).

56. J. Wang, W. Huang, Y. Wu, J. Hou, Y. Nie, H. Gu, J. Li, S. Hu, and H. Zhang, "MicroRNA-193 pro-proliferation effects for bone mesenchymal stem cells after low-level laser irradiation treatment through inhibitor of growth family, member 5," *Stem Cells Dev.* **21**, 2508–2519 (2012).

57. J. A. de Villiers, N. N. Houreld, and H. Abrahamse, "Influence of low intensity laser irradiation on isolated human adipose derived stem cells over 72 hours and their differentiation potential into smooth muscle cells using retinoic acid," *Stem Cell Rev.* **7**, 869–882 (2011).

58. B. Mvula, T. Mathope, T. Moore, and H. Abrahamse, "The effect of low level laser irradiation on adult human adipose derived stem cells," *Lasers Med. Sci.* **23**, 277–282 (2008).

59. B. Mvula, T. J. Moore, and H. Abrahamse, "Effect of low-level laser irradiation and epidermal growth factor on adult human adipose-derived stem cells," *Lasers Med. Sci.* **25**, 33–39 (2010).

60. J. Y. Wu, C. H. Chen, C. Z. Wang, M. L. Ho, M. L. Yeh, and Y. H. Wang, "Low-power laser irradiation suppresses inflammatory response of human adipose-derived stem cells by modulating intracellular cyclic AMP level and NF-kappaB activity," *PLoS One* **8**, e54067 (2013).

61. H. Tuby, L. Maltz, and U. Oron, "Implantation of low-level laser irradiated mesenchymal stem cells into the infarcted rat heart is associated with reduction in infarct size and enhanced angiogenesis," *Photomed. Laser Surg.* **27**, 227–233 (2009).

62. H. Zhang, J. F. Hou, Y. Shen, W. Wang, Y. J. Wei, and S. Hu, "Low level laser irradiation precondition to create friendly milieu of infarcted myocardium and enhance early survival of transplanted bone marrow cells," *J. Cell. Mol. Med.* **14**, 1975–1987 (2010).

63. U. Oron, L. Maltz, H. Tuby, V. Sorin, and A. Czerniak, "Enhanced liver regeneration following acute hepatectomy by low-level laser therapy," *Photomed. Laser Surg.* **28**, 675–678 (2010).

64. K. Choi, B. J. Kang, H. Kim, S. Lee, S. Bae, O. K. Kweon, and W. H. Kim, "Low-level laser therapy promotes the osteogenic potential of adipose-derived mesenchymal stem cells seeded on an acellular dermal matrix," *J. Biomed. Mater. Res. B. Appl. Biomater.* **101**, 919–928 (2013).

65. H. Kim, K. Choi, O. K. Kweon, and W. H. Kim, "Enhanced wound healing effect of canine adipose-derived mesenchymal stem cells with low-level laser therapy in athymic mice," *J. Dermatol. Sci.* **68**, 149–156 (2012).

66. D. H. Hawkins and H. Abrahamse, "The role of laser fluence in cell viability, proliferation, and membrane integrity of wounded human skin fibroblasts following helium-neon laser irradiation," *Lasers Surg. Med.* **38**, 74–83 (2006).

67. T. Akgul, M. Gulsoy, and H. O. Gulcur, "Effects of early and delayed laser application on nerve regeneration," *Lasers Med. Sci.* **29**, 351–357 (2014).

68. C. C. Yang, J. Wang, S. C. Chen, and Y. L. Hsieh, "Synergistic effects of low-level laser and mesenchymal stem cells on functional recovery in rats with crushed sciatic nerves," *J. Tissue Eng. Regen. Med.* (2013).

69. X. Wu, A. E. Dmitriev, M. J. Cardoso, A. G. Viers-Costello, R. C. Borke, J. Streeter, and J. J. Anders, "810 nm Wavelength light: an effective therapy for transected or contused rat spinal cord," *Lasers Surg. Med.* **41**, 36–41 (2009).

70. W. Xuan, F. Vatansever, L. Huang, Q. Wu, Y. Xuan, T. Dai, T. Ando, T. Xu, Y. Y. Huang, and M. R. Hamblin, "Transcranial low-level laser therapy improves neurological performance in traumatic brain injury in mice: effect of treatment repetition regimen," *PLoS One* **8**, e53454 (2013).

71. P. Avci, G. K. Gupta, J. Clark, N. Wikonkal, and M. R. Hamblin, "Low-level laser (light) therapy (LLLT) for treatment of hair loss," *Lasers Surg. Med.* **46**, 144–151 (2014).

72. R. J. Lanzafame, R. R. Blanche, A. B. Bodian, R. P. Chiacchierini, A. Fernandez-Obregon, and E. R. Kazmirek, "The growth of human scalp hair mediated by visible red light laser and LED sources in males," *Lasers Surg. Med.* **45**, 487–495 (2013).

73. J. J. Jimenez, T. C. Wikramanayake, W. Bergfeld, M. Hordinsky, J. G. Hickman, M. R. Hamblin, and L. A. Schachner, "Efficacy and Safety of a Low-level Laser Device in the Treatment of Male and Female Pattern Hair Loss: A Multicenter, Randomized, Sham Device-controlled, Double-blind Study," *Am. J. Clin. Dermatol.* (2014).

Chapter 9
Edema and Lymph Flow

The lymphatic system plays a critical role in the process of reducing inflammation and edema, as well as a major role in the immune response. It moves fluid (lymph) from interstitial spaces in tissues via a network of collecting vessels to the lymph nodes, where it is mostly emptied into the venous system. Some fluid moves further along the lymphatic chain to other lymph nodes and eventually empties into the thoracic duct. PBM reduces swelling, and it seems likely that the lymphatic system is involved, although limited evidence exists to confirm this.

A PubMed search for a range of PBM terms (see Chapter 1) AND edema OR oedema OR swelling returns over 50 abstracts. Most of these abstracts are for post-mastectomy lymphedema,[1,2] post-surgical swelling,[2–4] acute soft-tissue injury,[5] and arthritic joints.[6]

The mechanism by which light affects edema has not been adequately explored, although it makes sense that it should because nitric oxide (NO) modulates lymphatic vessel contraction and subsequent lymph flow,[7] and it has been established that PBM releases stores of NO[8–10] and subsequently improves blood flow.[11,12]

As with blood vessels, NO is produced by endothelial nitric oxide synthase (eNOS) in lymphatic endothelial cells, which in turn affects the dilation and force of lymph vessel contractions. Small amounts of NO are produced (by eNOS) when lymph vessels are stretched (by movement or a stretch/massage technique), and this leads to alternating periods of diastolic filling and systolic ejection of lymphangions (the tiny functional units of the collecting lymphatic system). Excessive amounts of NO produced by inducible nitric oxide synthase (iNOS) during inflammation can overwhelm the NO gradients produced by eNOS. The suppression of eNOS by iNOS disrupts the contraction/relaxation cycle in favor of excessive contraction and subsequent reduced flow.

How PBM resolves this situation is unknown, but clinical trials and laboratory studies report positive effects. Meneguzzo et al. investigated the effect of an 830-nm laser over lymph nodes on paw edema and inflammation. The edema was induced by carrageenan injection (CGN) into the plantar surface of 100 male mice hind paws. PBM was able to produce anti-inflammatory and pro-inflammatory effects just by treating inguinal lymph nodes alone. This effect was achieved whether treated before or after the carrageenan injection.[13]

There have been many systematic reviews of clinical trials on post-mastectomy lymphedema: Omar et al. performed a systematic review on PBM for breast-cancer-related lymphedema (BCRL). Eight clinical trials totaling 230 patients were found. The studies were assessed with the Physiotherapy Evidence Database scale and categorized according to Sackett's levels of evidence. Five studies were graded at evidence level II. Two studies were graded at evidence level III, and the remaining study was graded at evidence level V. They concluded that "there is moderate to strong evidence for the effectiveness of LLLT for the management of BCRL from five small studies of acceptable methodological quality. A dose of 1-2 J/cm^2 per point applied to several points covering the fibrotic area can reduce limb volume following BCRL."[5]

Smoot et al. also performed a systematic review of PBM on BCRL. They found nine studies for inclusion. They concluded that there was "moderate-strength evidence supporting the use of LLLT for the management of BCRL, with clinically relevant within-group reductions in volume and pain immediately after conclusion of LLLT treatments. Greater reductions in volume were found with the use of LLLT than in treatments without it. LLLT confers clinically meaningful reductions in arm volume and pain in women with BCRL."[1]

Stergioulas el al. compared three therapeutic protocols for treating edema in second-degree ankle sprains under placebo-controlled conditions. 47 soccer players with acute second-degree ankle sprains, were divided into three groups:

1. rest, ice, compression, and elevation (RICE);
2. RICE plus placebo laser; and
3. RICE plus PBM (two treatments per day for three days).

The volume of the edema was measured by water displacement. The group treated with PBM presented a statistically significant reduction in the volume of the edema after 24 h, 48 h, and 72 h. It was concluded that treatment with PBM was more effective than the traditional RICE modality.

Dae-Hyun Jang et al. investigated mechanism of PBM in a mouse tail model of lymphedema. Mice were divided into three groups (PBM, sham, and surgical control group). The PBM group was administered with PBM daily for 10 minutes a day for 12 days post-surgery. Macrophage activation, lymphatic vessel regeneration, and multiple VEGF factors were measured. The mice in the PBM group showed a significantly decreased thickness compared with the sham group at 10 and 12 days. An immunohistochemistry assay revealed that PBM reduced inflammation and induced new lymphatic vessel growth. They conclude that PBM has anti-inflammatory and lymphangiogenetic effects.[14]

Landucci et al. performed a clinical trial of PBM for the reduction of pain, swelling, and trismus after third molar extraction from 22 patients and immediately after extraction randomly selected right or left side. PBM was then applied (study group). The same extraction procedure was performed 21 days later on the other third molar without the application of PBM (control group). LLLT was applied at 10 points: four intraoral in close proximity to the socket, and six extraoral along the masseter muscle. Pain intensity was assessed using a visual analogue scale, swelling was measured as the distance from the tragus to the median base of the mentum, and trismus was assessed by the extent of mouth opening. Data was collected at four time points: before surgery, immediately after surgery, 48 h post-operation, and 7 days post-operation. Compared with the control group, the study group showed significant reductions in pain, swelling, and trismus at 48 h and 7 days post-operation. In conclusion, a single dose of LLLT was effective at reducing the post-operative discomforts (pain, swelling, and trismus) associated with third molar extraction surgery.[3]

Given the major role lymphatics play in reducing edema and inflammation, it is surprising how few clinical trials target them other than the lymphedema trials. The suggested treatment applies 30–100 mW/cm^2 for ~3 J/cm^2 to the regional lymph nodes twice a week (or, even better, daily).

References

1. B. Smoot, L. Chiavola-Larson, J. Lee, H. Manibusan, and D. D. Allen, "Effect of low-level laser therapy on pain and swelling in women with breast cancer-related lymphedema: a systematic review and meta-analysis," *J. Cancer Surviv.* **9**(2), 287–304 (2015).

2. A. Dirican, O. Andacoglu, R. Johnson, K. McGuire, L. Mager, and A. Soran, "The short-term effects of low-level laser therapy in the management of breast-cancer-related lymphedema," *Support Care Cancer* **19**(5), 685–690 (2011).

3. A. Landucci, A. C. Wosny, L. C. Uetanabaro, A. Moro, and M. R. Araujo, "Efficacy of a single dose of low-level laser therapy in reducing pain, swelling, and trismus following third molar extraction surgery," *Int. J. Oral Maxillofac. Surg.* (2015).

4. A. Markovic and L. Todorovic, "Effectiveness of dexamethasone and low-power laser in minimizing oedema after third molar surgery: a clinical trial," *Int. J. Oral Maxillofac. Surg.* **36**(3), 226–229 (2007).

5. M. T. Omar, A. A. Shaheen, and H. Zafar, "A systematic review of the effect of low-level laser therapy in the management of breast cancer-related lymphedema," *Support Care Cancer* **20**(11), 2977–2984 (2012).

6. A. P. Castano, T. Dai, I. Yaroslavsky, R. Cohen, W. A. Apruzzese, M. H. Smotrich, and M. R. Hamblin, "Low-level laser therapy for zymosan-induced arthritis in rats: Importance of illumination time," *Lasers in Surgery and Medicine* **39**(6), 543–550 (2007).

7. S. Chakraborty, M. J. Davis, and M. Muthuchamy, "Emerging trends in the pathophysiology of lymphatic contractile function," *Semin. Cell Dev. Biol.* **38**, 55–66 (2015).

8. U. H. Mitchell and G. L. Mack, "Low-level laser treatment with near-infrared light increases venous nitric oxide levels acutely: a single-blind, randomized clinical trial of efficacy," *Am. J. Phys. Med. Rehabil.* **92**(2), 151–156 (2013).

9. N. L. Lohr, A. Keszler, P. Pratt, M. Bienengraber, D. C. Warltier, and N. Hogg, "Enhancement of nitric oxide release from nitrosyl hemoglobin and nitrosyl myoglobin by red/near infrared radiation: potential role in cardioprotection," *J. Mol. Cell Cardiol.* **47**(2), 256–263 (2009).

10. R. Zhang et al., "Near infrared light protects cardiomyocytes from hypoxia and reoxygenation injury by a nitric oxide dependent mechanism," *J. Mol. Cell Cardiol.* **46**(1), 4–14 (2009).

11. K. A. Samoilova, N. A. Zhevago, N. N. Petrishchev, and A. A. Zimin, "Role of nitric oxide in the visible light-induced rapid increase of human skin microcirculation at the local and systemic levels: II. healthy volunteers," *Photomed. Laser Surg.* **26**(5), 443–449 (2008).

12. S. Benedicenti, I. M. Pepe, F. Angiero, and A. Benedicenti, "Intracellular ATP level increases in lymphocytes irradiated with infrared laser light of wavelength 904 nm," *Photomed. Laser Surg.* **26**(5), 451–453 (2008).

13. D. T. Meneguzzo, L. A. Lopes, R. Pallota, L. Soares-Ferreira, R. A. Lopes-Martins, and M. S. Ribeiro, "Prevention and treatment of mice paw edema by near-infrared low-level laser therapy on lymph nodes," *Lasers Med. Sci.* **28**(3), 973–980 (2013).

14. D. H. Jang, D. H. Song, E. J. Chang, and J. Y. Jeon, "Anti-inflammatory and lymphangiogenetic effects of low-level laser therapy on lymphedema in an experimental mouse tail model," *Lasers Med. Sci.* (2015).

Chapter 10
Augmenting Wound Healing with Photobiomodulation Therapy

Asheesh Gupta

10.1 Introduction

Wound healing is a dynamic, multifaceted, well-orchestrated, and highly efficient process that should proceed linearly to restore tissue homeostasis in response to injury. Wound repair proceeds through the coordinated integration of biological and molecular events in the extracellular wound micro-environment during four overlapping phases of hemostasis, inflammation, proliferation and tissue remodeling.[1] It includes the migration, adhesion, proliferation, and differentiation of various cell types, i.e., keratinocytes, fibroblasts, macrophages, mesenchymal stem cells, and endothelial cells, and their interaction with different cytokines, growth factors, and extracellular matrix (ECM) molecules. A cascade of healing events begins with the formation of a fibrin clot, which provides protection to the underlying tissues and serves as a provisional matrix through which cells can migrate and acts as a reservoir for growth factors. During inflammation, aggregated platelets release pro-inflammatory cytokines to recruit neutrophils and macrophages at the wound site. These inflammatory cells phagocytose debris and invading micro-organisms, and they also secrete mediators to stimulate the chemotaxis of cell types necessary for the proliferative phase. In the proliferative phase, fibroblasts, keratinocytes, and endothelial and smooth muscle cells migrate through the wound bed and proliferate, leading to re-epithelialization of the denuded surface. They also synthesize and deposit a provisional ECM, form new blood vessels (angiogenesis), and lead to contraction of the wound size. During the final stage, the newly formed granulation tissue is remodeled by the activity of matrix metalloproteinases (MMPs), which are balanced by the action of "tissue inhibitors of metalloproteinases" (TIMPs). MMPs reorganize the loose, newly regenerated dermis and strengthen the repaired tissue (by collagen cross-linking and scar maturation). Interactions between numerous cell types and the local release of a battery of growth factors and cytokines combine to influence the overall rate of wound repair.[2] This process is highly efficient in normal wound healing. However, chronic nonhealing wounds fail to progress through the expected ordered and reparative physiological healing process, and can require long-term treatment at high cost to both the patient and health-care provider.

Impaired wound healing may be a consequence of pathologic states associated with diabetes, venous stasis, pressure ulcers, or due to treatment with steroids, chemotherapy agents, or radiation. Poor healing can be found in injuries such as burns, frostbite, and military combat trauma. Nonhealing chronic wounds can be caused by a combination of multiple pathological abnormalities, i.e., dysregulated or stagnant inflammation, prolonged hypoxia, faulty angiogenesis, fibrosis, excessive ECM deposition, enhanced proteolysis, inappropriate MMPs, bacterial colonization/biofilms, excessive exudate and phenotypic changes in resident wound cells. Indeed, chronic nonhealing wounds exhibit numerous cellular and molecular abnormalities, most of which are attributed to dysregulated and dysfunctional interactions between cells and the ECM milieu.[3] Wound-healing abnormalities cause a great deal of physical and psychological discomfort and morbidity to affected patients. Delayed wound healing is one of the major therapeutic and economic issues in medicine today.

Research into different pharmacological and nonpharmacological modalities to augment wound healing is a developing area in modern biomedical sciences. Current efforts are being focused on enhancing the repair process through novel strategies, including pharmacotherapeutic agents, bioactive dressings, tissue-engineered scaffolds, gene therapy, stem-cell-based therapy, and biophysical therapeutic intervention using a light-based modality (photobiomodulation, PBM, or low-level laser/light therapy, LLLT). This chapter specifically addresses the current advances in light-based therapy (also known as PBM therapy) using medical red and near-infrared (NIR) light, the importance of radiant exposure parameters, interaction of light with tissue, the associated cellular and molecular mechanisms of PBM action, downstream effector molecules, the applications of PBM therapy in augmenting cutaneous acute and chronic wound healing, and future prospects.

10.2 Light-Based Healing Therapy: Photobiomodulation

Applications of light-based therapies, including PBM therapy and photodynamic therapy (PDT), have been demonstrated to be beneficial and relatively minimally invasive therapeutic modalities for several pathological conditions. Whereas PBM therapy uses red or NIR light alone to treat a variety of conditions, including the promotion of wound healing, prevention of tissue damage, reduction of edema, relief of pain and inflammation, and restoration of functions.[4] PDT uses a combination of visible light and nontoxic dyes (photosensitizers) to generate ROS that can kill infectious micro-organisms and cancer cells or destroy unwanted tissue (neo-vascularization in the choroid, atherosclerotic plaques in the arteries).[5]

The creative use of PBM therapy as a treatment for different pathological disorders arose after its discovery as a biophysical therapeutic healing modality by E. Mester in 1967. PBM is now achieving major attention in the biomedical research arena. Since 1967, the field of PBM has been constantly advancing, and it is now widely used for the treatment of normal and chronic dermal wound healing, muscle and nerve injuries,[5,6] attenuation of inflammation and pain[7] and photorejuvenation. PBM uses coherent light sources (lasers), noncoherent light sources consisting of filtered lamps or LEDs, or sometimes a combination of the two. PBM therapy uses low-power light (if a laser, the power is usually below 500 mW, depending on the target tissue) at a nonthermal, noninvasive irradiance to elicit biological responses from the cells and normalized cell function. In PBM, successful therapeutic outcomes require the selection of the optimal optical treatment parameters, including the illumination parameters (such as wavelength, fluence, fluence rate, pulse structure, etc.) and the treatment regimen. Optical dosages, i.e., fluence rate (mW/cm^2) and delivered fluence (J/cm^2), that are either markedly less or considerably more than the optimal choice of optical parameters can result in reduced efficacy of the treatment or even a negative therapeutic outcome. Indeed, the existence of the biphasic dose response has been held responsible for the publication of a number of negative studies, where it is highly likely that the results would have been positive if different optical parameters had been employed.[8–10]

Light–tissue interaction mainly depends on the wavelength, and light is affected by the tissue components that interact with the photons by absorption or scattering. In tissue, an "optical window" lies between wavelengths 600 and 1350 nm, where the effective tissue penetration of light is maximized due to the minimum light attenuation owing to lower absorption by heme-proteins, melanin, water, collagen, etc., and less scattering at longer wavelengths. Moreover, light possessing a shorter or higher wavelength than this region is absorbed by the tissue components (hemoglobin and myoglobin in the visible region, and tissue water content in the infrared region). The fact that red and NIR light can penetrate deeply into a tissue injury allows noninvasive treatment to be conducted for augmented healing processes.[4,11]

The operational mode PBM therapy can either be continuous wave or pulsed wave (CW or PW). Recent studies have shown that PW mode has biological and clinical effects that are different than those of CW mode. It has been demonstrated that PW is more efficacious than CW because there are quench periods (pulse-off times) of longer duration than the on-timings, which reduces tissue heating.[10] The biological explanation of the improved effects of PW is either due to some fundamental frequency that exists in biological systems in the range of 10–100 Hz or, alternatively, due to some biological process that has a time scale of a few milliseconds. It has been further revealed that LLLT in PW mode can better penetrate through melanin and other skin barriers, supporting the hypotheses that pulsing is beneficial in reaching deep target tissue and organs. Some recent studies have reported that PW mode is advantageous over CW mode, particularly in the context of healing deep tissue injuries and stroke management.[12,13]

10.3 Mechanisms of PBM Action

In PBM therapy, the photons of a light source penetrate deep into tissue, where they are absorbed in the cells and initiate photochemical and photobiological responses at the cellular and molecular levels.[14] In recent years, much knowledge has been gained regarding the cellular and molecular mechanisms of action of PBM, summarized in Fig. 10.1. It is generally accepted that cytochrome c oxidase (CCO, also known as complex-IV of the mitochondrial respiratory chain) absorbs light in the red (600–700 nm) and NIR (760–940 nm) regions by the redox active metal centers (two heme and two copper) and is the responsible photoacceptor molecule. The leading hypothesis suggested that the dissociation of NO (a physiologic regulator of CCO activity) rearranges downstream signaling effects, leading to an increase in electron transport, mitochondrial membrane potential, and ATP production.[15,16] Another hypothesis concerns light-sensitive ion channels, which can be activated allowing Ca^{+2} ions to enter the cell. After the initial photon absorption, several intracellular signaling pathways are activated via ROS, NO, cyclic AMP (cAMP), and Ca^{+2}, leading to the activation of transcription factors concerned with protein synthesis, ECM deposition, cell migration, proliferation, anti-inflammation, cell survival, and inhibition of apoptosis. Stem cells and progenitor cells appear to be chiefly susceptible to PBM therapy.[17]

During PBM, the absorption of photons by CCO leads to an increase in mitochondrial membrane potential and a short burst of ROS, which triggers some mitochondrial signaling pathways and produces cytoprotective, anti-oxidant, and anti-apoptotic effects in the cells. It has been shown that PBM-induced mitochondrial ROS production leads to the activation of the transcription factor NF-κB, which acts as a redox sensor. The NO that is released by photodissociation acts as a vasodilator as well as a dilator of lymphatic flow. Moreover, NO is also a potent signaling molecule and can activate a number of beneficial cellular pathways.[16]

It has been suggested that nonthermal irradiation forms of light in the red or NIR region activates retrograde light-sensitive cellular signaling events to

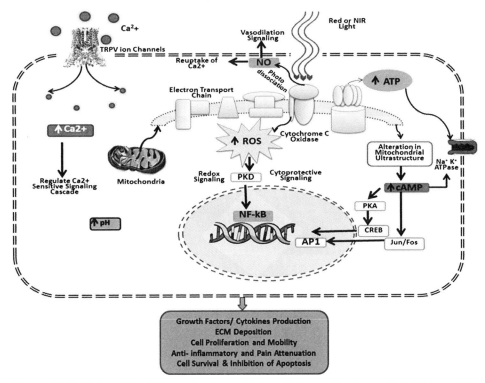

Figure 10.1 Schematic of the molecular and intracellular mechanisms of photobiomodulation. Photons are initially absorbed by mitochondrial chromophore (photoacceptor, cytochrome c oxidase (CCO)). Photon absorption leads to dissociation of inhibitory nitric oxide (NO) from CCO, leading to increased enzyme activity and ATP production and a short burst of reactive oxygen species (ROS), which in turn cause changes in the cellular redox potential, Ca^{2+} ions, and cyclic adenosine monophosphate (cAMP), and induce several transcription factors (NF-kB, AP-1, etc.). After photon absorption, light-sensitive ion channels can be activated, allowing Ca^{+2} ions to enter the cell. A photosignal transduction and amplification chain induced by red or NIR light leads to an increase in growth factor production, cell proliferation, cellular mobility, adhesion, and extracellular matrix deposition. AP1, activator protein 1; ATP, adenosine triphosphate; NF-kB, nuclear factor kappa B; and TRPV, transient receptor potential vanilloid.

transport the light signal from mitochondria to the nucleus and alter the cell metabolism and functions.[14] Besides CCO, a number of other nonmitochondrial molecules have been proposed to act as photoacceptors, depending on the wavelength of excitation. Flavins and flavoproteins, free porphyrins, hemoglobin and myoglobin, and "nanostructured water" (in the IR spectral region) have all been proposed to absorb photons and mediate photochemical and photobiological events. The establishment of a well-defined mechanistic approach towards PBM will help in unraveling the downstream pathways and effector molecules, which can boost future research endeavors and clinical applications of drug-free light-based therapy in wound healing.

10.4 PBM Therapy for Acute and Chronic Wound Healing

A wide range of PBM-induced healing effects on both acute and chronic wounds has been studied, such as partial thickness, incision, excision-type acute wounds, surgical scars, burns, diabetes, pressure ulcers etc. Many studies have also reported anti-inflammatory and anti-nociceptive effects provided by PBM therapy in both experimental studies and clinical trials.[4,5]

10.4.1 Acute wound healing

PBM has been studied extensively in acute experimental animal models of wound repair, and beneficial healing effects have been reported for this biophysical modality of treatment. PBM can improve cell proliferation, migration, and adhesion, and also prevent cell apoptosis at low-power red or NIR light illumination.[9] Red (630–680 nm) and NIR (800–830 nm; 904 nm) light can penetrate into a deep tissue injury, and so noninvasive treatment can be conducted for augmented healing processes. The use of PBM has been proposed as a means of stimulating different cells in the wound matrix and augmenting the healing process.

The *in vivo* studies have reported that PBM acts on multiple events of the wound repair process.[18–22] PBM is therefore believed to affect all phases of wound healing, i.e., inflammatory, granulation tissue formation, and remodeling phases.[5] It has been shown that PBM attenuates inflammation, induces cell proliferation;[22,23] promotes angiogenesis;[23,24] induces the proliferation and migration of fibroblasts and keratinocytes; [22,23] and allows faster wound contraction.[19,22,23] Furthermore, PBM increases mitochondrial metabolism and ATP synthesis,[14,25] accelerates collagen deposition, increases tensile strength,[22,26] and influences the level of prostaglandins (anti-nociceptive).[27] PBM was also shown to stimulate the expression of multiple genes related to cellular migration, proliferation, anti-apoptosis, and pro-survival elements[28,49] besides modulating the production of growth factors (bFGF, VEGF, PDGF, TGF-β, IGF-1) and cytokines (IL-1α, IL-8).[23,28,29]

PBM of the combined red (685 nm) and blue (470 nm) irradiation accelerated the process of re-epithelialization and the formation of cross-linked collagen fibers in the sutured skin incisions in a porcine model.[30] Red light (630 nm) accelerates skin wound healing by promoting fibrous-tissue and epidermal and endothelial cell proliferation in Japanese big-ear white rabbits.[31] In another study, maximally augmented healing was observed in groups irradiated with 810-nm light, followed by red (635 nm) light, as evidenced by enhanced cellular proliferation, re-epithelialization, and collagen deposition in partial-thickness dermal abrasion in mice.[5] Demidova-Rice et al.[19] reported that the 820-nm wavelength was highly effective for healing full-thickness dermal excisional wounds in mice. In clinical studies, PBM therapy with continuous 810-nm and pulsed 820-nm irradiation were found to be highly effective in improving surgical scars and facilitating wound contraction of partial-thickness wounds, respectively.[32,33]

10.4.2 Chronic wound healing

Many studies have demonstrated that both red and NIR light have a positive healing effect on chronic wounds in experimental animals and clinical studies. PBM therapy offers a drug-free, noninvasive, and easily performed modality to treat chronic nonhealing wounds, such as diabetic ulcers, burns, and pressure ulcers. NIR light around 810–830 nm and 904 nm have been found to have the best penetration into tissue and have shown beneficial healing effects for treating different kinds of chronic dermal wounds, muscles, and nerve injuries.

The PBM of NIR 810–830-nm irradiation accelerates diabetic and burn wound healing[34–36] and improve neurological performance in brain disorders.[37] Only a single exposure of 830-nm (3 J/cm^2) light augmented burn wound healing in mice, which was found equivalent to reference care Povidone–iodine ointment-treated wounds applied daily until complete healing.[38] Additive augmentation of full-thickness dermal wound healing, as evident by increased collagen, ATP levels, and cell proliferation, was observed in diabetic mice with low-power 830-nm irradiation and topical application of ubiquinone CoQ10.[35] Red (670 nm) and NIR (810 nm) light sources showed similar effects and improved the healing of second-degree burns in rats.[36] PBM with pulsed NIR 890-nm (11.7 J/cm^2) irradiation significantly increased the rate of wound closure in the deep second-degree burn model for rats.[39] Rocha et al.[40] demonstrated that PBM with superpulsed light (904 nm, 9500 Hz, 304.8 mW/cm^2, 18.288 J/cm^2) increased collagen accumulation and decreased oxidative and nitrosative stress during diabetic wound healing in mice. In a clinical study, Dahmardehei et al.[41] evaluated the efficacy of PBM on the prognosis of a split-thickness skin graft (STSG) in type-3 burns of diabetic patients. They reported that diabetic ulcers healed completely using PBM with 650-nm (2 J/cm^2) and 810-nm (6 J/cm^2) irradiation given before and after the STSG.

Fiorio et al.[42] assessed the PBM effects of a red laser (660 nm, 35 mW) on third-degree burns in rats and reported that laser irradiation resulted in a reduction in the inflammatory process and increased collagen deposition. Meireles et al.[43] evaluated the PBM efficacy of two different wavelengths (660 and 780 nm, 20 J/cm^2) on third-degree burns in diabetic rats. They reported that healing in the animals irradiated with 660 nm laser was more apparent at early stages with positive effects on inflammation, granulation tissue formation, fibroblast proliferation, collagen deposition, re-epithelialization, and local microcirculation. Red light (660 nm, 100 mW, 20 J/cm^2) enhanced dermal repair and showed that PBM is crucial during the early stage (proliferative stage) of second-degree burn wound healing in rats.[44] Red-light

(670 nm) irradiation significantly increases the wound closure rate in a murine pressure ulcer model.[45] PBM with superpulsed 904-nm irradiation (200-ns pulsewidth; 100 Hz; 0.7-mW mean output power; 0.4-mW/cm^2 average irradiance) attenuated the inflammatory response and augmented the healing of burn wounds in rats.[46] In a clinical study, Waibel et al.[47] evaluated the efficacy of a nonablative fractional Erbium laser (1,550 nm) for the treatment of burn scars and reported that PBM led to improved skin texture, dyschromia, and hypertrophy.

10.5 Pre-conditioning with PBM Therapy before Surgery

Pre-conditioning by ischemia, hyperthermia, hypothermia, hyperbaric oxygen, and other stressors is a rapidly growing area of investigation in biomedical arena that is used in different pathophysiological conditions where tissue injury may be expected. The damage caused by surgery, ischemic insult (heart attack), or stroke can be mitigated by pre-treating the local or distant tissue with low levels of a stress-inducing stimulus that can induce a protective response against subsequent major damage. A plethora of scientific evidence indicated that the application of PBM has evolved from a therapeutic modality for tissue repair, regeneration, dentistry, neuronal repair, and mitigation of pain and inflammation to its current progression as a pre-conditioning measure for neuronal pain, muscle injury, myocardial infarction, etc. It has been recently acknowledged that PBM can be effective if delivered to normal cells or tissue before the actual insult or trauma, in a pre-conditioning mode. Muscles are protected, nerves feel less pain, and PBM can protect cardiomyocytes against a subsequent heart attack, which supports wider use of PBM therapy as a pre-conditioning modality to prevent pain and increase healing after surgical/medical procedures and possibly to increase athletic performance.[37,48]

10.6 Conclusions and Future Perspectives

In aggregate, PBM can be considered as a promising painless, non-invasive, drug-less, biophysical healing modality owing to its numerous applications. The light sensitivity of a variety of effector molecules strongly suggests that PBM could be used in light-based healing therapy for both acute and chronic nonhealing wounds, especially when conventional therapies have failed or have unacceptable side effects. Although there is general unanimity on the efficacy of the PBM effect and some consensus on the mechanism by which the light–tissue interaction results in PBM, it remains controversial for many researchers working in mainstream medicine. To address the limitations of PBM therapy, researchers have recently placed even more emphasis on better understanding biological mechanistic insights, establishing better guidelines with standardized treatment protocols, maintaining consistency in measuring radiant exposure parameters, and systematically controlling clinical studies.

References

1. A. J. Singer and R. A. Clark, "Cutaneous wound healing," *N. Engl. J. Med.* **341**, 738–46 (1999).
2. S. Schreml, R. M. Szeimies, L. Prantl, M. Landthaler, and P. Babilas, "Wound healing in the 21st century," *J. Am. Acad. Dermatol.* **63**, 866–81 (2010).
3. G. S. Schultz and A. Wysocki, "Interactions between extracellular matrix and growth factors in wound healing," *Wound Repair Regen.* **17**, 153–162 (2009).
4. A. Gupta and M. R. Hamblin, History and fundamentals of low-level laser (light) therapy, In: *Handbook of Photomedicine.* CRC Press, Taylor and Francis, New York, pp. 43–52 (2013).
5. A. Gupta, P. Avci, M. Sadasivam, R. Chandran, N. Parizotto, D. Vecchio, W. C. de Melo, T. Dai, L. Y. Chiang, and M. R. Hamblin, "Shining light on nanotechnology to help repair and regeneration," *Biotechnol. Adv.* **31**, 607–31 (2013).
6. J. J. Anders, R. J. Lazalame, and P. R. Arany, "Low-level light/laser therapy versus photobiomodulation therapy," *Photomed. Laser Surg.* **33**, 183–184 (2015).
7. S. R. Barretto, G. C. de Melo, J. C. Santos et al., "Evaluation of anti-nociceptive and anti- inflammatory activity of low-level laser therapy on temporomandibular joint inflammation in rodents," *J. Photochem. Photobiol. B: Biol.* **129**, 135–142 (2013).
8. P. Avci, A. Gupta, M. Sadasivam, D. Vecchio, Z. Pam, N. Pam, and M. R. Hamblin, "Low-level laser (light) therapy (LLLT) in skin: stimulating, healing, restoring," *Semin. Cutan. Med. Surg.* **32**, 41–52 (2013).
9. Y. Y. Huang, A. C. Chen, J. D. Carroll, and M. R. Hamblin, "Biphasic dose response in low level light therapy," *Dose Response* **7**, 358–383 (2009).
10. J. T. Hashmi, Y. Y. Huang, S. K. Sharma et al., "Effect of pulsing in low-level light therapy," *Lasers Surg. Med.* **42**, 450–466 (2010).
11. C. P. Sabino, A. M. Deana, T. M. Yoshimura et al., "The optical properties of mouse skin in the visible and near infrared spectral regions," *J. Photochem. Photobiol. B. Biol.* **160**, 72–78 (2016).
12. T. Ando, W. Xuan, T. Xu, T. Dai, S. K. Sharma, G. B. Kharkwal, Y. Y. Huang, Q. Wu, M. J. Whalen, S. Sato, and M. Obara, "Comparison of therapeutic effects between pulsed and continuous wave 810-nm

wavelength laser irradiation for traumatic brain injury in mice," *PLoS One* **6**, e26212 (2011).

13. J. Joensen, K. Ovsthus, R. K. Reed, S. Hummelsund, V. V. Iversen, R. Á. Lopes-Martins, and J. M. Bjordal, "Skin penetration time-profiles for continuous 810 nm and Superpulsed 904 nm lasers in a rat model," *Photomed. Laser Surg.* **30**, 688–94 (2012).

14. P. Salvatore and T. Karu, "Absorption of monochromatic and narrow band radiation in the visible and near IR by both mitochondrial and non-mitochondrial photoacceptors results in photobiomodulation," *J. Photochem. Photobiol. B. Biol.* **140**, 344–358 (2014).

15. N. Lane, "Cell biology: power games," *Nature* **443**, 901–903 (2006).

16. L. F. de Freitas and M. R. Hamblin, "Proposed mechanisms of photobiomodulation or low-level light therapy," *IEEE J. Selected Topics Quantum Electronics* **22**, 700417 (2016).

17. D. Bisht, S. C. Gupta, V. Misra, V. P. Mital, and P. Sharma, "Effect of low intensity laser radiation on healing of open skin wounds in rats," *Indian J. Med. Res.* **100**, 43–46 (1994).

18. M. R. Hamblin, M. V. P. Sousa, P. R. Arany et al., "Low-level laser (light) therapy and photobiomodulation: The Path Forward," *Proc. of SPIE* **9309**, (2015) [doi :10.1117/12.2084049].

19. T. N. Demidova-Rice, E. V. Salomatina, A. N. Yaroslavsky, I. M. Herman, and M. R. Hamblin, "Low-level light stimulates excisional wound healing in mice," *Lasers Surg. Med.* **39**, 706–715 (2007).

20. H. Chung, T. Dai, S. K. Sharma et al., "The nuts and bolts of low-level laser (light) therapy," *Annals of Biomedical Engineering* **40**, 516–533 (2012).

21. S. Dixit, A. Maiya, L. Rao, M. A. Rao, B. A. Shastry, and L. Ramachandra, "Photobiomodulation by helium neon and diode lasers in an excisional wound model: A single blinded trial," *Adv. Biomed. Res.* **1**, 38 (2012).

22. A. Gupta, T. Dai, and M. R. Hamblin, "Effect of red and near infrared wavelengths on low-level laser (light) therapy induced healing of partial-thickness dermal abrasions in mice," *Lasers Med. Sci.* **29**, 257–65 (2014).

23. T. Fushimi, S. Inui, T. Nakajima et al., "Green light emitting diodes accelerate wound healing: characterization of the effect and its molecular basis in vitro and in vivo," *Wound Repair Regen.* **20**, 226–235 (2012).

24. C. H. Chen, H. S. Hung, and S. H. Hsu, "Low-energy laser irradiation increases endothelial cell proliferation, migration, and eNOS gene expression possibly via PI3K signal pathway," *Lasers Surg. Med.* **40**, 46–54 (2008).

25. W. P. Hu, J. J. Wang, C. L. Yu et al., "Helium-neon laser irradiation stimulates cell proliferation through photostimulatory effects in mito-chondria," *J. Invest. Dermatol.* **127**, 2048–2057 (2007).

26. V. Prabhu, S. B. Rao, S. Chandra et al., "Spectroscopic and histological evaluation of wound healing progression following low level laser therapy (LLLT)," *J. Biophotonics* **5**, 168–184 (2012).

27. R. T. Chow, M. I. Johnson, R. A. Lopes-Martins, and J. M. Bjordal, "Efficacy of low-level laser therapy in the management of neck pain: a systematic review and meta-analysis of randomised placebo or active-treatment controlled trials," *Lancet.* **374**, 1897–1908 (2009)

28. Y. Zhang, S. Song, C. C. Fong, C. H. Tsang, Z. Yang, and M. Yang, "cDNA microarray analysis of gene expression profiles in human fibroblast cells irradiated with red light," *J. Invest Dermatol.* **120**, 849–57 (2003).

29. P. V. Peplow, T. Y. Chung, B. Ryan, and G. D. Baxter. "Laser photobiomodulation of gene expression and release of growth factors and cytokines from cells in culture: a review of human and animal studies," *Photomed. Laser Surg.* **29**, 285–304 (2011).

30. M. Figurova, V. Ledecky, M. Karasova et al., "Histological assessment of a combined low-level laser/light-emitting diode therapy (685 nm/470 nm) for sutured skin incisions in a porcine model: a short report," *Photomed. Laser Surg.* **34**, 53–55 (2015).

31. Y. Li, J. Zhang, X. Yanfeng et al., "The histopathological investigation of red and blue light emitting diode on treating skin wounds in Japanese big ear white rabbit," *PLoS One* **11**, e0157898 (2016).

32. A. Capon, G. Iarmarcovai, D. Gonnelli, N. Degardin, G. Magalon, and S. Mordon, "Scar prevention using laser-assisted skin healing (LASH) in plastic surgery," *Aesthetic Plast. Surg.* **34**, 438–46 (2010).

33. J. T. Hopkins, T. A. McLoda, J. G. Seegmiller et al., "Low-level laser therapy facilitates superficial wound healing in humans: A triple-blind, sham-controlled study," *J. Athl. Train.* **39**, 223–229 (2004).

34. L. Dancakova, T. Vasilenko, I. Kovac, K. Jakubcova, M. Holly, V. Revajova, F. Sabol, Z. Tomori, M. Iversen, P. Gal, and J. M. Bjordal, "Low-level laser therapy with 810 nm wavelength improves skin wound healing in rats with streptozotocin-induced diabetes," *Photomed. Laser Surg.* **32**, 198–204 (2014).

35. Z. Mao, J. H. Wu, T. Dong et al., "Additive enhancement of wound healing in diabetic mice by low-level light and CoQ10," *Sci. Rep.* **6**, (2016) [doi: 10.1038/srep20084].

36. G. B. Chiarotto, L. M. Neves, M. A. Esquisatto et al., "Effects of laser irradiation (670-nm InGaP and 830-nm GaAlAs) on burn of second-degree in rats," *Lasers Med. Sci.* **29**, 1685–93 (2014).

37. M. R. Hamblin, "Shining light on the head: Photobiomodulation for brain disorders," *BBA Clinical.* (2016) [doi: 10.1016/j.bbacli.2016.09.002].

38. B. Rathnakar, B. S. Rao, V. Prabhu et al., "Photo-biomodulatory response of low-power laser irradiation on burn tissue repair in mice," *Lasers Med. Sci.* (2016) [doi: 10.1007/s10103-016-2044-2].

39. A. Ezzati, M. Bayat, and A. Khoshvaghti, "Low-level laser therapy with a pulsed infrared laser accelerates second-degree burn healing in rat: a clinical and microbiologic study," *Photomed. Laser Surg.* **28**, 603–11 (2010).

40. J. C. T. Rocha, C. Ferraresi, M. R. Hamblin et al., "Low-level laser therapy (904 nm) can increase collagen and reduce oxidative and nitrosative stress in diabetic wounded mouse skin," *J. Photochem. Photobiol. B. Biol.* **164**, 96–102 (2016).

41. M. Dahmardehei, N. Kazemikhoo, R. Vaghardoost et al., "Effects of low level laser therapy on the prognosis of split thickness skin graft in type 3 burn of diabetic patients: a case series," *Lasers Med. Sci.* **31**, 497–502 (2016).

42. F. B. Fiorio, R. Albertini, E. C. Pinto Leal-Junior, and P. T. Camillo de Carvalho, "Effect of low-level laser therapy on types I and III collagen and inflammatory cells in rats with induced third-degree burns," *Lasers Med. Sci.* **29**, 313–319 (2014).

43. G. C. S. Meireles, J. N. Santos, P. O. Chagas, A. P. Moura, and A. L. B. Pinheiro. "Effectiveness of laser photobiomodulation at 660 or 780 nanometers on the repair of third-degree burns in diabetic rats," *Photomed. Laser Surg.* **26**, 47–54 (2008).

44. E. T. Trajano, L. A. da Trajano, M. A. dos Santos Silva et al., "Low-level red laser improves healing of second-degree burn when applied during proliferative phase," *Lasers Med. Sci.* **30**, 1297–1304 (2015).

45. R. J. Lanzafame, I. Stadler, A. F. Kurtz, R. Connelly, P. A. Timothy, P. Brondon, and D. Olson, "Reciprocity of exposure time and irradiance on energy density during photoradiation on wound healing in a murine pressure ulcer model," *Lasers in Surgery and Medicine* **39**, 534–542 (2007)

46. A. Gupta, G. K. Keshri, A. Yadav et al., "Superpulsed (Ga-As, 904 nm) low-level laser therapy (LLLT) attenuates inflammatory response and enhances healing of burn wounds," *J. Biophotonics* **8**, 489–501 (2015).

47. J. Waibel, A. J. Wulkan, M. Lupo et al., "Treatment of burn scars with the 1,550 nm nonablative fractional Erbium laser," *Lasers Surg. Med.* **44**, 441–6 (2012).

48. T. Agarwal, G. K. Gupta, V. Rai, J. D. Carroll, and M. R. Hamblin, "Pre-conditioning with low-level laser (light) therapy: light before the storm," *Dose Response* **12**, 619–649 (2014).

49. A. C. Chen, P. R. Arany, Y. Y. Huang et al., "Low-level laser therapy activates NF-kB via generation of reactive oxygen species in mouse embryonic fibroblasts," *PloS One* **6**, e22453 (2011).

Chapter 11
Photobiomodulation in Human Muscle Tissue for Better Sports Performance*

11.1 Introduction

Photobiomodulation (PBM) by low-level laser therapy (LLLT) and light-emitting diode therapy (LEDT) provides several benefits for muscle tissue as evidenced by *in vitro* and *in vivo* studies, and clinical trials. Among these benefits, this chapter covers two recent and very important effects reported in the current literature:

1. the prevention of muscle damage after exercise, including delayed onset muscle soreness; and
2. the improvement of muscle performance (demonstrated by increases in muscle torque, power, or work), workload capacity, fatigue resistance, functional or sport activity, and exercise recovery.

Therefore, this chapter covers the majority of clinical trials that have been published up to February 2016 that aimed at increasing muscle performance and exercise recovery or preventing muscle damage with PBM in healthy volunteers/ athletes. Studies with different purposes were not included.

The use of PBM to prevent muscle damage has primarily been investigated in animal models, irradiating skeletal muscles before a bout of intense exercise (referred to in this chapter as "muscular pre-conditioning") and by following the muscle damage with measurements of the creatine kinase (CK) levels in the bloodstream. To the best of our knowledge, the first study that used PBM via LLLT to prevent muscle damage was performed by Lopes-Martins et al.[1] in rats. These authors investigated the effects of different doses of a 655-nm laser

---

*Based on material first printed in C. Ferraresi, Y. Y. Huang, and M. R. Hamblin, "Photobiomodulation in human muscle tissue: an advantage in sports performance?" *J. Biophotonics* **9**(11–12), 1273–1299 (2016).

(0.5 J/cm^2, 1.0 J/cm^2, and 2.5 J/cm^2) to prevent muscle fatigue and muscle damage (CK) induced by neuromuscular electrical stimulation. This study reported a LLLT dose response to decreased CK activity.

Another experimental study used exercise-trained rats on an inclined treadmill and measured the inhibition of inflammation, reduction of CK activity, and reduction of oxidative stress. They also found increases in the resistance to oxidative stress (increased activity of superoxide dismutase, SOD) 24 h and 48 h after exercise.[2] These previous studies and other similar reports[1–6] were important in establishing a scientific basis to conduct clinical trials for the prevention of muscle damage with PBM.

Regarding the clinical trials of improved muscle performance and exercise recovery, the first studies published were on delayed-onset muscle soreness[7,8] and resistance to muscle fatigue[9,10] during one or a few bouts of exercise; and improved muscle strength[11] and resistance to muscle fatigue[12] after exercise training programs combined with PBM.

This chapter reviews the literature regarding the use of PBM through LLLT and LEDT in clinical trials investigating muscle performance, prevention of damage, and delayed onset muscle soreness and fast muscle recovery in upper- and lower-limb muscles over the two last decades. All parameters used in these studies are summarized in Tables 11.1–11.3.

11.2 Literature Review

11.2.1 Acute responses in exercises with *biceps brachii* muscles

The first known study that investigated the effects of LEDT (a cluster of 32 LEDs, 950 nm) on delayed onset muscle soreness after fatigue induction of the *biceps brachii* muscle in an isokinetic dynamometer was conducted by Vinck et al.[8] The authors reported no significant difference between LEDT and placebo therapies regarding peak torque and pain. However, using a similar methodology, Douris et al.[7] applied LEDT (cluster of 36 LEDs, 880 nm and 660 nm) on the *biceps brachii* after an elbow flexion/extension exercise with free weights, and found a significant decay in delayed onset muscle soreness after 48 h when comparing LEDT to the control group.

Using a muscular pre-conditioning protocol, Leal, Jr. et al.[10] applied LLLT (655 nm) to the *biceps brachii* muscle before elbow flexion/extension until exhaustion on a Scott bench. PBM was applied to four points of the *biceps brachii*, and then a series of maximum voluntary contractions (MVCs) were applied with a load of 75%. The number of repetitions increased significantly in all of the volunteers that received muscular pre-conditioning compared to the placebo group but with no significant difference regarding blood lactate and time expended to accomplish the exercise. Moreover, similar studies were conducted by the same research group, investigating the muscular pre-conditioning with LLLT (830 nm) applied to four points of

Table 11.1 Clinical trials of PBM in acute responses in exercises with upper limb muscles.

Source	PBM Parameters	Muscle and Exercise	Mode of Irradiation
Vinck et al.[8]	Cluster with 32 LEDs (950 nm) Diode area 18 cm² 160 mW, 3.2 J/cm² (360 s) 1 site of irradiation per limb	*biceps brachii* via elbow flexion (isokinetic dynamometer)	Contact, after exercise
Douris et al.[7]	Cluster with 36 LEDs: 32 @ 880 nm, 80 s, 8 J/cm²4 @ 660 nm, 80 s, 8 J/cm² Diode area 5 cm² 100 mW/cm² 2 sites of irradiation per limb	*biceps brachii* (1 site of irradiation at the point of muscle-tendon junction, and 1 site of irradiation 5 cm above) via elbow flexion (Scott bench)	Contact, after exercise
Leal, Jr. et al.[10]	Diode laser (655 nm) Diode area 0.1 cm² 50 mW, 500 J/cm², 5 W/cm², 5 J per diode (100 s) 4 sites of irradiation per limb (20 J)	*biceps brachii* via elbow flexion (Scott bench), maximum voluntary contraction until exhaustion	Contact, muscular pre-conditioning
Leal, Jr. et al.[13]	Diode laser (830 nm) Diode area 0.0028 cm² 100 mW, 35.7 W/cm², 5 J (50 s), 1,785 J/cm² 4 sites of irradiation per limb (20 J)	*biceps brachii* via elbow flexion (Scott bench), maximum voluntary contraction until exhaustion	Contact, muscular pre-conditioning
de Almeida et al.[14]	Diode laser (660 nm) Diode area 0.0028 cm² 50 mW, 17.85 W/cm², 5 J (100 s), 1,785 J/cm² 4 sites of irradiation per limb: 20 J **versus** Diode laser (830 nm) Diode area 0.0028 cm² 50 mW, 17.85 W/cm², 5 J (100 s), 1,785 J/cm² 4 sites of irradiation per limb (20 J)	*biceps brachii* via elbow flexion (Scott bench), maximum voluntary contraction (60 s)	Contact, muscular pre-conditioning
Leal, Jr. et al.[15]	Cluster with 5 diode lasers (810 nm) Diode area 0.0364 cm² 200 mW, 5.495 W/cm², 6 J per diode (30 segundos), 164.85 J/cm² 30 J per site of irradiation: 5 × 6 J 2 sites of irradiation per limb (60 J)	*biceps brachii* via elbow flexion (Scott bench), maximum voluntary contraction until exhaustion	Contact, muscular pre-conditioning

(*continued*)

Table 11.1 Continued

Source	PBM Parameters	Muscle and Exercise	Mode of Irradiation
Leal, Jr. et al.[16]	Cluster with 69 LEDs LED area 0.2 cm^2 mW 150 mW/cm^2 0.3-J LED 660 nm (30 s), 1.5 J/cm^2 0.9-J LED 850 nm (30 s), 4.5 J/cm^2 41.7 J per site of irradiation (30 s) 1 site of irradiation per limb (41.7 J)	*biceps brachii* via elbow flexion (Scott bench), maximum voluntary contraction until exhaustion	Contact, muscular pre-conditioning
Borges et al.[17]	LED (630 nm) LED area 1.77 cm^2 300 mW, 169.49 mW/cm^2, 9 J (30 s), 5.1 J/cm^2 4 sites of irradiation per limb (36 J)	*biceps brachii* via elbow flexion (Scott bench), 30 eccentric contraction	Contact, muscular pre-conditioning
Felismino et al.[18]	Diode laser (808 nm) Diode area 0.0028 cm^2 100 mW, 35.71 W/cm^2, 1 J (10 s), 357.14 J/cm^2 4 sites of irradiation per limb (4 J)	*biceps brachii* via elbow flexion (biceps curl), 10 sets of 10 repetitions	Contact, between sets of exercise
Higashi et al.[19]	Diode laser (808 nm) Diode area 0.0028 cm^2 100 mW, 35.7 W/cm^2, 7 J (70 s), 2,500 J/cm^2 8 sites of irradiation per limb (56 J)	*biceps brachii* via elbow flexion	Contact, muscular pre-conditioning
Larkin-Kaiser et al.[20]	Cluster with 2 laser diodes (800 nm and 970 nm) Diode area not provided 3 W (50% duty cycle), 1.5 W of average power output 24 J per point 15 sites of irradiation per limb (360 J)	*biceps brachii* via elbow flexion (isokinetic dynamometer)	Contact, muscular pre-conditioning

Table 11.2   Clinical trials of PBM in acute responses to exercises with lower limb muscles.

Reference	PBM Parameters	Muscle and Exercise	Irradiation and Moment
Gorgey et al.[9]	4 diode lasers (808 nm), 500 mW, 8.3 mW/cm², 7 J (10 min) and 3 J (5 min); 1 site of irradiation	*quadriceps femoris*; Maximum voluntary contraction (isokinetic dynamometer)	Scanning, muscular pre-conditioning
Leal, Jr. et al.[21]	Diode laser (830 nm), 0.0028-cm² area, 100 mW; Volleyball athletes [4 J (40 s), 1,428.57 J/cm²]; Soccer athletes [3 J (30 s), 1,071.43 J/cm²]; 5 sites of irradiation per limb: 20 J (volleyball) and 15 J (soccer)	*rectus femoris*; Wingate test	Contact, muscular pre-conditioning
Leal, Jr. et al.[22]	Diode laser (810 nm), 0.036-cm² area, 200 mW, 5.5 W/cm², 6 J (30 s), 164.84 J/cm²; 2 sites of irradiation per limb (12 J) **versus** 69 LEDs (0.2-cm² area): 34 LEDs (660 nm), 10 mW, 50 mW/cm², 0.3 J, 30 s, 1.5 J/cm² 35 LEDs (850 nm), 30 mW; 150 mW/cm², 0.9 J, 30 s, 4.5 J/cm² 41.7 J per site of irradiation, 2 sites of irradiation per limb (83.4 J)	*rectus femoris*; Wingate test	Contact, muscular pre-conditioning
Denis et al.[23]	69 LEDs (0.2-cm² area): 34 LEDs (660 nm), 10 mW; 50 mW/cm², 0.30 J, 30 s, 1.5 J/cm² 35 LEDs (950 nm), 15 mW; 75 mW/cm², 0.45 J, 30 s, 2.25 J/cm² 25.95 J per site of irradiation, 4 sites of irradiation per limb (103.8 J)	*rectus femoris* (2), *vastus lateralis* (1), and *vastus medialis* (1); Wingate test	Contact, between 2° and 3° Wingate

(continued)

Table 11.2 Continued

Reference	PBM Parameters	Muscle and Exercise	Irradiation and Moment
Leal, Jr. et al.[24]	69 LEDs (0.2-cm² area): 34 LEDs 660 nm, 10 mW, 50 mW/cm², 0.3 J, 30 s, 1.5 J/cm² 35 LEDs 850 nm; 30 mW; 150 mW/cm², 0.9 J, 30 s, 4.5 J/cm² 41.7 J per site of irradiation, 5 sites of irradiation per limb (208.5 J) **versus** Cryotherapy (water immersion for 5 minutes at 5°C)	quadriceps femoris (2), hamstrings (2), and gastrocnemius (1); 3 Wingate tests	Contact, after exercise
Baroni et al.[25]	5 diode lasers (810 nm, 0.029-cm² area); 200 mW, 6.89 W/cm²; 6 J per diode (30 s), 206.89 J/cm²; 30 J per site of irradiation (5 × 6 J), 6 sites of irradiation per limb (180 J)	vastus medialis (2), vastus lateralis (2), and rectus femoris (2); Max. voluntary contraction (isokinetic dynamometer)	Contact, muscular pre-conditioning
Baroni et al.[26]	69 LEDs (0.2-cm² area): 34 LEDs 660 nm, 10 mW, 50 mW/cm², 0.3 J, 30 s, 1.5 J/cm² 35 LEDs 850 nm; 30 mW; 150 mW/cm², 0.9 J, 30 s, 4.5 J/cm² 41.7 J per site of irradiation (30 s), 3 sites of irradiation per limb (125.1 J)	rectus femoris (1), vastus medialis (1), and vastus lateralis (1); Max. voluntary contraction (isokinetic dynamometer)	Contact, muscular pre-conditioning
Antonialli et al.[27]	1 diode laser (905 nm), 0.44-cm² area, 0.3125 mW, 0.07 mW/cm² 4 LEDs (875 nm), 0.9-cm² area, 17.5 mW, 19.44 mW/cm² 4 LEDs (640 nm), 0.9-cm² area, 15 mW, 16.66 mW/cm² 10 J per site of irradiation (76 s), 30 J per site of irradiation (228 s), and 50 J per site of irradiation (381 s); 6 sites of irradiation per limb (60 J, 180 J, 300 J)	vastus medialis (2), vastus lateralis (2), and rectus femoris (2); Eccentric contractions (isokinetic dynamometer)	Contact, muscular pre-conditioning
Toma et al.[28]	Diode laser (808 nm), 0.00785-cm² area, 100 mW, 12.7 W/cm², 7 J (70 s), 892 J/cm² 8 sites of irradiation per limb (56 J)	rectus femoris (8); Knee extension (extensor chair)	Contact, muscular pre-conditioning

Study	Parameters	Muscle (sites); Exercise	Mode
dos Santos Maciel et al.[29]	Diode laser (780 nm), 0.2-cm² area, 30 mW, 0.15 W/cm², 0.81 J (27 s), 4 J/cm²; 29 sites of irradiation per limb (23.49 J)	*tibialis anterior* (29); Ankle dorsiflexion (isokinetic dynamometer)	Contact, muscular pre-conditioning
de Brito Viera et al.[30]	Diode laser (808 nm), 0.0028-cm² area; 100 mW, 35.71 W/cm², 4 J (40 s), 1,428.57 J/cm²; 5 sites of irradiation per limb (20 J × 3 = 60 J)	*rectus femoris* (3), *vastus lateralis* (1), *vastus medialis* (1); Knee extension (isokinetic dynamometer)	Contact, between sets of exercise
Vassao et al.[31]	Diode laser (808 nm), 0.028-cm² area, 100 mW, 35.71 W/cm², 7 J (70 s), 250 J/cm²; 8 sites of irradiation per limb (56 J)	*rectus femoris* (8), *vastus lateralis* (1), *vastus medialis* (1); Knee extension (isokinetic dynamometer)	Contact, muscular pre-conditioning
Ferraresi et al.[32]	200 LEDs: 100 LEDs (850 nm, IR) arranged in 25 clusters of 4, 130 mW, 185.74 mW/cm² 100 LEDs (630 nm, RED) arranged in 25 clusters of 4, 80 mW Groups: 105 J (20 s), total per limb: 315 J 210 J (40 s), total per limb: 630 J 315 J (60 s), total per limb: 945 J Placebo: 0 J (30 s)	Whole *quadriceps femoris*, hamstrings, and *triceps surae*; Before volleyball games	Contact, muscular pre-conditioning
de Marchi et al.[33]	5 diode lasers (810 nm), 0.0364-cm² area, 200 mW, 5.495 W/cm², 6 J per diode (30 s), 164.85 J/cm², 30 J per site of irradiation (5 × 6 J), 12 sites of irradiation per limb (360 J)	*vastus medialis* (2), *vastus lateralis* (2), *rectus femoris* (2), hamstrings (4), and gastrocnemius (2); Running on a treadmill until exhaustion	Contact, muscular pre-conditioning
da Silva Alves et al.[34]	7 diode lasers (850 nm), 0.05-cm² area, 100 mW, 2 W/cm², 2 J per diode (20 s), 40 J/cm²; 14 J per site of irradiation: (7 × 2 J), 4 sites of irradiation per limb (56 J)	*vastus medialis* (1), *vastus lateralis* (1), *rectus femoris* (1), and gastrocnemius (1); Running on a treadmill until exhaustion	Contact, muscular pre-conditioning
Ferraresi et al.[35]	50 LEDs (850 nm), 0.2-cm², 50 mW, 250 mW/cm², 0.75 J per diode (15 s), 3.75 J/cm²; 37.5 J per muscle group (50 × 0.75 J), total energy delivered: 450 J	*biceps brachii* and *triceps brachii*, external oblique and *latissimus dorsi*, femoral quadriceps, hamstrings, *tibialis anterior* and *peroneus longus*, and gastrocnemius and soleus; Running on a treadmill until exhaustion	Contact, muscular pre-conditioning

Table 11.3 Clinical trials of PBM in chronic responses in exercises with lower limb muscles.

Reference	PBM Parameters	Muscle and Exercise	Irradiation and Moment
Ferraresi et al.[11]	6 diode lasers (808 nm), 0.0028-cm² area, 60 mW, 21.42 W/cm², 0.6 J per diode (10 s), 214.28 J/cm²; 3.6 J per site of irradiation (0.6 J × 6), 7 sites of irradiation per limb (25.2 J)	*quadriceps femoris*: 7 sites uniformly distributed; Leg press training and isokinetic dynamometer	Contact, after exercise
Viera et al.[12]	6 diode lasers (808 nm), 0.0028-cm² area, 60 mW, 21.42 W/cm², 0.6 J per diode (10 s), 214.28 J/cm²; 3.6 J per site of irradiation (0.6 J × 6), 5 sites of irradiation per limb (18 J)	*quadriceps femoris*: 5 sites uniformly distributed; Cycle ergometer training and isokinetic dynamometer	Contact, after exercise
Paolillo et al.[36]	2 panels with 2,000 LEDs (850 nm), 1,110-cm² panel area; 2,000 LEDs (850 nm), 31 mW/cm²; 14,400 J (both lower limbs), 30 minutes, 55.8 J/cm²	Whole thigh; Treadmill training	Without contact, during exercise
Paolillo et al.[37]	2 panels with 2,000 LEDs (850 nm), 1,110-cm² panel area; 2,000 LEDs (850 nm), 100 mW, 39 mW/cm², 45 minutes, 108 J/cm²	Whole thigh; Treadmill training	Without contact, during exercise
Dos Reis et al.[38]	6 diode lasers (830 nm), 0.0028-cm² area, 60 mW, 21.42 W/cm², 0.6 J per diode (10 s), 214.28 J/cm²; 3.6 J per site of irradiation (0.6 J × 6), 7 sites of irradiation per limb (25.2 J)	*quadriceps femoris*: 7 sites uniformly distributed; Knee extension	Contact, muscular pre-conditioning/ after exercise
Baroni et al.[39]	5 diode lasers (810 nm), 0.029-cm² area, 200 mW, 6.89 W/cm², 6 J per diode (30 s), 206.89 J/cm²; 30 J per site of irradiation (8 × 6 J), 8 sites of irradiation per limb (240 J)	*vastus medialis* (2), *vastus lateralis* (3), and *rectus femoris* (3); Eccentric training in isokinetic dynamometer	Contact, muscular pre-conditioning

biceps brachii,[13] as well as red (660 nm) and infrared (830 nm) wavelenghts applied to the *biceps brachii* muscle before maximum voluntary contractions on a Scott bench.[14] These authors identified significant differences between the placebo group and both groups irradiated with LLLT, but without any difference between the two wavelengths regarding the peak torque developed by each group irradiated.

Applying a muscular pre-conditioning protocol on 2 sites of the *biceps brachii* during 30 s, Leal, Jr. et al.[15] reported an increased number of repetitions and time of contraction, and decreased lactate levels in blood, CK, and C-rective protein. The PBM used in this study was delivered by a cluster of five laser diodes (810 nm). Similar results were reported by the same research group[16] using a cluster of 69 LEDs (850 nm and 660 nm) applied to one site of the *biceps brachii* muscle during muscular pre-conditioning of elbow flexion/extension with a load of 75% of MVCs on a Scott bench. The LEDT group showed an increased number of repetitions and longer duration of exercise compared to the placebo group. LEDT also decreased the blood levels of lactate, CK and C-reactive protein compared to placebo group.

While investigating the effects of LEDT (640 nm) when applied after an exercise protocol to induce muscle damage by eccentric elbow flexion/extension, Borges et al.[17] reported delayed-onset muscle soreness and slower decay in isometric force in the LEDT group when compared to the placebo. The authors also reported less restriction (or a smaller decrease in the range of motion) in the LEDT group 24 h, 48 h, 72 h, and 96 h after the induction of muscle damage. In a similar study, Felismino et al.[18] applied LLLT (808 nm) to the *biceps brachii* muscle between sets of 10 series of 10 repetitions with a load corresponding to 50% of the single maximum repetition (1 RM) during exercise consisting of elbow flexion/extension on a Scott bench. The results of this study pointed to a significant reduction in muscle damage (CK) 72 h after the exercise test compared to the placebo group. However, there was no significant difference in muscle performance (load) between the groups.

As mentioned earlier, although several studies have reported the benefits of PBM on *biceps brachii*, Higashi et al.[19] did not find any positive effects of PBM on *biceps brachii* subjected to an exercise protocol on a Scott bench. These authors used a muscular pre-conditioning protocol applying LLLT (808 nm) to eight sites of irradiation on the *biceps brachii*. There was no significant increment in the number of repetitions and no reduction of lactate levels in the blood. Finally, Larkin-Kaiser et al.[20] in a recent crossover study enrolling men and women applied a muscular pre-conditioning protocol with LLLT (800 nm and 970 nm) to *biceps brachii* muscle at 15 points. Although only a very small result when compared with the placebo group, the LLLT group had a minor decay in the maximum voluntary isometric contraction assessed by an isokinetic dynamometer, and it had no significant effect on muscle point tenderness. Figure 11.1 represents sites of irradiation on muscles

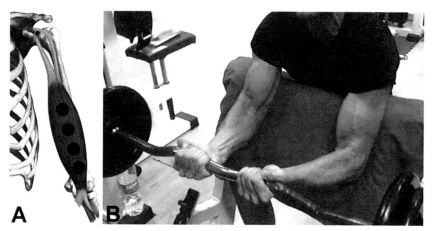

Figure 11.1 (a) Muscular pre-conditioning irradiating multiple sites or points of the *biceps brachii*. (b) Exercise test on a Scott bench.

and an exercise test for upper limbs. Table 11.1 presents all of the parameters of PBM in acute responses to exercises with upper limb muscles.

11.2.2 Acute responses in exercises with *quadriceps femoris* muscles

One of the first studies published in this research field was conducted by Gorgey et al.[9] The authors performed a muscular pre-conditioning protocol applying LLLT (808 nm) for 5 minutes (scanning mode) with low energy (3 J) and high energy (7 J) on the *quadriceps femoris* muscles before inducing fatigue by neuromuscular electrical stimulation. Although apparently less fatigue of LLLT groups compared to control, there was no significant results comparing the groups.

Leal, Jr. et al.[21] irradiated the *rectus femoris* muscle before Wingate tests in a muscular pre-conditioning study design. These authors reported no significant effects of the LLLT (830 nm) on muscle performance, but the levels of CK and lactate in the bloodstream were decreased when compared to the placebo group. Leal, Jr. et al.[22] conducted another study using the Wingate test and compared the effects of LLLT (single diode, 810 nm) to LEDT (cluster of 69 LEDs, 850 nm and 660 nm) on the muscle performance of athletes. LLLT or LEDT was applied to two sites of the *rectus femoris* muscle during a muscular pre-conditioning protocol. LEDT decreased CK levels in the blood compared to the placebo and LLLT groups. However, there was no improvement in muscle performance or reduction in lactate levels in the bloodstream of the LEDT group compared to the placebo and LLLT groups. Similar results were reported by Denis et al.,[23] who also did not find positive results when LEDT (cluster of 69 LEDs, 950 nm and 660 nm) was applied during the rest intervals of the Wingate tests. These authors reported no significant differences in muscle peak power, fatigue index, and blood lactate levels when compared to the placebo group.

Using the Wingate test, Leal, Jr. et al.[24] compared the effects of LEDT (cluster of 69 LEDs, 850 nm and 660 nm) to the use of cold-water immersion for promoting muscle recovery. Six athletes performed three Wingate tests on nonconsecutive days and received either LEDT or cold-water immersion of their lower limbs (5°C for five minutes) as therapy. LEDT was applied to two sites of the *quadriceps femoris* muscles, two sites of the hamstrings, and two sites of the *triceps surae*. Comparing both groups, LEDT significantly decreased levels of CK and lactate in blood but was not able to increase muscle work in the Wingate test and did not reduce C-reactive protein.

Assessing muscle performance by an exercise protocol of eccentric exercise in isokinetic dynamometer, Baroni et al.[25] also used muscular pre-conditioning with LLLT (cluster of five laser diodes, 810 nm) applied to six sites of the *quadriceps femoris* muscles. The authors reported an improved maximum voluntary contraction immediately and 24 h after the exercise protocol, found increased lactate dehydrogenase (LDH) activity at 48 h after exercise, and the CK in the blood decreased after 24 h and 48 h when compared to the placebo group. However, the delayed-onset muscle soreness was not improved by LLLT. This same research group[26] also investigated the effects of the same LEDT cluster (69 LEDs, 850 nm and 660 nm) applied to three sites of the *quadriceps femoris* muscles before a fatigue exercise protocol performed in an isokinetic dynamometer for knee flexion/extension. The authors reported that LEDT was able to decrease the decay of the peak torque that could be exerted compared to the placebo group.

With a similar protocol of exercise in an isokinetic dynamometer to the previous study,[26] Antonialli et al.[27] used a diode laser (905 nm) and LEDs (640 nm and 875 nm) in the same device to stimulate muscle recovery when applied as muscular pre-conditioning to the *quadriceps femoris* muscles before a fatigue protocol with eccentric contractions and maximum voluntary contractions in an isokinetic dynamometer. Muscular pre-conditioning using LLLT and LEDs was performed three minutes before the exercise protocol. The authors reported that light energies of 10 J and 30 J per site of irradiation increased the peak torque of maximum voluntary contraction immediately, and this effect lasted for 96 h after the muscular pre-conditioning. Delayed muscle soreness was reduced significantly using light energies of 30 J and 50 J when compared with the placebo group. Finally, these authors reported a significant reduction of CK with light energies of 10 J, 30 J, and 50 J.

Toma et al.[28] used muscular pre-conditioning with LLLT (808 nm) on the *quadriceps femoris* muscles and assessed muscle fatigue by surface electromyography during 60 s of leg-extension exercise, measuring also the maximal number of repetitions. The authors reported an increased number of repetitions in the LLLT group compared to the placebo, but surface electromyography showed no statistical difference. In a similar study, Dos

Santos Maciel et al.[29] used a muscular pre-conditioning protocol with LLLT (780 nm) applied to the *tiabialis anterior* and investigated muscle fatigue in an isokinetic dynamometer associated with surface electromyography analysis. These authors reported an increased torque exterted by the *tiabialis anterior* muscle with muscular pre-conditioning, but muscle fatigue analyzed by surface electromyography was not reduced, and lactate levels in the blood were not different between the groups.

On the other hand, de Brito Vieira et al.[30] applied LLLT (808 nm) to five sites of the *quadriceps femoris* muscles between 3 sets of 20 maximum voluntary repetitions in an isokinetic dynamometer during a single training session. Two days after the training session, all volunteers were evalutated through the number of maximum repetitions of knee flexion/extension in an isokinetic dynamometer in conjunction with surface electromyography to identify muscle fatigue. The authors reported increased number of repetitions in the LLLT group and lower muscle fatigue compared to the placebo group. Similarly, while investigating the responsivess of elderly woman to PBM, Vassao et al.[31] applied LLLT (808 nm) to eight sites of the *rectus femoris* before a fatigue protocol in an isokinetic dynamometer along with surface electromyography and blood lactate analysis. The LLLT group decreased the blood levels of lactate and reduced muscle fatigue assessed by surface electromyography, but it did not improve muscle performance in the isokinetic dynamometer.

Regarding the use of PBM in the sports field with the goal to translate laboratory findings to clinical practice, Ferraresi et al.[32] used an array of 200 LEDs (100 LEDs at 850 nm, and 100 LEDs at 630 nm) to test the effectiveness of LEDT for the prevention of muscle damage. The authors applied muscular pre-conditioning with LEDT to the *quadriceps femoris*, hamstring, and *triceps surae* muscles of professional volleyball players before each official match during a national championship to prevent muscle damage (CK). In addition, this study tested four light energies: 105 J, 210 J, 315 J, and placebo. The authors reported that the light energies that effectively prevent the rise in CK were 210 J and 315 J, whereas 105 J and the placebo allowed a significant increase in CK to occur in the blood 24 h after each official match. Figure 11.2 represents the sites of irradiation on muscles and exercise test for lower limbs in an isokinetic dynamometer.

11.2.3 Acute responses during exercise on a treadmill

Several studies in the literature have reported the acute effects of PBM on muscles when applied in muscular pre-conditioning regimens and on exercises performed on a treadmill. de Marchi et al.[33] used a cluster of five laser diodes (810 nm) applied to *quadriceps femoris* muscles, hamstrings and *triceps surae* before a protocol of progressive and maximum effort on a treadmill. This study showed that LLLT increased the relative and absolute oxygen uptake, as well as the time of running on treadmill, when compared with the placebo

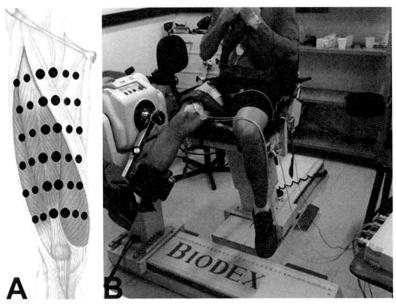

Figure 11.2 (a) Muscular pre-conditioning irradiating multiple sites or points of the *quadriceps femoris* muscles in order to cover the entire muscle group. (b) Exercise testing in an isokinetic dynamometer along with surface electromyography.

group. In addition, LDH, muscle damage (CK), and lipid peroxidation (thiobarbituric acid reactive substances, TBARS) were significantly higher in the placebo group. Finally, the superoxide dismutase enzyme activity was lower only in the placebo group after exercise.

da Silva Alves et al.[34] investigated the effects of PBM on cardiopulmonary exercise testing in conjunction with electromyographic analysis. The authors applied muscular pre-conditioning with a cluster of seven laser diodes (850 nm) to three sites of *quadriceps femoris* muscles (one *vastus lateralis*, one *vastus medialis*, and one *rectus femoris*) and one site of gastrocnemius muscles. Compared to the placebo, LLLT increased peak O_2 uptake and cardiovascular efficiency but had no effect on electromyographic analysis.

After analyzing the kinetics of oxygen uptake, Ferraresi et al.[35] conducted a randomized, double-blind, placebo-controlled trial with an elite runner athlete. The authors applied muscular pre-conditioning to the lower and upper limbs and trunk muscles using an array of 50 LEDs (850 nm) before high-intensity, constant-workload running exercise on a treadmill. Compared to placebo therapy, LEDT improved the speed of muscular VO_2 adaptation (~ -9 s), decreased the O_2 deficit (~ 10 L), increased the VO_2 from the slow component phase ($\sim +348$ ml·min^{-1}), and increased the time limit of exercise before fatigue ($\sim +589$ s). LEDT also decreased the CK in blood (muscle damage) and markers of muscle damage and fatigue (alanine and lactate levels) analyzed in urine by proton nuclear magnetic resonance spectroscopy

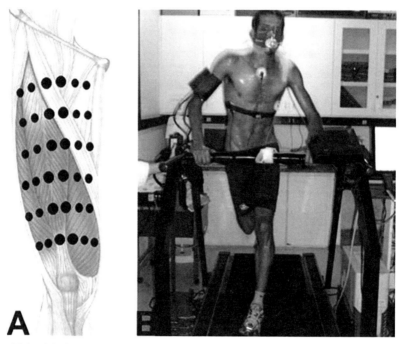

Figure 11.3 (a) Muscular pre-conditioning irradiating multiple sites or points of the *quadriceps femoris* muscles in order to cover the entire muscle group. (b) Cardiopulmonary exercise testing on a treadmill.

(^{1}H NMR). Figure 11.3 shows the sites of irradiation on muscles and exercise testing on treadmill. Table 11.2 presents all of the parameters of PBM employed to acute responses in exercise with lower limb muscles.

11.2.4 Chronic responses in clinical trials

Ferraresi et al.[11] studied the effects of LLLT (a cluster of 6 laser diodes, 808 nm) on a strength-training program using a load of 80% of 1RM, 2 days per week during 12 weeks. Immediately after each training session, LLLT was applied to seven regions of the *quadriceps femoris* muscles. The authors reported an increased load in the 1 RM of the LLLT group compared to the control and non-LLLT training groups. Furthermore, only the LLLT group increased the peak torque assessed by an isokinetic dynamometer.

Regarding resistance to muscle fatigue, Vieira et al.[12] measured the effects of LLLT (cluster of 6 laser diodes, 808 nm) on moderate training using a cycle ergometer performed three days per week for nine weeks. LLLT was applied to five sites of the *quadriceps femoris* muscles immediately after each training session. The authors reported that only the LLLT group showed a reduced fatigue index of the knee extensor muscles in an isokinetic dynamometer.

Paolillo et al.[36] investigated the effects of LEDT combined with physical training in post-menopausal women for 12 weeks. Training sessions were performed twice a week with 30 minutes of exercise on a treadmill. During each training session, the LEDT group received LEDT (850 nm) using two panels of LEDs placed 15 cm from the women's thighs. The authors reported increased muscle power and work of the knee extensor muscles assessed by an isokinetic dynamometer when compared to the training group without LEDs, which had a higher fatigue index. In addition, the follow-up at six months of this study showed a decreased time for recovery of the heart rate after exercise.[37]

Dos Reis et al.[38] tried to find the best time to apply PBM to muscles by comparing the effectiveness of LLLT (830 nm) applied to the *quadriceps femoris* muscles as muscular pre-conditioning or after an exercise protocol of leg extension with 75% of 1 RM. The authors reported that there was no significant difference regarding the number of maximum repetitions performed by all groups. However, the lactate and CK levels in blood were lower in the group that received LLLT after the exercise protocol when compared to the placebo and pre-exercise LLLT groups.

Finally, Baroni et al.[39] assessed the effects of LLLT (cluster of five laser diodes, 810 nm) applied as muscular pre-conditioning on *quadriceps femoris* muscles during an eccentric training program in isokinetic dynamometer, twice a week for eight weeks. Knee extensor muscle thickness increased in the LLLT group compared to the placebo group (15% versus 9%) assessed by ultrasonography, as well as isometric peak torque (20.5% versus 13.7%) and eccentric peak torque (32.2% versus 20.0%) in an isokinetic dynamomenter. Figure 11.4 shows

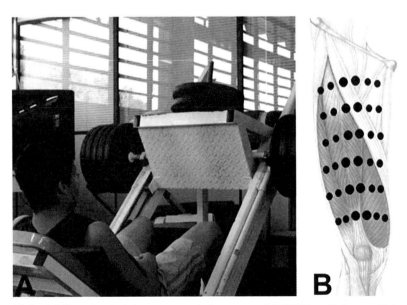

Figure 11.4 (a) Exercise training program in leg press. (b) PBM irradiating multiple sites or points of the *quadriceps femoris* muscles to cover the entire muscle group after each training session.

the exercise training program and sites of irradiation on muscles of lower limbs after a training session. Table 11.3 presents all parameters of PBM in chronic responses in exercises with lower limb muscles.

There are still many unanswered question remaining in the field of PBM and exercise:

1. Which is the best wavelength to use?
2. When is best time to apply PBM to muscles (before, during, or after exercise?
3. Which are the best doses and parameters?
4. How many points or sites of irradiation should be used?
5. How does PBM interact with muscle tissue to increase sports performance?

These questions will certainly be raised by health professionals and sports physiologists when considering the possibility of using PBM to improve sports performance. Based on the present literature review, wavelengths have ranged mainly from red (630–660 nm) and near-infrared (808–950 nm) regions. However, although a previous study did not find significant difference between red and infrared LLLT for muscle performance in upper limbs,[14] there is a preference for infrared wavelengths possibly because of their better penetration into muscle tissue. Conversely, it is important to note the increased frequency of mixed red and infrared wavelengths made available by new clusters of lasers/LEDs for PBM (see Tables 11.1–11.3).

Regarding the adequate moment to irradiate muscle tissue, the current literature reports two main strategies for the use of PBM to increase muscle performance and exercise recovery in clinical trials aiming at improved sports performance. The first strategy is the use of muscular pre-conditioning, i.e., irradiation of muscle tissue 3–5 minutes before exercise. There are several pieces of scientific evidence in favor of muscular pre-conditioning[40–42] when the purpose is to increase sports performance or reduce the damage and pain of a single bout of exercise, i.e., acute response simulating a competition. This strategy seems to be valid for this purpose; however, recent studies suggested that five minutes may not necessarily be the best time. Ferraresi et al.[43] reported that after 3–6 h after muscular pre-conditioning in rats, the performance increased more than 300–600% compared to sham and muscular pre-conditioning only five minutes before exercise. In addition, muscular pre-conditioning conducted 40–60 minutes before official matches involving professional volleyball players was able to decrease muscle damage (CK in bloodstream).[32] The second strategy applies PBM by LLLT or LEDT immediately after exercise in order to accelerate muscle recovery,[38,40] mainly in exercise training programs.[11,44] In addition, the use of PBM as muscular pre-conditioning in exercise training programs seems to improve the potential gains of training, including better defense against oxidative stress, improved muscle cell proliferation, higher muscle energy contents (glycogen and adenosine tri-phosphate, ATP) and mitochondrial metabolism.[44]

The parameters of PBM reported in the literature present a large degree of variability. The power of the light, time of irradiation, energy of the light, dose, and irradiance have not generally been very similar among the studies. One of the main factors that contribute to this variability is the diversity of devices available and how they are used by researchers. In addition, the optimal parameters of wavelength, light energy, power, timing, and treatment repetition frequency still remain as questions to be solved. However, based on the present review, it is possible to establish a range for the aforementioned parameters to guide the clinical practitioner. For the upper-limb studies (*biceps brachii*) with positive effects in acute responses, the power of the light ranged from 50–300 mW and the total energy from 4–60 J. For the lower limbs (*quadriceps femoris*) with positive effects in acute responses, the power of the light ranged from 40–200 mW and the total energy from 28–315 J.

Regarding the number of points or sites of irradiation on muscle tissue, the literature has reported an increased number, mainly when applied to the lower limbs. It is logical and in accordance with previous studies to suggest to irradiate the largest area as possible over the muscles.[11,40]

There are several mechanisms of action for PBM to explain the benefits to muscle tissue and consequently its ability to enhance sports performance. Several of these mechanisms have been described previously and can be summarized as improvements in

1. energy metabolism,
2. oxidative stress defenses,
3. prevention and repair of muscle damage,
4. modulation of gene expression, and
5. better excitability of muscle fibers.[40]

Finally, if the use of PBM becomes widespread in high-performance sports, especially before or during athletic competitions, then organizations such as the World Anti-Doping Agency (WADA) or the International Olympic Committee (IOC) will need to discuss whether or not PBM will be allowed. If it is not allowed, how could the authorities detect light exposure of muscles or of athletes in general? Discussions about this issue are inevitable.

References

1. R. A. Lopes-Martins et al., "Effect of low-level laser (Ga-Al-As 655 nm) on skeletal muscle fatigue induced by electrical stimulation in rats," *J. Appl. Physiol.* **101**(1), 283–288 (2006) [doi: 10.1152/japplphysiol.01318.2005].
2. X. G. Liu, Y. J. Zhou, T. C. Liu, and J. Q. Yuan, "Effects of low-level laser irradiation on rat skeletal muscle injury after eccentric exercise,"

Photomed. Laser. Surg. **27**(6), 863–869 (2009) [doi: 10.1089/pho.2008. 2443].

3. D. A. Sussai et al., "Low-level laser therapy attenuates creatine kinase levels and apoptosis during forced swimming in rats," *Lasers Med. Sci.* **25**(1), 115–120 (2010) [doi: 10.1007/s10103-009-0697-9].

4. E. C. Leal, Jr. et al., "Effect of low-level laser therapy (GaAs 904 nm) in skeletal muscle fatigue and biochemical markers of muscle damage in rats," *Eur. J. Appl. Physiol.* **108**(6), 1083–1088 (2010) [doi: 10.1007/ s00421-009-1321-1].

5. P. de Almeida et al., "Low-level laser therapy improves skeletal muscle performance, decreases skeletal muscle damage and modulates mRNA expression of COX-1 and COX-2 in a dose-dependent manner," *Photochem. Photobiol.* **87**(5), 1159–1163 (2011) [doi: 10.1111/j.1751-1097. 2011.00968.x].

6. L. A. Santos et al., "Effects of pre-irradiation of low-level laser therapy with different doses and wavelengths in skeletal muscle performance, fatigue, and skeletal muscle damage induced by tetanic contractions in rats," *Lasers Med. Sci.* **29**(5), 1617–1626 (2014) [doi: 10.1007/ s10103-014-1560-1].

7. P. Douris et al., "Effect of phototherapy on delayed onset muscle soreness," *Photomed. Laser Surg.* **24**(3), 377–382 (2006) [doi: 10.1089/pho.2006.24.377].

8. E. Vinck, B. Cagnie, P. Coorevits, G. Vanderstraeten, and D. Cambier, "Pain reduction by infrared light-emitting diode irradiation: a pilot study on experimentally induced delayed-onset muscle soreness in humans," *Lasers Med. Sci.* **21**(1), 11–18 (2006) [doi: 10.1007/s10103-005-0366-6].

9. A. S. Gorgey, A. N. Wadee, and N. N. Sobhi, "The effect of low-level laser therapy on electrically induced muscle fatigue: a pilot study," *Photomed. Laser Surg.* **26**(5), 501–506 (2008) [doi: 10.1089/pho.2007.2161].

10. E. C. Leal, Jr. et al., "Effect of 655-nm low-level laser therapy on exercise-induced skeletal muscle fatigue in humans," *Photomed. Laser Surg.* **26**(5), 419–424 (2008) [doi: 10.1089/pho.2007.2160].

11. C. Ferraresi et al., "Effects of low level laser therapy (808 nm) on physical strength training in humans," *Lasers Med. Sci.* **26**(3), 349–358 (2011) [doi: 10.1007/s10103-010-0855-0].

12. W. H. Vieira, C. Ferraresi, S. E. Perez, V. Baldissera, and N. A. Parizotto, "Effects of low-level laser therapy (808 nm) on isokinetic muscle performance of young women submitted to endurance training: a randomized controlled clinical trial," *Lasers Med. Sci.* **27**(2), 497–504 (2012) [doi: 10.1007/s10103-011-0984-0].

13. E. C. Leal, Jr. et al., "Effect of 830 nm low-level laser therapy in exercise-induced skeletal muscle fatigue in humans," *Lasers Med. Sci.* **24**(3), 425–431 (2009) [doi: 10.1007/s10103-008-0592-9].

14. P. de Almeida et al., "Red (660 nm) and infrared (830 nm) low-level laser therapy in skeletal muscle fatigue in humans: what is better?" *Lasers Med. Sci.* **27**(2), 453–458 (2012) [doi: 10.1007/s10103-011-0957-3].

15. E. C. Leal, Jr. et al., "Effects of low-level laser therapy (LLLT) in the development of exercise-induced skeletal muscle fatigue and changes in biochemical markers related to postexercise recovery," *J. Orthop. Sports Phys. Ther.* **40**(8), 524–532 (2010) [doi: 10.2519/jospt.2010.3294].

16. E. C. Leal, Jr. et al., "Effect of cluster multi-diode light emitting diode therapy (LEDT) on exercise-induced skeletal muscle fatigue and skeletal muscle recovery in humans," *Lasers Surg. Med.* **41**(8), 572–577 (2009) [doi: 10.1002/lsm.20810].

17. L. S. Borges et al., "Light-emitting diode phototherapy improves muscle recovery after a damaging exercise," *Lasers Med. Sci.* **29**(3), 1139–1144 (2014) [doi: 10.1007/s10103-013-1486-z].

18. A. S. Felismino et al., "Effect of low-level laser therapy (808 nm) on markers of muscle damage: a randomized double-blind placebo-controlled trial," *Lasers Med. Sci.* **29**(3), 933–938 (2014) [doi: 10.1007/s10103-013-1430-2].

19. R. H. Higashi et al., "Effects of low-level laser therapy on biceps braquialis muscle fatigue in young women," *Photomed. Laser Surg.* **31**(12), 586–594 (2013) [doi: 10.1089/pho.2012.3388].

20. K. A. Larkin-Kaiser, E. Christou, M. Tillman, S. George, and P. A. Borsa, "Near-infrared light therapy to attenuate strength loss after strenuous resistance exercise," *J. Athl. Train.* **50**(1), 45–50 (2015) [doi: 10.4085/1062-6050-49.3.82].

21. E. C. Leal, Jr. et al., "Effect of 830 nm low-level laser therapy applied before high-intensity exercises on skeletal muscle recovery in athletes," *Lasers Med. Sci.* **24**(6), 857–863 (2009) [doi: 10.1007/s10103-008-0633-4].

22. E. C. Leal, Jr. et al., "Comparison between single-diode low-level laser therapy (LLLT) and LED multi-diode (cluster) therapy (LEDT) applications before high-intensity exercise," *Photomed. Laser Surg.* **27**(4), 617–623 (2009) [doi: 10.1089/pho.2008.2350].

23. R. Denis, C. O'Brien, and E. Delahunt, "The effects of light emitting diode therapy following high intensity exercise," *Phys. Ther. Sport* **14**(2), 110–115 (2013) [doi: 10.1016/j.ptsp.2012.03.014].

24. E. C. Leal, Jr. et al., "Comparison between cold water immersion therapy (CWIT) and light emitting diode therapy (LEDT) in short-term skeletal muscle recovery after high-intensity exercise in athletes–preliminary results," *Lasers Med. Sci.* **26**(4), 493–501 (2011) [doi: 10.1007/s10103-010-0866-x].

25. B. M. Baroni et al., "Low level laser therapy before eccentric exercise reduces muscle damage markers in humans," *Eur. J. Appl. Physiol.* **110**(4), 789–796 (2010) [doi: 10.1007/s00421-010-1562-z].

26. B. M. Baroni, E. C. Leal, Jr., J. M. Geremia, F. Diefenthaeler, and M. A. Vaz, "Effect of light-emitting diodes therapy (LEDT) on knee extensor muscle fatigue," *Photomed. Laser Surg.* **28**(5), 653–658 (2010) [doi: 10.1089/pho.2009.2688].

27. F. C. Antonialli et al., "Phototherapy in skeletal muscle performance and recovery after exercise: effect of combination of super-pulsed laser and light-emitting diodes," *Lasers Med. Sci.* **29**(6), 1967–1976 (2014) [doi: 10.1007/s10103-014-1611-7].

28. R. L. Toma et al., "Effect of 808 nm low-level laser therapy in exercise-induced skeletal muscle fatigue in elderly women," *Lasers Med. Sci.* **28**(5), 1375–1382 (2013) [doi: 10.1007/s10103-012-1246-5].

29. T. Dos Santos Maciel et al., "Phototherapy effect on the muscular activity of regular physical activity practitioners," *Lasers Med. Sci.* **29**(3), 1145–1152 (2014) [doi: 10.1007/s10103-013-1481-4].

30. V. H. de Brito Vieira et al., "Use of low-level laser therapy (808 nm) to muscle fatigue resistance: a randomized double-blind crossover trial," *Photomed. Laser Surg.* **32**(12), 678–685 (2014) [doi: 10.1089/pho.2014.3812].

31. P. G. Vassao, R. L. Toma, H. K. Antunes, H. T. Tucci, and A. C. Renno, "Effects of PBM on the fatigue level in elderly women: an isokinetic dynamometry evaluation," *Lasers Med. Sci.* **31**(2), 275–282 (2015) [doi: 10.1007/s10103-015-1858-7].

32. C. Ferraresi et al., "Light-emitting diode therapy (LEDT) before matches prevents increase in creatine kinase with a light dose response in volleyball players," *Lasers Med. Sci.* **30**(4), 1281–1287 (2015) [doi: 10.1007/s10103-015-1728-3].

33. T. De Marchi et al., "Low-level laser therapy (LLLT) in human progressive-intensity running: effects on exercise performance, skeletal muscle status, and oxidative stress," *Lasers Med. Sci.* **27**(1), 231–236 (2012) [doi: 10.1007/s10103-011-0955-5].

34. M. A. da Silva Alves et al., "Acute effects of low-level laser therapy on physiologic and electromyographic responses to the cardiopulmonary exercise testing in healthy untrained adults," *Lasers Med. Sci.* **29**(6), 1945–1951 (2014) [doi: 10.1007/s10103-014-1595-3].

35. C. Ferraresi et al., "Muscular pre-conditioning using light-emitting diode therapy (LEDT) for high-intensity exercise: a randomized double-blind placebo-controlled trial with a single elite runner," *Physiother Theory Pract.* 1–8. (2015) [doi: 10.3109/09593985.2014.1003118].

36. F. R. Paolillo et al., "Effects of infrared-LED illumination applied during high-intensity treadmill training in postmenopausal women," *Photomed. Laser Surg.* **29**(9), 639–645 (2011) [doi: 10.1089/pho.2010.2961].

37. F. R. Paolillo et al., "Infrared LED irradiation applied during high-intensity treadmill training improves maximal exercise tolerance in postmenopausal

women: a 6-month longitudinal study," *Lasers Med. Sci.* **28**(2), 415–422 (2013) [doi: 10.1007/s10103-012-1062-y].

38. F. A. Dos Reis et al., "Effects of pre- or post-exercise low-level laser therapy (830 nm) on skeletal muscle fatigue and biochemical markers of recovery in humans: double-blind placebo-controlled trial," *Photomed. Laser Surg.* **32**(2), 106–112 (2014) [doi: 10.1089/pho.2013.3617].

39. B. M. Baroni et al., "Effect of low-level laser therapy on muscle adaptation to knee extensor eccentric training," *Eur. J. Appl. Physiol.* **115**(3), 639–647 (2015) [doi: 10.1007/s00421-014-3055-y].

40. C. Ferraresi, M. R. Hamblin, and N. A. Parizotto, "Low-level laser (light) therapy (LLLT) on muscle tissue: performance, fatigue and repair benefited by the power of light," *Photon. Lasers Med.* **1**(4), 267–286 (2012) [doi: 10.1515/plm-2012-0032].

41. E. C. Leal, Jr. et al., "Effect of phototherapy (low-level laser therapy and light-emitting diode therapy) on exercise performance and markers of exercise recovery: a systematic review with meta-analysis," *Lasers Med. Sci.* **30**(2), 925–939 (2013) [doi: 10.1007/s10103-013-1465-4].

42. P. A. Borsa, K. A. Larkin, and J. M. True, "Does phototherapy enhance skeletal muscle contractile function and postexercise recovery? A systematic review," *J. Athl. Train.* **48**(1), 57–67 (2013) [doi: 10.4085/1062-6050-48.1.12].

43. C. Ferraresi et al., "Time response of increases in ATP and muscle resistance to fatigue after low-level laser (light) therapy (LLLT) in mice," *Lasers Med. Sci.* **30**(4), 1259–1267 (2015) [doi: 10.1007/s10103-015-1723-8].

44. C. Ferraresi et al., "Light-emitting diode therapy in exercise-trained mice increases muscle performance, cytochrome c oxidase activity, ATP and cell proliferation," *J. Biophoton.* **8**(9), 740–754 (2014) [doi: 10.1002/jbio.201400087].

Chapter 12
Photobiomodulation in Bone: Studies *in vitro, in vivo*, and Clinical Applications

Cleber Ferraresi, Fernanda Freire, and Michael R. Hamblin

12.1 Photobiomodulation in Bone

Bone tissue comprises different types of cells, such as osteoblasts, osteocytes, and osteoclasts. Osteoblasts are cells responsible for bone matrix synthesis and bone mineralization, and for secreting type-I collagen, proteoglycan, alkaline phosphatase, and osteocalcin. Osteocytes are cells that originate from osteoblasts and became incorporated within the osteoid matrix that is formed and then calcified to become mature bone. These cells are localized deeply within the bone matrix and are well organized. Osteoclasts are the cells responsible for degrading bone and for resorption of mineralized bone during the process of bone remodeling, which is required during repair of bone tissue. In addition, the bone mass (mineralized matrix) is composed of collagen and inorganic components—such as hydroxyapatite, calcium, and phosphate—conferring tensile strength to bones and providing a well-arranged structure that can bear loads and protect against sheer stress.[1–3]

The process of healing bone fractures is formally separated into the following phases:

- immediate response to injury,
- inflammatory phase,
- ossification, and
- bone remodeling.

These stages are all characterized by the proliferation and differentiation of different bone cells, deposition of extracellular matrix, and expression of specific genes and cell-signaling molecules. In this context, the transcription factor Runx2 controls the development of osteoblasts and the expression of extracellular matrix proteins during differentiation. The receptor activator of NF-κB ligand (RANKL) has been credited as the key transcription factor for osteoclast differentiation and activation, and it has been shown to bind to a receptor activator of NF-κB (RANK) on the surface of osteoclast cells. Moreover, bone morphogenetic proteins have an important regulatory role in bone regeneration, affecting osteoblast differentiation and bone remodeling by regulating osteoclasts during the process of bone resorption.[1–4]

There are some diseases that adversely affect bone repair/regeneration, such as osteoporosis and diabetes mellitus. Osteoporosis is a skeletal disease characterized by the reduction or lowering of bone mass, and the deterioration of the micro-architecture of the bone tissue, which increases bone frailty and the risk of fractures; it is becoming a major public health issue. In addition, the low bone mineral density in osteoporosis possibly induces a delay in fracture healing and also poor-quality bone repair, mainly in the vertebrae, proximal femur (femoral neck), and the wrist.[5–7]

Diabetes mellitus is a heterogeneous and debilitating metabolic disease characterized by defective insulin secretion and, consequently, chronically high blood-glucose levels. This disease is frequently associated with major dysfunctions in many organ systems of the human body, including bone tissue. Diabetes can decrease bone mass and reduce mineral density, which directly affects the micro-architecture of bone tissue. Moreover, diabetes can decrease bone formation via a reduction of osteoblast activity, slow down the healing of bone fractures, and decrease the biomechanical properties of the bone due to changes in the balance between bone formation and bone resorption. Finally, diabetes mellitus also promotes osteoporosis, osteopenia, and poor healing of bone fractures.[8–10]

Biomaterial implants and some physical therapies, such as low-intensity pulsed ultrasound and photobiomodulation (PBM) or low-level laser therapy (LLLT), have been used to accelerate bone fracture healing or to modulate bone cells for the improvement of bone repair. The recent literature has reported the use of biomaterials as an implant for bone substitution or as a material to serve as a biocompatible matrix upon which osteoblasts can proliferate and form new bone. Bioactive glasses and glass–ceramics, such as Bio-Oss® and Biosilicate®, are examples of biomaterials used to induce osteogenesis and help bone fracture healing.[4,5,1]

The literature has reported the use of LLLT to improve bone fracture healing in normal, osteoporotic/osteopenic, or diabetic animal models *in vivo*, and to promote bone cell modulation *in vitro* studies. LLLT can increase angiogenesis and modulate the formation of new bone tissue, stimulating the metabolism and proliferation of osteoblasts and osteoclasts, modulating the inflammatory process, and stimulating the gene expression of pro-osteogenic factors.[1,8,12–14] Therefore, this chapter summarizes studies published in the last few years about the use of PBM to stimulate bone cells *in vitro*, affect bone tissue in experimental models, and help bone problems in clinical trials. Table A.1 in the Appendix summarizes all of the employed PBM parameters and the main findings reported in the studies involving bone (see Fig. 12.1).

12.2 *in vitro* Studies with Bone Cells

Ozawa et al.[15] investigated the effects of LLLT (830 nm, 500 mW, 3.8 J/cm^2) on bone cells during different stages of cell culture, such as cellular proliferation (osteoblasts), bone nodule formation, alkaline phosphatase activity, and osteocalcin gene expression in rat calvarial bone cells. These authors reported an increased proliferation of bone cells (1.3–1.7-fold) compared with the control group. Bone nodule formation was also increased on the 1st day of irradiation (1.7-fold) to the 13th day (1.2-fold) with LLLT, but on the 14th there was no difference between the LLLT and control groups. Regarding the alkaline phosphatase activity, there was a peak increase in the LLLT group compared to the control on the 9th day of irradiation (2.3-fold), and then on the 18th and 21th the LLLT group decreased compared with the control group. Finally, osteocalcin gene expression increased in the LLLT group (1.6-fold) on the 1st day. The authors concluded that LLLT could promote a stimulatory effect on cell proliferation and bone formation during the early stages of cell culture.

Osteoclast precursor cells, which are cells responsible for bone resorption, were irradiated with LLLT (810 nm, 50 mW, 9.33 J/cm^2, 27.99 J/cm^2,

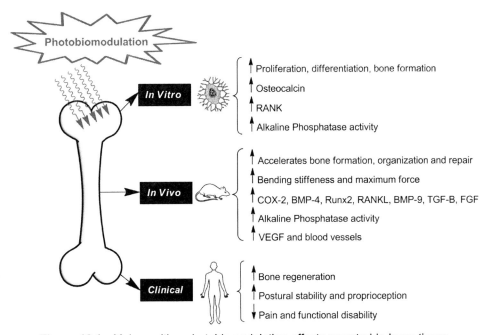

Figure 12.1 Main positive photobiomodulation effects reported in bone tissue.

55.98 J/cm^2, and 93.30 J/cm^2) once a day for eight days and compared to the control group (no treatment).[3] This study reported significantly higher proliferation with light doses of 9.33 J/cm^2, 27.99 J/cm^2, and 55.98 J/cm^2; increased immunoexpression of RANK (receptor activator of NF-κB) on the 2nd, 3rd, 4th, 6th, and 8th days; and higher bone resorption when compared with the control group, suggesting that LLLT promoted the differentiation and activation of osteoclasts via RANK expression.

Jawad et al.[16] recently evaluated the effects of different power levels and light doses of LLLT (940 nm) on osteoblast cells during the proliferation and differentiation stages. The authors applied 100 mW (22.92 J/cm^2, and 45.85 J/cm^2), 200 mW (45.85 J/cm^2, and 91.79 J/cm^2), and 300 mW (68.78 J/cm^2, and 137.57 J/cm^2) once a day for 7 days and compared all of the LLLT groups with the control group using cell viability (MTT assay: 3-(4,5-dimethylthiazol-2yl)-2,5 diphenyl tetrazolium bromide), alkaline phosphatase activity, and osteocalcin activity. The MTT assay revealed higher proliferation of all of the LLLT groups, especially on the 7th day, when compared with the control group. Moreover, LLLT 300 mW (137.57 J/cm^2) promoted the highest proliferation rate between LLLT groups. Cell differentiation was increased in all groups treated with LLLT on the 7th day. The best treatment to increase alkaline phosphatese activity was LLLT 100 mW (45.85 J/cm^2), and the osteocalcin activity was LLLT 200 mW (91.79 J/cm^2). Therefore, this study showed the important role of LLLT in osteoblast proliferation and differentiation with a clear dose response.

PBM by pulsed LLLT (915 nm) was used to irradiate human osteoblast-like cells in a model of bone wounding in cell culture.[13] LLLT (1 W, 100 Hz, duty cycle of 50% corresponding to an average power of 575 mW) was applied with single doses of 5 J/cm^2, 10 J/cm^2, or 15 J/cm^2 on the cell cultures. Compared to the control group (no treatment), groups receiving doses of 5 J/cm^2 and 10 J/cm^2 were the first to reach complete wound closure 72 h after irradiation, followed by 15 J/cm^2 at 96 h, whereas the control group displayed only partial wound healing after 96 h. Moreover, when a cell-proliferation inhibitor (Mitomycin C) was applied, doses of 10 and 15 J/cm^2 were able to maintain improved wound healing compared with the control group. However, there was no significant difference between the LLLT and control groups regarding cell viability and DNA quantification. After 24 h, COL1A1 (collagen type-I alpha 1) gene expression was increased in all groups treated with LLLT compared with the control group, and LLLT 15 J/cm^2 had the highest level of COL1A1 expression at 24 h and 72 h. The control group increased gene expression of TGFbeta1 (transforming growth factor beta-1-like) at 48 h compared with 5 J/cm^2 and 15 J/cm^2, and LLLT 10 J/cm^2 decreased TGFbeta1 compared with the control group at 72 h. In conclusion, the authors reported PBM with a dose response in cell migration and increased collagen deposition by osteoblasts in the wound-healing model *in vitro*.

12.3 Bone Injury in Animal Models

One of the first studies investigating the effects of PBM on bone tissue was reported by Barushka et al.[17] who applied LLLT (632 nm, 6 mW, 31 J/cm^2) to surgical defects (hole injury) created in rat bones (tibia). Compared with the control group, on the 5th and 6th days after the bone defect there was an increase in alkaline phosphatase activity; tartrate-resistant acid phosphatase (TRAP), which is characteristic of cells from the macrophage/osteoclast lineage, increased sharply on the 12th day; and calcium accumulation showed a peak on the 11th day. Histomorphometrical analysis revealed a rapid accumulation of reparative new bone in the LLLT group 10, 13, and 15 days after the bone defect. The authors concluded that LLLT could improve bone repair approximately twofold when compared with the control group.

Years later, another study investigated the effects of the LLLT (632 nm, 1 mW, 31.5 J/cm^2, 94.5 J/cm^2) on angiogenesis in the injured tibias of rats.[18] The mechanical injury model was similar to a previous study[17] of the creation of a surgical hole in rat tibias. LLLT was applied 24 h after the surgical procedure and repeated once a day for 7 or 14 days. Histological analysis quantified the newly-formed blood vessels and the injured area. Compared to the control group, LLLT (94.5 J/cm^2) increased blood vessels after 7 days. However, both LLLT dose levels decreased the number of blood vessels after 14 days. There was no increase in blood vessels in the control group between 8 and 15 days after the surgical injury.

Batista et al.[19] tried to reverse the compromise in bone tissue healing induced by radiotherapy (ionizing radiation) by using LLLT (830 nm, 100 mW, 210 J/cm^2, 6 J, 120 s, 0.028 cm^2) in a model of a surgical bone defect in rat femurs. Radiotherapy was applied to both the femur and tibia with a single anterior field, delivering 30 Gy in only one session. After 4 weeks, the authors created a surgical bone defect in the femur; LLLT was applied immediately after the surgical defect and every 48 h for 7 days. There was good bone repair only in bone that had not received previous radiotherapy, and the LLLT group expressed higher amounts of newly formed bone. However, groups that received radiotherapy were not responsive to LLLT.

The effects of LLLT on bone repair assessed by radiologic (x-ray) and histopathological analysis were reported by Briteno-Vazquez et al.[20] Bone defects were made surgically in rat tibias and then treated with LLLT (850 nm, 100 mW, 8 J/cm^2, 64 s, 0.04 cm^2) every 24 h after the surgery for 10 days. Compared with the control group, LLLT presented higher bone consolidation (x-ray) after 10 days of irradiation. Furthermore, histopathological analysis reported an increase in fibroblasts and angiogenesis in the LLLT group.

Batista et al.[21] investigated the effects of LLLT (830 nm, 100 mW, 210 J/cm^2, 6 J, 120 s, 0.028 cm^2) on bone repair in rats. LLLT was applied immediately after bone surgery and every 48 h for 7, 15, and 21 days. In addition, LLLT was applied to the femur of rats (nonsurgical area). This study reported improvement in new bone formation during early stages of bone healing in the LLLT group when compared with the control (no treatment). However, there were no LLLT effects on bone healing when applied to a nonsurgical area.

Regarding the expression of inflammatory markers during bone repair, Matsumoto et al.[22] investigated the effects of LLLT (735 nm, 18 mW, 16 J/cm^2) applied every 48 h for 15 days, starting 24 h after the bone defect was surgically created in the rat tibia. Compared with the control group, LLLT increased the amount of newly formed bone tissue and cyclo-oxygenase-2 (COX-2) immunostaining after 14 days, suggesting better bone repair in the LLLT group mediated by an up-regulation of COX-2 expression in bone cells.

A recent study developed by Sella et al.[23] investigated the effects of LLLT (808 nm, 20 mW, 37 J/cm^2, 1 J, 5 s, 0.027 cm^2) on healing a complete bone fracture in rat femurs. This study assessed healing on days eight, 13, and 18 after the surgical fracture. Compared with the control group, the LLLT group showed decreased inflammatory infiltration on day 13, better periosteal formation on days 13 and 18, and increased new bone formation on all days (eight, 13, and 18). In addition, immunoexpression of osteocalcin was higher on day eight in the LLLT group, but the control and LLLT groups presented comparable results for the immunoexpression of osteopontin and osteonectin. Finally, this study suggested that LLLT could be an adjunct therapy to treat nonunion fractures

12.3.1 Laser versus ultrasound

After comparing the effects of PBM by LLLT (780 nm, 30 mW, 112.5 J/cm^2) with low-intensity pulsed ultrasound (LIPUS, 1.5 MHz, 30 mW/cm^2) and a control group (no treatment) with respect to the bone repair of rat tibias for 12 sessions (five times a week), Lirani-Galvao et al.[12] reported a higher maximum load at failure (bending test), a higher number of osteoblasts, and more new bone formation compared to the LIPUS and control groups. Moreover, the LIPUS group increased the number of osteoclasts, suggesting major bone resorption. The authors concluded that LLLT could stimulate bone repair by increasing bone formation, whereas LIPUS increases bone resorption.

A very similar study by Favaro-Pipi et al.[11] compared the effects of LIPUS (1.5 MHz, 1:4 duty cycle, 30 mW/cm^2, 20 min) and LLLT (830 nm, 30 mW, 50 J/cm^2, 0.51 J, 47 s, 0.028 cm^2) on surgically induced bone defects in rat tibias. Compared to the control group, the authors reported an intense, newly formed area of bone with highly vascularized connective tissue in the LLLT group 13 and 25 days after the bone defect (injury). In addition, this study suggested that LLLT produced better effects on bone repair compared with LIPUS. However, Oliveira et al.[24], using similar parameters of LLLT (830 nm, 100 mW, 120 J/cm^2, 3.4 J, 0.028 cm^2, 34 s) and LIPUS (1.5 MHz, pulse frequency of 1 KHz, 30 mW/cm^2, 20 min), reported no difference between either treatments regarding biomechanical analysis and the newly formed area of bone. Both treatments were superior compared to the control group.

12.3.2 Osteoporotic rats

The effectiveness of LLLT on bone repair was also investigated with animal models of osteoporosis in rats. Pires-Oliveira et al.[6] applied LLLT (904 nm, 10 kHz, 50 mW, 50 mJ/cm^2) 24 h after surgery to create a bone defect in the tibia of rats that had been rendered osteoporotic by ovariectomy, delivering repeated treatments every 48 h until the 7th and 21th days. There was an increase in new bone formation with LLLT on the 7th day compared to the control group. There was no significant difference between LLLT and control group on the 21th day.

In a similar study, Bossini et al.[25] reported similar effects of two LLLT doses on the bone repair of osteoporotic rats. LLLT (830 nm, 100 mW, 60 J/cm^2 or 120 J/cm^2, 1.7 J or 3.4 J, 17 or 34 s, 0.028 cm^2) was applied to bone defects on the 2nd, 4th, 6th, 8th, 10th, and 12th days post-surgery. Both light doses of LLLT increased the amounts of newly formed bone, presented higher deposition of collagen fibers, better organization of collagen fibers, and higher immunoexpression of COX-2 and vascular endothelial growth factor (VEGF)) compared to the control group. However, there was no difference between the LLLT treatments and control group regarding the biomechanical properties of the bone in the three-point bending test. The authors suggested that the improvement of bone repair in osteoporotic rats was produced by LLLT, which stimulates new bone formation and angiogenesis.

12.3.3 Biomaterials

Beyond the use of LLLT to repair bone defects or fractures, recent studies have investigated the combination of biomaterials and LLLT to further improve bone repair. Bossini et al.[5] induced bone defects in the tibias of osteoporotic rats and filled the holes with a bioactive glass–ceramic composite (Biosilicate®) and treated them with LLLT (830 nm, 100 mW, 60 J/cm^2 or 120 J/cm^2, 1.7 J or 3.4 J, 17 or 34 s, 0.028 cm^2) on days 2, 4, 6, 8, 10, and 12 post-surgery. Compared to control group (without Biosilicate® and or LLLT treatments), Biosilicate® plus LLLT (60 J/cm^2 and 120 J/cm^2) presented higher newly formed areas of bone, higher amounts of collagen, greater immunoexpression of VEGF and COX-2, and higher maximal loads in the bending test. The authors concluded that Biosilicate® combined with LLLT is beneficial for bone repair.

Conversely, while using a very similar study design, Fangel et al.[26] reported that LLLT (830 nm, 120 J/cm^2, 3.4 J, 34 s, 0.028 cm^2) did not promote any improvement in the biomechanical properties of the bone when used as the sole therapy. However, when LLLT was applied in conjunction with Biosilicate®, the maximal load to induce bone fracture and the energy absorption were higher (but without significance in the three-point bending test). The authors concluded that Biosilicate® alone or in conjunction with LLLT improves the biomechanical properties of bone healing in osteopenic rats.

Pinheiro et al.[27] recently assessed the efficacy of LLLT (780 nm, 50 mW, 16 J/cm^2, 8 J, 0.5 cm^2) with or without wire osteosynthesis, with or without hydroxyapatite for the guided regeneration of tibial fractures in rabbits. When comparing all of the different groups with Raman spectroscopy, the group treated with wire osteosynthesis combined with hydroxyapatite and LLLT showed the highest readings, whereas wire osteosynthesis and hydroxyapatite alone presented the lowest Raman estimation of the peaks for calcium hydroxyapatite. The authors concluded that LLLT in conjunction with hydroxyapatite and guided regeneration was effective in improving bone healing in fractures in rabbits.

Using a model of calvarial defects in rabbits, Rasouli Ghahroudi et al.[28] assessed the effects of LLLT (810 nm, 300 mW, 4 J/cm^2), a biomaterial (Bio-Oss®), and a combination of both therapies for 20 days of treatment. LLLT was applied immediately post-surgery and every 48 h for the next 20 days. After 4 and 8 weeks, the animals were sacrificed for histomorphometric analysis. There was no significant difference between all of the groups with respect to inflammation. However, there was an increase in newly formed bone in LLLT plus Bio-Oss® during the 4th (41%) and 8th (47%) weeks, followed by the Bio-Oss® 4th (35%) and 8th (41%), LLLT 4th (27%) and 8th (25%), and control 4th (15%) and 8th (18%) groups. Therefore, this study suggested that LLLT in conjunction with Bio-Oss® could promote better bone healing.

12.3.4 Gene expression

In order to investigate the mechanisms of LLLT on bone repair, Favaro-Pipi et al.[1] measured the time course of the gene expression of osteogenic genes during bone healing. Bone defects in the tibias of rats were created surgically and treated after 24 h with LLLT (830 nm, 30 mW, 50 J/cm^2, 1.4 J, 47 s, 0.028 cm^2), with a 48-h interval for 7, 13, and 25 days. On the 13th day there was an up-regulation of BMP-4 (bone morphogenetic protein 4) gene expression in the bone of the LLLT group. Additionally, on the 25th day, the gene expression levels of alkaline phosphatase and runt-related transcription factor 2 (Runx2)) were up-regulated in the LLLT group when compared with the control group. The authors suggested that LLLT could improve bone repair particularly during the later stages due to up-regulation of osteogenic gene expression and stimulation of new bone formation with osteogenic activity.

Fernandes et al.[2] also investigated the effects of LLLT on the bone repair of rats by analyzing the expression levels of osteogenic genes. The bone defect was created surgically, and LLLT (830 nm; 30 mW; 100 J/cm^2; 2.8 J; 94 s; 0.028 cm^2) was applied immediately once (12 h), twice (36 h), thrice (3 days), or five times (5 days) at intervals of 24 h. Compared to the control group, LLLT at 12 h and 36 h showed new bone formation on days 3 and 5 post-surgery. Regarding gene expression, Runx2 was up-regulated at 12 h and 3 days after the bone defect; alkaline phosphatase was up-regulated after 36 h and 3 days; and osteocalcin was also up-regulated after 3 and 5 days. This study suggested that LLLT could modulate the inflammatory process as well as accelerate bone repair via the differential expression of osteogenic genes.

Tim et al.[29] recently used a similar bone defect induced surgically in rat tibias. These authors compared LLLT (830 nm, 100 mW, 120 J/cm^2, 3.4 J, 34 s, 0.028 cm^2) to a control group (without treatment) with respect to bone repair for 15, 30, and 45 days. LLLT was applied immediately after bone surgery and repeated every 48 h. Compared to the control, the LLLT group showed less inflammatory infiltrate as well as better tissue organization 15 and 30 days post-surgery. In addition, the LLLT group presented greater amounts of newly formed bone after 15 days. Regarding the inflammatory markers, the immunoexpression of COX-2 was not up-regulated in either group at any experimental period. However, BMP-9 immunoexpression was higher in the LLLT group at 30 days as well Runx2 at 45 days. There was no difference between groups regarding the immunoexpression of RankL and no difference regarding the biomechanical properties of the bone during a three-point bending test. This study suggested that LLLT could accelerate bone repair by increasing the newly formed bone and activating osteogenic factors.

Finally, the LLLT effects on gene expression using large-scale micro-arrays was analyzed with markers for osteogenesis,[30] inflammation, and angiogenesis[14] with the same study design. LLLT (830 nm, 30 mW, 1000 J/cm^2, 2.8 J, 94 s, 0.0028 cm^2) was applied immediately after the surgical defect was created in the rat tibia and again every 24 h for 3, 5, and 7 days. Gene expression was analyzed after 12 h, 36 h, 3 days, 5 days, and 7 days after the bone defect was created. Compared with the control group, the LLLT up-regulated expression of transforming growth factor beta (TGF-β), bone morphogenetic protein (BMP), fibroblast growth factor (FGF), and Runx2 corroborate the increase in newly formed bone at the surgical site.[30] Furthermore, LLLT modulated the expression of genes related to inflammation and angiogenesis at 36 h and days 3 and 7, suggesting accelerated bone repair during the early stages of bone healing.[14]

12.3.5 Diabetic rats

Diabetes can be induced in rats by the administration of streptozotocin. These animals were subjected to surgical bone injury in the tibia and treated with

LLLT (632 nm, 10 mW, 66.8 J/cm^2 or 369.4 J/cm^2) or no (placebo group).[31] Bone repair of the partial osteotomy in the tibia was analyzed using a bending test until bone fracture occurred, and the surface area of the bone defect was measured. The authors did not find significant results when comparing the LLLT group with the placebo and control groups.

A study[31] assessed the effects of LLLT (890 nm, 70 W, 3000 Hz, 23.3 J/cm^2 or 11.6 J/cm^2) once a day for 7 days with respect to the biomechanical resistance of bone repair in diabetic rats. Compared to the control group, LLLT (11.6 J/cm^2) increased the bending stiffness and maximum force until bone fracture occurred. Moreover, in a very similar study, Bayat et al.[8] investigated the effects of LLLT (632 nm; 10 mW; 28.6 J/cm^2 or 382.2 J/cm^2) on bone in diabetic rats. The authors applied LLLT during 14 consecutive days and analyzed biomechanical properties of the bone. Compared with the respective control groups, stiffness assessed by bending test was higher in the LLLT (382.2 J/cm^2) group and maximum load until the bone fracture was higher in the LLLT (28.6 J/cm^2) group. Regarding histological assessment, LLLT 382.2 J/cm^2 was the best group to significantly increase the density of bone lamellae meshwork in diabetic rats tibias.

Patrocinio-Silva et al.[10] evaluated the effects of LLLT (808 nm, 100 mW, 120 J/cm^2, 3.3 J, 33 s, 0.028 cm^2) on the femur and tibia of rats during 6 weeks (18 sessions), 3 times a week, on nonconsecutive days. Compared with the control group, LLLT presented smaller areas of bone resorption (osteoclast activity), increased cortical area, higher immunoexpression of Runx2 and RANKL, higher bone-mineral content, higher density, and better resistance to fracture (three-point bending test).

12.4 Bone Healing in Clinical Trials

There are a few studies that have reported the effects of PBM in clinical trials. One of the first studies was conducted by AboElsaad et al.[32] investigating the effects of LLLT (830 nm, 40 mW, 4 J/cm^2, 60 s) applied to infra-bony periodontal defects after surgery and on days 3, 5, and 7 in conjunction with repair with a bioactive glass. After 3 months, there was a significant reduction in the probing depths with LLLT compared with the control (bioactive glass treatment alone), as well as less defect fill. After 6 months, both treatments did not present significant differences.

Angeletti et al.[33] investigated the effects of LLLT on bone regeneration in mid-palatal anterior sutures after surgery to assist maxillary expansion. The patients were subjected to an osteotomy in the maxillary bone and then treated with LLLT (830 nm, 100 mW, 140 J/cm^2, 8.4 J, 84 s, 0.06 cm^2) for eight sessions every 48 h. Compared to the control group (no treatment), the LLLT group showed better bone regeneration (assessed by digital radiographs and optical density analysis) at all post-surgery times (1, 2, 3, 4, and 7 months follow-up).

LLLT was also used to treat periostitis related to sports activity in adult men.[34] This study applied LLLT [a cluster with five laser diodes (850 nm each, 200 mW), 12 LEDs (670 nm each, 10 mW), 8 LEDs (880 nm each, 25 mW), and 8 LEDs (950 nm each, 15 mW); totaling 1,440 mW, 43.2 J, 1.4 J/cm², 60 s, 31.2 cm²] on the lower legs three times per day for 5 days. Compared with the control group, LLLT decreased the pain score and had a positive effect on proprioception tests, such as postural stability and limits of stability.

Finally, Chang et al.[35] used LLLT to treat closed bone fractures in human wrists and hands. These authors applied LLLT (830 nm, with an average power of 60 mW, 10 Hz, 9.71 J/cm², 600 s) five times per week for 2 weeks. This study assessed pain with a visual analog scale, functional disability by questionnaire, hand and finger grip strength by dynamometer, and radiographic signs of bone healing before and after 2 weeks of follow-up. After treatment and at the follow-up periods, compared with the control group, LLLT decreased pain and functional disability, increased hand and finger grip strength, and improved bone healing by radiography. Therefore, the authors concluded that LLLT could promote pain relief and improve bone healing in closed bone fractures in the human wrist and hand.

References

1. E. Favaro-Pipi et al., "Low-level laser therapy induces differential expression of osteogenic genes during bone repair in rats," *Photomed. Laser Surg.* **29**(5), 311–317 (2011) [doi: 10.1089/pho.2010.2841].

2. K. R. Fernandes et al., "Effects of low-level laser therapy on the expression of osteogenic genes related in the initial stages of bone defects in rats," *J. Biomed. Opt.* **18**(3), 038002 (2013) [doi:10.1117/1.JBO.18.3.038002].

3. N. Aihara, M. Yamaguchi, and K. Kasai, "Low-energy irradiation stimulates formation of osteoclast-like cells via RANK expression in vitro," *Lasers Med. Sci.* **21**(1), 24–33 (2006) [doi: 10.1007/s10103-005-0368-4].

4. K. N. Pinto et al., "Effects of biosilicate® scaffolds and low-level laser therapy on the process of bone healing," *Photomed. Laser Surg.* **31**(6), 252–260 (2013) [doi: 10.1089/pho.2012.3435].

5. P. S. Bossini et al., "Biosilicate® and low-level laser therapy improve bone repair in osteoporotic rats," *J. Tissue Eng. Regen. Med.* **5**(3), 229–237 (2011) [doi: 10.1002/term.309].

6. D. A. Pires-Oliveira, R. F. Oliveira, S. U. Amadei, C. Pacheco-Soares, and R. F. Rocha, "Laser 904 nm action on bone repair in rats with osteoporosis," *Osteoporosis International* **21**(12), 2109–2114 (2010) [doi: 10.1007/s00198-010-1183-8].

7. Z. Mohsenifar et al., "Evaluation of the effects of pulsed wave LLLT on tibial diaphysis in two rat models of experimental osteoporosis, as

examined by stereological and real-time PCR gene expression analyses," *Lasers Med. Sci.* **31**(4), 721–732 (2016) [doi: 10.1007/s10103-016-1916-9].

8. M. Bayat, S. Abdi, F. Javadieh, Z. Mohsenifar, and M. R. Rashid, "The effects of low-level laser therapy on bone in diabetic and nondiabetic rats," *Photomed. Laser Surg.* **27**(5), 703–708 (2009) [doi: 10.1089/pho.2008.2351].

9. F. Javadieh, M. Bayat, S. Abdi, Z. Mohsenifar, and S. Razi, "The effects of infrared low-level laser therapy on healing of partial osteotomy of tibia in streptozotocin-induced diabetic rats," *Photomed. Laser Surg.* **27**(4), 641–646 (2009) [doi: 10.1089/pho.2008.2370].

10. T. L. Patrocinio-Silva et al., "The effects of low-level laser irradiation on bone tissue in diabetic rats," *Lasers Med. Sci.* **29**(4), 1357–1364 (2014) [doi: 10.1007/s10103-013-1418-y].

11. E. Favaro-Pipi et al., "Comparative study of the effects of low-intensity pulsed ultrasound and low-level laser therapy on bone defects in tibias of rats," *Lasers Med. Sci.* **25**(5), 727–732 (2010) [doi: 10.1007/s10103-010-0772-2].

12. A. P. Lirani-Galvao, V. Jorgetti, and O. L. da Silva, "Comparative study of how low-level laser therapy and low-intensity pulsed ultrasound affect bone repair in rats," *Photomed. Laser Surg.* **24**(6), 735–740 (2006) [doi: 10.1089/pho.2006.24.735].

13. M. Tschon, S. Incerti-Parenti, S. Cepollaro, L. Checchi, and M. Fini, "Photobiomodulation with low-level diode laser promotes osteoblast migration in an in vitro micro wound model," *J. Biomed. Opt.* **20**(7), 78002 (2015) [doi: 10.1117/1.JBO.20.7.078002].

14. C. R. Tim et al., "Effects of low level laser therapy on inflammatory and angiogenic gene expression during the process of bone healing: A microarray analysis," *J. Photochem. Photobiol. B* **154**, 8–15 (2016) [doi: 10.1016/j.jphotobiol.2015.10.028].

15. Y. Ozawa, N. Shimizu, G. Kariya, and Y. Abiko, "Low-energy laser irradiation stimulates bone nodule formation at early stages of cell culture in rat calvarial cells," *Bone* **22**(4), 347–354 (1998).

16. M. M. Jawad et al., "Effect of 940 nm low-level laser therapy on osteogenesis in vitro," *J. Biomed. Opt.* **18**(12), 128001 (2013) [doi: 10.1117/1.JBO.18.12.128001].

17. O. Barushka, T. Yaakobi, and U. Oron, "Effect of low-energy laser (He-Ne) irradiation on the process of bone repair in the rat tibia," *Bone* **16**(1), 47–55 (1995).

18. I. Garavello, V. Baranauskas, and M. A. da Cruz-Hofling, "The effects of low laser irradiation on angiogenesis in injured rat tibiae," *Histol. Histopathol.* **19**(1), 43–48 (2004).

19. J. D. Batista et al., "Effect of low-level laser therapy on repair of the bone compromised by radiotherapy," *Lasers Med. Sci.* **29**(6), 1913–1918 (2014) [doi: 10.1007/s10103-014-1602-8].

20. M. Briteno-Vazquez et al., "Low power laser stimulation of the bone consolidation in tibial fractures of rats: a radiologic and histopathological analysis," *Lasers Med. Sci.* **30**(1), 333–338 (2015) [doi: 10.1007/s10103-014-1673-6].

21. J. D. Batista, S. Sargenti-Neto, P. Dechichi, F. S. Rocha, and R. M. Pagnoncelli, "Low-level laser therapy on bone repair: is there any effect outside the irradiated field?" *Lasers Med. Sci.* **30**(5), 1569–1574 (2015) [doi: 10.1007/s10103-015-1752-3].

22. M. A. Matsumoto, R. V. Ferino, G. F. Monteleone, and D. A. Ribeiro, "Low-level laser therapy modulates cyclo-oxygenase-2 expression during bone repair in rats," *Lasers Med. Sci.* **24**(2), 195–201 (2009) [doi: 10.1007/s10103-008-0544-4].

23. V. R. Sella et al., "Effect of low-level laser therapy on bone repair: a randomized controlled experimental study," *Lasers Med. Sci.* **30**(3), 1061–1068 (2015) [doi: 10.1007/s10103-015-1710-0].

24. P. Oliveira et al., "Comparison of the effects of low-level laser therapy and low-intensity pulsed ultrasound on the process of bone repair in the rat tibia," *Rev. Bras. Fisioter.* **15**(3), 200–205 (2011).

25. P. S. Bossini et al., "Low level laser therapy (830nm) improves bone repair in osteoporotic rats: similar outcomes at two different dosages," *Exp. Gerontol.* **47**(2), 136–142 (2012) [doi: 10.1016/j.exger.2011.11.005].

26. R. Fangel et al., "Biomechanical properties: effects of low-level laser therapy and Biosilicate® on tibial bone defects in osteopenic rats," *J. Appl. Biomater. & Functional Mater.* **12**(3), 271–277 (2014) [doi: 10.5301/jabfm.5000198].

27. A. L. Pinheiro et al., "The efficacy of the use of IR laser phototherapy associated to biphasic ceramic graft and guided bone regeneration on surgical fractures treated with wire osteosynthesis: a comparative laser fluorescence and Raman spectral study on rabbits," *Lasers Med. Sci.* **28**(3), 815–822 (2013) [doi: 10.1007/s10103-012-1166-4].

28. A. A. Rasouli Ghahroudi et al., "Effect of low-level laser therapy irradiation and Bio-Oss graft material on the osteogenesis process in rabbit calvarium defects: a double blind experimental study," *Lasers Med. Sci.* **29**(3), 925–932 (2014) [doi: 10.1007/s10103-013-1403-5].

29. C. R. Tim et al., "Low-level laser therapy enhances the expression of osteogenic factors during bone repair in rats," *Lasers Med. Sci.* **29**(1), 147–156 (2014) [doi: 10.1007/s10103-013-1302-9].

30. C. R. Tim et al., "Effects of low-level laser therapy on the expression of osteogenic genes during the initial stages of bone healing in rats: a microarray analysis," *Lasers Med. Sci.* **30**(9), 2325–2333 (2015) [doi: 10.1007/s10103-015-1807-5].

31. S. Abdi, M. Bayat, F. Javadieh, Z. Mohsenifar, and F. Rezaie, "The effects of helium-neon light therapy on healing of partial osteotomy of the

tibia in streptozotocin induced diabetic rats," *Photomed. Laser Surg.* **27**(6), 907–912 (2009) [doi: 10.1089/pho.2008.2421].

32. N. S. AboElsaad et al., "Effect of soft laser and bioactive glass on bone regeneration in the treatment of infra-bony defects (a clinical study)," *Lasers Med. Sci.* **24**(3), 387–395 (2009) [doi: 10.1007/s10103-008-0576-9].

33. P. Angeletti, M. D. Pereira, H. C. Gomes, C. T. Hino, and L. M. Ferreira, "Effect of low-level laser therapy (GaAlAs) on bone regeneration in midpalatal anterior suture after surgically assisted rapid maxillary expansion," *Oral Surg. Oral Med. Oral Pathol. Oral Radiol. Endod.* **109**(3), e38–46 (2010) [doi: 10.1016/j.tripleo.2009.10.043].

34. C. C. Chang et al., "Five-day, low-level laser therapy for sports-related lower extremity periostitis in adult men: a randomized, controlled trial," *Lasers Med. Sci.* **29**(4), 1485–1494 (2014) [doi: 10.1007/s10103-014-1554-z].

35. W. D. Chang, J. H. Wu, H. J. Wang, and J. A. Jiang, "Therapeutic outcomes of low-level laser therapy for closed bone fracture in the human wrist and hand," *Photomed. Laser Surg.* **32**(4), 212–218 (2014) [doi: 10.1089/pho.2012.3398].

Chapter 13
Photobiomodulation in Cartilage: *in vitro, in vivo,* and Clinical Trials*

Cleber Ferraresi, Fernanda Freire, and Michael R. Hamblin

13.1 Photobiomodulation in Cartilage

Cartilage is a tissue that develops following the differentiation of mesenchymal cells into chondroblasts, which in turn become chondrocytes that specialize in synthesizing an extracellular matrix rich in proteoglycans, elastin, and collagen. Chondrocytes are embedded within a dense extracellular matrix that is distributed in several cartilage layers classified as superficial, transitional, radial, and calcified zones. Differentiated chondrocytes are responsible for maintaining the homeostasis of the cartilage, adjusting the synthesis and catabolism of the extracellular matrix. However, adult chondrocytes do not divide, and the cell population in cartilage is supplied by new cells arriving as a result of diffusion from outside, limiting the capacity of cartilage to undergo self-regeneration. In this context, cartilage is avascular (contains no blood vessels), which contributes to the poor self repair of this tissue.[1–4]

Because cartilage has only a limited capacity for self healing, any kind of damage can produce major complications, especially if this damage occurs in articular cartilage. Any chondral and osteochondral damage will cause disabilities and poor quality of life in young people and especially in elderly subjects.[4] Moreover, during pathological conditions such as arthritis and osteoarthritis, the homeostasis of the cartilage is disturbed, and a cascade of biochemical and cellular reactions are responsible for the accumulating destruction of this tissue. Inflammation and an imbalance between anabolic and catabolic factors can result in the destruction of cartilage tissue, causing pain and loss of function.[3,5,6]

---

*Based on material first printed in M. R. Hamblin, M. V. P. de Sousa, and T. Agarwal, Eds., *Handbook of Low-Level Laser Therapy*, Pan Stanford Publishing, Singapore (2016).

Arthritis and osteoarthritis are very common joint diseases, mainly in elderly people, that produce symptoms such as inflammation, pain, edema, distension of the joint capsule, alteration in the synovium (synovitis), reduction in the range of motion in the joint, degradation of articular cartilage, and loss of subchondral bone, all of which cause physical disability.[7–10] In particular, synovitis promotes an overproduction of pro-inflammatory mediators, including cytokines, nitric oxide (NO), and tumor necrosis factor alpha (TNF-α). These mediators can inhibit the synthesis of the extracellular matrix as the chondrocytes attempt to restore the cartilage damage. In addition, these cytokines can up-regulate the gene expression of matrix metalloproteinases (MMPs) that will also degrade the remaining extracellular matrix.[9,10]

Several studies have investigated the effects of PBM on chondrocyte cells in experimental models of arthritis and osteoarthritis, and in clinical trials with patients suffering from osteoarthritis. PBM has been mainly carried out by LLLT and used as an alternative therapeutic strategy to nonsteroidal anti-inflammatory drugs to treat arthritis and osteoarthritis because these drugs can cause many side effects.[8] LLLT has demonstrated positive effects in the reduction of inflammation, improvement in the degradation of the extracellular matrix, reduction in swelling (edema) and pain, and restoration of homeostasis in the cartilage and joint. However, the efficacy of PBM, especially in clinical trials, has not yet been proved conclusively.

This chapter covers studies published in the last few years about the effects of PBM using LLLT or light-emitting-diode therapy (LEDT) on cartilage tissue. Therefore, recent studies *in vitro* involving chondrocytes, experimental animal models, and clinical trials of arthritis and osteoarthritis have been included. The mechanisms of action of the PBM are not the purpose of this chapter and are not discussed in detail. Table A.2 summarizes all of the parameters of PBM that have been reported and the main findings in the studies involving cartilage (Fig. 13.1).

13.2 *in vitro* Studies with Cartilage-Related Cells

One of the first studies investigating the effects of PBM used LLLT on chondrocytes was performed by Jia et al.[11] These authors isolated chondrocytes from the condyles of rabbit femurs, cultured them, and then irradiated them with different doses of LLLT (632.8 nm; 2, 4, 6, 8, 10, and 12 mW; 1, 2, 3, 4, 5, and 6 J/cm^2; 390 s; 0.785 cm^2) three times every 24 h. One day after LLLT doses of 4–6 J/cm^2, there were increased numbers of cells (more proliferation) compared to the control group. Moreover, doses of 4–5 J/cm^2 gave better increases in cell growth and increased synthesis and secretion of glycosaminoglycans and collagen-type-II-forming extracellular matrix. Therefore, this study suggested that LLLT may have some clinical relevance in the repair of articular cartilage.

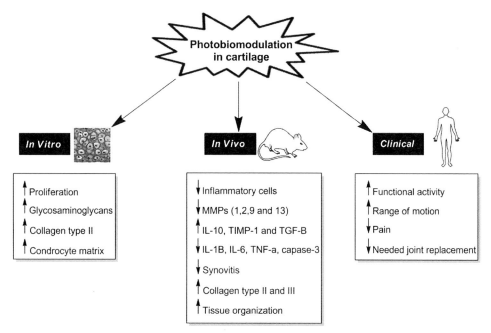

Figure 13.1   Main positive PBM effects reported in cartilage tissue.

Kushibiki et al.[3] assessed the effects of LLLT on the differentiation of chondrocytes and expression levels of chondrogenic genes in prechondrogenic cells (ATDC5 cells). The authors induced chondrogenic differentiation of ATDC5 cells with LLLT (405 nm, 100 mW/cm^2, 180 s) and incubation in a chondrogenic differentiation medium. After 14 days of LLLT, compared with the control group (non-irradiated cells), the LLLT group had increased collagen content and up-regulation of gene expression of collagen type II. Moreover, the expression levels of aggrecan (a gene related to the early chondrocyte matrix) and SOX-9 and DEC-1 (positive transcription factors for chondrogenesis) were up-regulated. In addition, LLLT decreased the expression of AP-2α (a negative transcription factor for chondrogenesis) one day after irradiation. No differences were noted between the groups one day after irradiation regarding AP-2α expression. The authors suggested a possible therapeutic benefit of LLLT to control the differentiation of chondrocytes at a site inside the body (joint) in order to diminish damage and restore cartilage tissue.

13.3 Cartilage Injury in Animal Models

13.3.1 Osteochondral injury

Kamali et al.[12] induced a surgical osteochondral defect in the knee joint (patellar groove) of rabbits and investigated whether LLLT (890 nm, 60 W,

1.5 KHz, 4.8 J/cm^2, 300 s) could improve the healing function. LLLT was applied twice a week for 4, 8, and 16 weeks, and biomechanical tests were performed to assess the joint healing in LLLT and control groups. LLLT increased the equilibrium stiffness of the knee joint after 8 weeks of treatment, but at 4 and 16 weeks there was no difference between the LLLT and control groups regarding the instantaneous and equilibrium stiffness of the knee.

Bayat et al.[13] also investigated the effects of LLLT on an osteochondral defect in the patellar groove of rabbits and assessed the histological outcomes. These authors applied LLLT (632.8 nm, 10 mW, 148.4 J/cm^2, 466 s, 0.0314 cm^2) three times a week for 2, 4, 8, and 16 weeks. After 2 weeks of treatment, the control group showed accelerated osteochondral healing compared with the LLLT group. However, after 4 and 16 weeks, the LLLT group reversed and presented faster healing than the control group. Conversely, Bayat et al.[2] used a similar study design, where LLLT (890 nm, 1500 Hz, 60 W, 4.8 J/cm^2, 1 cm^2) was applied twice a week for 2 weeks and 1, 2, and 4 months, but did not produce significantly better histological outcomes compared with the control group.

Using the same model of a surgically induced osteochondral defect in the femoral patellar groove in rabbits, Javadieh et al.[4] analyzed the effects of LLLT (632.8 nm, 10 mW, 148.4 J/cm^2, 466 s, 0.0314 cm^2) on the biomechanical properties of osteochondral healing. LLLT was applied 3 times a week for 16 weeks. The authors reported no significant differences between the LLLT and control group regarding the biomechanical properties of instantaneous stiffness and maximum force that could be exerted.

13.3.2 Arthritis and osteoarthritis

de Morais et al.[8] induced arthritis in the knee joints with intra-articular injections of zymosan in rats. The authors assessed the effects of LLLT and LEDT on edema, vascular permeability, and articular hyperalgesia (pain). LLLT (685 nm or 830 nm, 20 mW, 2.5 J/cm^2, 2 J, 100 s, 0.8 cm^2) or LEDT (628 ± 30 nm, 20 mW, 2.5 J/cm^2, 2 J, 100 s, 0.8 cm^2) was applied immediately, 1 h, and 2 h after zymosan-induced arthritis. LLLT, both 685 nm and 830 nm, significantly inhibited edema (23%) and reduced vascular permeability (24%) and hyperalgesia (59%). However, LEDT had no significant effects on the arthritis.

Using the same model of zymosan-induced arthritis, Carlos et al.[7] evaluated the effects of LLLT on the influx of inflammatory cells, pro-inflammatory mediators, MMP activity, and cartilage repair in the knee joint of rats. LLLT (660 nm, 10 mW, 2.5 J/cm^2, 0.1 J, 10 s, 0.04 cm^2) was applied to the knee joint immediately, 1 h, and 2 h after the injection of zymosan. Six hours after injection, treatment with LLLT significantly inhibited the total leucocyte influx, including fewer polymorphonuclear and mononuclear cells in the knee joint; reduced the activity of MMP-2 and MMP-9; decreased the release of IL-1β (interleukin 1β) and IL-6 (interleukin 6); and allowed the percentage of collagen fibers to remain at near-normal levels (comparable to joints without zymosan injection). These results demonstrated an effective reduction in inflammation and protease secretion (gelatinases), suggesting less degradation of collagen and a protective effect of LLLT on cartilage tissue.

Using another model of arthritis induced by papain (another proteolytic enzyme), Alves et al.[6] analyzed the effects of LLLT on MMP-2, MMP-9, and amounts of collagen (type I and III) in the knee joint of rats. LLLT (808 nm, 50 mW or 100 mW, 142 J/cm^2, 4 J, 40 or 80 s, 0.028 cm^2) was applied immediately after the induction of arthritis and repeated three times a week for 7, 14, and 21 days. Both LLLT therapies (50 mW and 100 mW) decreased collagen type III, MMP-2, and MMP-9, and increased collagen type I after 7, 14, and 21 days. Moreover, LLLT (50 mW) was more effective in reducing the expression of MMP-9 at all experimental time points. The authors concluded that both LLLT therapies (50 mW and 100 mW) were able to modulate MMPs and repair the cartilage, but 50-mW LLLT was more efficient, probably due to the longer time of irradiation compared with LLLT at 100 mW.

Corroborating these results, Alves et al.[9] used the same study design and LLLT parameters and reported that 50-mW LLLT was more efficient than 100-mW LLLT in reducing cellular inflammation and down-regulating the gene expression of IL-1β and IL-6. Conversely, LLLT (100 mW, 4 J) was more efficient in reducing the gene expression of TNF-α (tumor necrosis factor alpha), contrasting with the results published by dos Santos et al.[10] that reported a significant reduction in TNF-α gene expression with 2-J LLLT.

Using the same model of arthritis as Alves et al.[6] and with very similar methodology, dos Santos et al.[10] evaluated the effects of two LLLT dosages on the expression of inflammatory mediators in acute joint inflammation in rats. The authors applied LLLT (808 nm, 50 mW, 71.4 J/cm^2 or 142.8 J/cm^2, 2 J or 4 J, 40 s or 80 s, 0.028 cm^2) and reported that both LLLT dosages decreased the number of inflammatory cells compared with the arthritis group without treatment. In addition, 2-J LLLT decreased the gene expression of IL-1β and increased IL-10, whereas 4-J LLLT decreased IL-6. Finally, 2-J LLLT was more effective in reducing the gene expression of TNF-α. The authors concluded that a single application of LLLT with 2 J could efficiently modulate inflammation in the knee joint of rats.

Wang et al.[5] used a model of osteoarthritis in rabbits produced by the transection of the anterior cruciate ligament that studied pain; synovitis; the expression of beneficial factors such as transforming growth factor beta (TGF-β), insulin-like growth factor 1 (IGF-1), tissue inhibitor of metallo-proteinase 1 (TIMP-1), bone morphogenetic protein 2 (BMP-2), and bone morphogenetic protein 7 (BMP-7); the expression of detrimental factors such as IL-1β, nitric oxide synthase (iNOS), and metallopeptidases 1, 3, and 13 (MMP-1, MMP-3, and MMP-13); and extracellular matrix genes such as aggrecan and collagen type II. LLLT (830 nm, 50 mW, 4.8 J/cm^2, 0.13 J, 0.028 cm^2) was applied three times a week for 2, 4, 6, and 8 weeks, and decreased synovitis only in the long term (6 and 8 weeks). There was less damage in the femoral condyle cartilage, and LLLT promoted pain relief (6 and 8 weeks) compared with the control group (no treatment). Moreover, LLLT decreased the gene expression of detrimental factors such as IL-1β, iNOS, and MMP-3 at 6 and 8 weeks, and MMP-1 and MMP-13 at 8 weeks. Regarding beneficial factors, LLLT increased gene expression of TIMP-1 at 6 and 8 weeks, and TGF-β at 8 weeks. Finally, genes related to the extracellular matrix such as collagen type II and aggrecan were up-regulated at 8 weeks after LLLT. This study revealed an important protective effect of LLLT against cartilage degradation and synovitis in a model of progressive osteoarthritis in rabbits.

Using the same model of anterior cruciate ligament transection, Bublitz et al.[14] assessed the protective effect of LLLT against osteoarthritis in rats. The authors applied LLLT (808 nm, 30 mW, 10 J/cm^2, 0.3 J, 10 s; or 50 J/cm^2, 1.4 J, 47 s, 0.028 cm^2) immediately after the surgery and every 48 h for 3 weeks. When comparing the LLLT groups with the control, there was no difference in the number of chondrocytes or the immunoexpression of IL-1β and MMP-13. The cartilage area was larger in the untreatment control group but showed disorganization and irregularities with signs of degradation. The LLLT groups showed better tissue organization, especially with the dose of 10 J/cm^2 and also had higher content of proteoglycans. The authors concluded that LLLT with doses of 10 J/cm^2 and 50 J/cm^2 prevented the progression of morphological alteration (damage) of articular cartilage during osteoarthritis.

Assis et al.[15] evaluated the effects of LLLT either as a sole therapy or in conjunction with aerobic exercise training in rats with osteoarthritis induced by an anterior cruciate ligament transection. LLLT (808 nm, 50 mW, 50 J/cm^2, 1.4 J, 28 s, 0.028 cm^2) was applied three times a week for 8 weeks immediately after the exercise when combined with exercise training. Aerobic exercise was performed on a treadmill without inclination, with a velocity of 16 m/min for 50 min/day, three times a week for 8 weeks. Descriptive histological analysis revealed that all of the treated groups (LLLT, exercise, or a combination of both) had better organization of cartilage, fewer irregularities, and more chondrocytes, corroborating a better Osteoarthritis Research Society International (OARSI) score. All of the treated groups showed reduced expression of IL-1β, caspase-3, and MMP-13, with lower expression of caspase-3 in the LLLT-and-exercise group. The authors concluded that LLLT and exercise training were able to prevent cartilage damage and modulate the inflammatory process in the knee osteoarthritis model in rats.

Mangueira et al.[16] used Raman spectroscopy to evaluate the effects of LLLT on biochemical markers in cartilage tissue and the surrounding area in a model of osteoarthritis induced by injecting collagenase in the knee of rats. This study applied two LLLT treatments (660 nm or 780 nm, 30 mW, 7.5 J/cm², 10 s, 0.3 J, 0.04 cm²) 12 h after a second injection of collagenase (4th day) and repeated every 24 h for 14 days. 660-nm LLLT led to higher amounts of collagen type III by histomorphometric analysis. Principal component analysis and the Mahalanobis distance used in Raman spectroscopy revealed higher increases in collagen type II and III in the LLLT groups, suggesting an accelerated process of cartilage repair.

Fekrazad et al.[1] combined mesenchymal stem cells with LLLT and assessed the effects of both therapies in combination to repair cartilage damage in rabbits. The authors harvested bone-marrow mesenchymal stem cells from rabbits, and then cultured and suspended them on a scaffold of collagen type I. The authors implanted this scaffold loaded with stem cells in the osteochondral defect made in the patellar groove in the same rabbits that were used to harvest the stem cells. Afterward, LLLT (808 nm, 30 mW, 8.5 J/cm², 0.6 J, 20 s, 0.070 cm²) was applied to the knee immediately after the surgery and every 48 h for 3 weeks. Histological analysis showed no difference between LLLT and control (only stem cells implanted) regarding the formation of new cartilage and inflammation, but LLLT increased the formation of new bone. The authors concluded that although they found possibly better osteochondral healing with LLLT in combination with stem cells, the improvement was not due to extra cartilage formation.

13.4 Cartilage Healing in Clinical Trials: Arthritis and Osteoarthritis

Arthritis and osteoarthritis have been the principal conditions used to study the effects of PBM on cartilage tissue in humans. There have been several reports of human clinical trials published showing the effects of PBM on arthritis/osteoarthritis. For this reason, this chapter summarizes recent reports of the use of LLLT to manage this pathophysiological condition.

The efficacy of LLLT as an adjuvant therapy combined with exercise in the treatment of osteoarthritis was investigated by Alfredo et al.[17] These authors conducted a randomized, double-blind, placebo-controlled trial to assess the pain, functionality, range of motion, muscular strength, and quality of life of patients with knee osteoarthritis. The authors set up a program of physical exercise three times a week for 8 weeks that aimed to strengthen the knees and improve the range of motion, balance coordination, and motor learning. In addition, the LLLT group received active LLLT (904 nm, 20 W, 700 Hz, 60 mW average power, pulse of 4.3 ms, 6 J/cm², 3 J, 50 s, 0.5 cm²) in conjunction with the physical exercise program. The LLLT treatment gave better functional activity when compared with the control group (without LLLT), and only the LLLT group reduced pain and also increased the range of motion and functional activity. The authors suggested that LLLT, when combined with exercise, is effective to manage osteoarthritis in human knee joints.

Alghadir et al.[18] performed a single-blinded randomized study to assess the effects of LLLT on pain and functional activity in patients with chronic osteoarthritis. The authors applied LLLT (850 nm, 100 mW, 48 J/cm^2, 6 J, 60 s) two times a week for 4 weeks, and the placebo group received no effective LLLT. In addition, all patients received a home exercise program. Pain intensity was significantly reduced with LLLT at rest (47%) and also during movement (40%) compared with the placebo group. In addition, the functional activity was improved with LLLT. The authors concluded that LLLT could be used as an effective therapy to relieve pain and improve functional activity in patients with osteoarthritis.

Al Rashoud et al.[19] treated knee osteoarthritis with LLLT applied at acupuncture points in conjunction with an exercise program in a randomized double-blind trial. LLLT (830 nm, 30 mW, 4 J/cm^2, 1.2 J, 40 s, 0.280 cm^2) was applied to the five acupuncture points in the LLLT group, and straight leg raise exercises five times a day were prescribed for all patients. The authors reported a significant reduction in pain with LLLT at 6 weeks and 6 months after the intervention, and an improvement in knee function at the last treatment session and after 6 months. These results showed that in both the short term and long term LLLT could manage osteoarthritis and improve functional activity.

Nakamura et al.[20] assessed the effectiveness of LLLT for pain relief (visual analogue scale) and improvement in joint function by range of motion analysis in patients with chronic osteoarthritis and degenerative meniscal tears. The authors applied LLLT (830 nm; 1 W; 20 J/cm^2; 30 J; 30 s; 1.5 cm^2) on the knee twice a week for 4 weeks. There was a significant reduction in pain. However, there was no significant improvement in the range of motion.

Similar results were seen in another study that applied LLLT (810 nm, 80 W, average power of 50 mW, 3000 Hz, 200 ns, 6 J/cm^2, 6 J, 120 s, 1 cm^2) or LLLT (890 nm, 50 W, average power of 30 mW, 3000 Hz, pulse of 200 ns, 10 J/cm^2, 17 J, 588 s, 1.764 cm^2) to the knee joint three times a week for 12 sessions.[21] The authors reported a significant reduction in the pain of patients with osteoarthristis of the knee when treated with LLLT.

The effects of LLLT in combination with low-intensity ultrasound therapy on hand osteoarthritis were investigated recently by Paolillo et al.[22] The authors compared the use of LLLT plus ultrasound therapy with and without therapeutic exercise on pain relief and hand grip strength in women with osteoarthritis. Low-intensity ultrasound (1 MHz, 1 W/cm^2, pulse 1:1, duty cycle 50%, 3.5 cm^2) and LLLT (808 nm; 100 mW; 7 J/cm^2; 18 J; 180 s; 2.5 cm^2) were applied after therapeutic exercise on five regions of the hand, once a week for 12 weeks. There was no improvement in hand grip for any group. However, pain decreased in the LLLT-and-ultrasound group and also in the LLLT/ultrasound/therapeutic exercise group. The authors concluded that LLLT combined with low-intensity ultrasound is beneficial for pain relief in patients with hand osteoarthritis.

LLLT (810 nm, 30 mW, 20 mW/cm^2, 3.6 J/cm^2, 5.4 J, 180 s, 1.5 cm^2) was combined with hyaluronic-acid injections in patients with osteoarthritis in order to verify possible positive effects in the degenerated cartilage tissue in the knee joint.[23] This prospective, double-blind, and placebo-controlled study enrolled patients with tri-compartmental knee arthritis. Two treatments were administered three times a week for 6 weeks:

A. conventional physical therapy combined with placebo LLLT and saline injection, and
B. conventional physical therapy combined with active LLLT and hyaluronic-acid injection every 6 months.

The authors reported a significant reduction in the requirement to progress to knee joint replacement surgery with treatment B (1 patient out of 70) compared with treatment A (15 patients out of 70).

These aforementioned results were corroborated by Ip,[24] who used the same LLLT parameters (810 nm, 30 mW, 20 mW/cm^2, 3.6 J/cm^2, 5.4 J, 180 s, 1.5 cm^2) with and without conventional physical therapy in a prospective randomized cohort study with a follow-up in 6 years. There were no hyaluronic-acid injections into the patient's knee joints. Ip[24] reported that only one patient needed knee joint replacement (1 patient out of 50) in the LLLT-and-conventional-physical-therapy group. On the other hand, 9 patients needed joint replacement after conventional physical treatment (9 out of 50).

Melo Mde et al.[25] combined LLLT with neuromuscular electrical stimulation in order to improve the muscle architecture and functional capacity of elderly patients with knee osteoarthritis. The patients received LLLT or electrical stimulation on their *quadriceps femoris* muscles (18–32 minutes of symmetric biphasic rectangular current, 80 Hz, pulse of 400 μs, and stimulation intensity fixed near the maximal tolerated); LLLT (810 nm, 200 mW, 111 J/cm^2 or 116 J/cm^2, 4 J or 6 J, 20 s or 30 s, 0.036 cm^2) over the intercondylar line; or LLLT and electrical stimulation twice a week, every 48 h at least, for 8 weeks. After the treatment period, only electrical stimulation or the combined therapies promoted increases in muscle thickness (27–29%). All therapies increased functional capacity in the walk test (5–9%) without any difference between them. The authors concluded that LLLT was not effective to potentiate the use of electrical stimulation to increase the muscle thickness or functional capacity of patients with knee osteoarthritis.

Finally, there are several review articles with and without meta-analysis that report the effects of PBM in the management of arthritis or osteoarthritis.[26–30] However, these reviews are somewhat contradictory about the effectiveness of PBM to reduce inflammation and pain, increase functional capacity, and postpone joint replacement. The main problem discussed in this research field is the biphasic dose-response relationship that is typical of PBM therapy. The World Association for Laser Therapy (WALT) has published recommendations to guide clinicians to choose the parameters for several types of treatment, including arthritis that has been diagnosed in several joints.[32]

References

1. Y. L. Jia and Z. Y. Guo, "Effect of low-power He-Ne laser irradiation on rabbit articular chondrocytes in vitro," *Lasers Surg. Med.* **34**(4), 323–328 (2004) [doi: 10.1002/lsm.20017].

2. T. Kushibik, T. Tajiri, Y. Ninomiya, and K. Awazu, "Chondrogenic mRNA expression in prechondrogenic cells after blue laser irradiation," *J. Photochem. Photobiol. B* **98**(3), 211–215 (2010) [doi: 10.1016/j. jphotobiol.2010.01.008].

3. F. Kamali, M. Bayat, G. Torkaman, E. Ebrahimi, and M. Salavati, "The therapeutic effect of low-level laser on repair of osteochondral defects in rabbit knee," *J. Photochem. Photobiol. B* **88**(1), 11–15 (2007) [doi: 10. 1016/j.jphotobiol.2007.04.010].

4. M. Bayat, F. Javadieh, and M. Dadpay, "Effect of He-Ne laser radiation on healing of osteochondral defect in rabbit: a histological study," *J. Rehabil. Res. Dev.* **46**(9), 1135–1142 (2009).

5. M. Bayat, F. Kamali, and M. Dadpay, "Effect of low-level infrared laser therapy on large surgical osteochondral defect in rabbit: a histological study," *Photomed. Laser Surg.* **27**(1), 25–30 (2009) [doi: 10.1089/pho. 2008.2253].

6. F. Javadieh, M. Bayat, and G. Torkaman, "Evaluation of low-level laser therapy with a He-Ne laser on the healing of an osteochondral defect using a biomechanical test," *Photomed. Laser Surg.* **28**(3), 423–428 (2010) [doi: 10.1089/pho.2008.2434].

7. J. F. de Jesus et al., "Low-level laser therapy in IL-1beta, COX-2, and PGE2 modulation in partially injured Achilles tendon," *Lasers Med. Sci.* **30**(1), 153–158 (2014) [doi: 10.1007/s10103-014-1636-y].

8. N. C. de Morais et al., "Anti-inflammatory effect of low-level laser and light-emitting diode in zymosan-induced arthritis," *Photomed. Laser Surg.* **28**(2), 227–232 (2010) [doi: 10.1089/pho.2008.2422].

9. F. P. Carlos et al., "Protective effect of low-level laser therapy (LLLT) on acute zymosan-induced arthritis," *Lasers Med. Sci.* **29**(2), 757–763 (2014) [doi: 10.1007/s10103-013-1413-3].

10. A. C. Alves et al., "Effect of low-level laser therapy on metalloproteinase MMP-2 and MMP-9 production and percentage of collagen types I and

III in a papain cartilage injury model," *Lasers Med. Sci.* **29**(3), 911–919 (2014) [doi: 10.1007/s10103-013-1427-x].

11. A. C. Alves et al., "Effect of low-level laser therapy on the expression of inflammatory mediators and on neutrophils and macrophages in acute joint inflammation," *Arthritis. Res. Therapy* **15**(5), R116 (2013) [doi: 10.1186/ar4296].

12. S. A. dos Santos et al., "Comparative analysis of two low-level laser doses on the expression of inflammatory mediators and on neutrophils and macrophages in acute joint inflammation," *Lasers Med. Sci.* **29**(3), 1051–1058 (2014) [doi: 10.1007/s10103-013-1467-2].

13. P. Wang et al., "Effects of low-level laser therapy on joint pain, synovitis, anabolic, and catabolic factors in a progressive osteoarthritis rabbit model," *Lasers Med. Sci.* **29**(6), 1875–1885 (2014) [doi: 10.1007/s10103-014-1600-x].

14. C. Bublitz et al., "Low-level laser therapy prevents degenerative morphological changes in an experimental model of anterior cruciate ligament transection in rats," *Lasers Med. Sci.* **29**(5), 1669–1678 (2014) [doi: 10.1007/s10103-014-1546-z].

15. L. Assis et al., "Aerobic exercise training and low-level laser therapy modulate inflammatory response and degenerative process in an experimental model of knee osteoarthritis in rats," *Osteoarthritis and Cartilage* **24**(1), 169–177 (2016) [doi: 10.1016/j.joca.2015.07.020].

16. N. M. Mangueira et al., "Effect of low-level laser therapy in an experimental model of osteoarthritis in rats evaluated through Raman spectroscopy," *Photomed. Laser Surg.* **33**(3), 145–153 (2015) [doi: 10.1089/pho.2014.3744].

17. R. Fekrazad et al., "Effects of photobiomodulation and mesenchymal stem cells on articular cartilage defects in a rabbit model," *Photomed. Laser Surg.* **34**(11), 543–549 (2016) [doi: 10.1089/pho.2015.4028].

18. P. P. Alfredo et al., "Efficacy of low level laser therapy associated with exercises in knee osteoarthritis: a randomized double-blind study," *Clinical Rehabil.* **26**(6), 523–533 (2012) [doi: 10.1177/0269215511425962].

19. A. Alghadir, M. T. Omar, A. B. Al-Askar, and N. K. Al-Muteri, "Effect of low-level laser therapy in patients with chronic knee osteoarthritis: a single-blinded randomized clinical study," *Lasers Med. Sci.* **29**(2), 749–755 (2014) [doi: 10.1007/s10103-013-1393-3].

20. A. S. Al Rashoud, R. J. Abboud, W. Wang, and C. Wigderowitz, "Efficacy of low-level laser therapy applied at acupuncture points in knee osteoarthritis: a randomised double-blind comparative trial," *Physiotherapy* **100**(3), 242–248 (2014) [doi: 10.1016/j.physio.2013.09.007].

21. T. Nakamura et al., "Low Level Laser Therapy for chronic knee joint pain patients," *Laser Therapy* **23**(4), 273–277 (2014) [doi: 10.5978/islsm.14-OR-21].

22. H. Soleimanpour et al., "The effect of low-level laser therapy on knee osteoarthritis: prospective, descriptive study," *Lasers Med. Sci.* **29**(5), 1695–1700 (2014) [doi: 10.1007/s10103-014-1576-6].

23. A. R. Paolillo, F. R. Paolillo, J. P. Joao, H. A. Joao, and V. S. Bagnato, "Synergic effects of ultrasound and laser on the pain relief in women with hand osteoarthritis," *Lasers Med. Sci.* **30**(1), 279–286 (2015) [doi: 10.1007/s10103-014-1659-4].

24. D. Ip and N. Y. Fu, "Can combined use of low-level lasers and hyaluronic acid injections prolong the longevity of degenerative knee joints?" *Clinical Interventions in Aging* **10**, 1255–1258 (2015) [doi: 10.2147/CIA.S86907].

25. D. Ip, "Does addition of low-level laser therapy (LLLT) in conservative care of knee arthritis successfully postpone the need for joint replacement?" *Lasers Med. Sci.* **30**(9), 2335–2339 (2015) [doi: 10.1007/s10103-015-1814-6].

26. O. Melo Mde, K. D. Pompeo, G. A. Brodt, B. M. Baroni, D. P. da Silva, Jr., and M. A. Vaz, "Effects of neuromuscular electrical stimulation and low-level laser therapy on the muscle architecture and functional capacity in elderly patients with knee osteoarthritis: a randomized controlled trial," *Clinical Rehabil.* **29**(6), 570–580 (2015) [doi: 10.1177/0269215514552082].

Chapter 14

Photobiomodulation in Tendons: Effects *in vitro*, *in vivo*, and Clinical Use

Cleber Ferraresi, Fernanda Freire, and Michael R. Hamblin

14.1 Photobiomodulation in Tendons

Tendons (structures that connect muscles to bones) are composed of a dense connective tissue containing fibroblasts and extracellular matrix, including glycoproteins, elastin, proteoglycans, multiple saccharides, and collagen fibrils, which is the majority component by weight. In normal conditions, type-I collagen provides tensile strength to the tendon, and type-III collagen is distributed among bundles of type-I collagen.[1,2] The tensile stiffness of collagen fibrils is due to their geometrical configuration, wherein the alignment of the individual fibrils confers resistance to the mechanical tension exerted by the muscle contraction, transmitting the muscle contraction forces to the bone in order to produce the movement of the limb.[3]

However, as a result of injuries combined with different kinds of extraneous factors (obesity, trauma, prolonged use of drugs such as antibiotics and corticosteroids, repetitive stress in work activities, and recreational sports activities), tendon tissue can develop a painful condition called tendinopathy that is characterized by an inflammatory process, biochemical changes in the extracellular matrix, and loss of biomechanical properties, such as lower resistance to tensile forces. Classified as a degenerative disease, tendinopathies generally have a poor ability to spontaneously heal, and the chronic conditions can sometimes lead to the complete rupture of the tendons, which requires surgical repair.[3–6]

During the inflammatory process, many pro-inflammatory cytokines and mediators are produced, such as interleukin-1beta (IL-1β), tumor necrosis factor-alpha (TNF-α), cyclooxigenase-2 (COX-2), and prostaglandin E2 (PGE2).

These inflammatory markers can stimulate the remodeling of the extracellular matrix by an over-expression of matrix metalloproteinases (MMPs) that in turn hydrolyze collagens type I and III and proteoglycans, impairing tendon healing and weakening tendons in some cases. Moreover, inflammation causes an inhibition of the synthesis of collagen type I, impairing the repair process and making the tendon more susceptible to rupture.[4,6,7]

The healing process of tendons is associated with the proliferation and migration of different specialized types of cells, such as tenoblasts and tenocytes, that are responsible for the synthesis of additional collagen fibrils, controlling their orientation, and also encouraging angiogenesis.[3,5,8] However, without adequate treatment, a tendon rarely recovers its original strength and elasticity.

The clinical management of the tendon healing process has been attempted using different therapies and physical strategies such as exercise and PBM, which have shown some positive outcomes in terms of less pain and improved functional activity.[9] Eccentric exercises are considered to be a well-established therapy that promotes a significant increase in collagen synthesis in the tendon and improved alignment of the fibrils, and it has become an important tool to treat tendinopathy.[8,10] Moreover, recent studies *in vitro* and *in vivo* have reported positive effects of PBM using LLLT and LEDT during the tendon healing process. These benefits include a reduction in the inflammatory process, an increase in collagen synthesis, higher tensile strength, improved angiogenesis, and better knowledge of the mechanisms of actions of PBM. Therefore, this chapter covers studies published in the last few years about the use of PBM to stimulate tendon cells *in vitro*, treat tendinopathies in experimental models, and test PBM in clinical trials. Table A.3 in the Appendix summarizes all of the parameters of PBM and the main findings reported in the studies involving tendons (Fig. 14.1).

14.2 *in vitro* Studies with Tendon Cells

Several studies have investigated the effects of LLLT on the Achilles tendon, concentrating on inflammation and improving the healing process. Despite considerable evidence in favor of LLLT, the mechanisms of action has not been fully understood. For this reason, Tsai et al.[11] investigated the effects of LLLT on tenocyte proliferation, the secretion of nitric oxide (NO), and the expression of proliferating cell nuclear antigen (PCNA) and cyclins D1, E, A, and B1. Primary tenocyte cells were cultured from the Achilles tendons of rats and treated with LLLT (660 nm, 50 mW, 1 J/cm^2, 1.5 J/cm^2, 2 J/cm^2 and 2.5 J/cm^2). Compared to the control group,

- 2-J/cm^2 LLLT significantly increased the number of tenocytes;
- all LLLT doses increased the nitrite concentration;

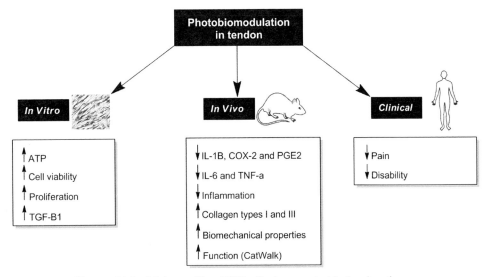

Figure 14.1 Main positive PBM effects reported in tendon tissue.

- doses of 1 J/cm^2, 1.5 J/cm^2, and 2 J/cm^2 up-regulated the expression of PCNA; and
- doses of 1.5 J/cm^2, 2 J/cm^2, and 2.5 J/cm^2 increased the expression of cyclins E, A, and B1, producing a LLLT dose response in primary cultured tenocytes of rats.

Chen et al.[12] also conducted an *in vitro* study in order to identify the mechanisms of action governing PBM in the Achilles tenocytes of rats, similar to the previous study.[11] Pulsed LLLT (904 nm, 5000–7000 Hz, peak power 27 W, average power of 2.4 mW, 0.5 J/cm^2, 1 J/cm^2, 2 J/cm^2, and 4 J/cm^2) was applied to cultured cells and compared to a control group. The authors reported that 1-J/cm^2 LLLT increased the viability of cells 24 h and 48 h after treatment, raised the amounts of ATP (adenosine tri-phosphate) from 30 min to 4 h, and increased the intracellular Ca^{2+} at 15 and 30 minutes, PCNA and collagen type-I expression after 24 h, and TGF-β1 (transforming growth factor beta-1-like) after 72 h.

14.3 Achilles Tendon Injury in Animal Models

The majority of animal models of tendon injury have concentrated on the inflammatory process and the expression of enzymes such as MMPs, which are responsible for remodeling the extracellular matrix in Achilles tendons.

Neves et al.[3] investigated the effects of PBM using LLLT (830 nm) on Achilles tendon healing in rats after a partial injury caused by blunt trauma (weight drop). These authors applied different powers of light—40, 60, 80, and 100 mW—with the same dose (30 J/cm^2) each day for 5 consecutive days.

Compared to the sham group, this study showed higher amounts of type-III collagen produced by light at higher powers (60–100 mW), and type-I collagen was increased with 80 mW. However, the alignment of the collagen fibers, considered to be very important for the biomechanical resistance of the tendon, was not improved by LLLT when analyzed by birefringence optical retardation measurements.

Marcos et al.[4] conducted an experimental study with rats in order to compare the effects of PBM using LLLT (810 nm, 100 mW, 1 J and 3 J) to sodium diclofenac (a nonsteroidal anti-inflammatory drug commonly used to treat tissue inflammation) to improve the biomechanical and biochemical properties of the Achilles tendon. The authors injected collagenase into the peritendinous area to produce tissue damage and treated the rats with LLLT or intramuscular sodium diclofenac after 1 h. LLLT (especially 3 J) was able to significantly reduce the gene expression of biochemical markers of inflammation and tissue remodeling such as COX-2, TNF-α, MMP-3, MMP-9, MMP-13, and PGE$_2$, and it also preserved the biomechanical properties of the tendon comparable to the control group, measured by performing a loading–unloading sequence of the tendon until rupture.

Another study by Marcos et al.[6] compared the effects of a single intramuscular dose of diclofenac and a single application of LLLT (810 nm, 100 mW, 1 J and 3 J) on the mechanical properties and expression of MMP-3, MMP-9, and MMP-13 in the Achilles tendon after an induced acute injury by injected collagenase in rats. The authors reported that diclofenac after 7 days did not reduce MMP production, and it led to weakness and low elasticity of the tendon. On the other hand, LLLT treatment (1 J) showed a protective effect, reducing the expression of MMPs and restored the mechanical properties of the tendon similarly to the control 7 days after the treatment.

Acute and sub-acute tendon injuries involve tissue inflammation and the reduction of this process is one of the main objectives of treatment. Having these perspectives in mind, de Jesus et al.[7] investigated the effects of LLLT (780 nm, 70 mW, 17.5 J/cm^2) on inflammatory mediators in rats with an injured Achilles tendon induced by blunt trauma, such as in the previous study.[3] The authors applied LLLT once (1 day), three times (3 days), or seven times (7 days). Compared to the control group (without blunt trauma), LLLT groups treated for 3 and 7 days showed very similar results regarding the concentration of IL-1β (interleukin 1 beta), COX-2, and PGE2 by immunohistochemical analysis. These results showed a positive effect of PBM to control the inflammatory process during tendon healing and better synthesis and alignment of collagens type I and III. de Jesus et al.[13] used the same study design and LLLT parameters to investigate the effects of PBM on synthesis and alignment of collagen types I and III. The authors concluded that PBM did not affect the alignment of collagen fibers I and III, but increased the percentage of collagen type I in the LLLT groups treated for 3 and 7 days.

Using a model of traumatic tendon injury, Casalechi et al.[5] investigated the effects of LLLT (830 nm, 50 mW, 6 J) on tendon inflammation (inflammatory cells), collagen content, and biomechanical properties (stiffness and strength to rupture) on the 7th and 14th days after treatments. Inflammatory cells were higher in the group without treatment, followed by the diclofenac group, and then lowest in the LLLT group on the 7th day. On the 14th day, the group without treatment still showed a high number of inflammatory cells, whereas the LLLT and diclofenac groups had fewer inflammatory cells. The collagen content in the control group on the 7th day showed collagen type I and III in the same proportion, the diclofenac group had a predominance of type-II collagen, and the LLLT group had more type-I collagen. On the 14th day, the LLLT group retained more type-I collagen, whereas the diclofenac group showed the same proportion of collagens type I and III. The stiffness and force required to rupture was increased in the LLLT group 14 days after treatment, whereas the diclofenac group decreased its biomechanical properties, suggesting deleterious effects of diclofenac treatment.

More studies were conducted to identify the effects of PBM on inflammatory markers in the Achilles tendon after injury. Recently Xavier et al.[1] used light-emitting-diode therapy (LEDT) as PBM in tendinitis of Achilles tendon induced by collagenase. LEDT (880 nm; 22 mW; 7.5 J/cm^2) was applied 12h after the induction of tendinitis and repeated at 48h intervals between irradiations until the 7th or 14th day. Compared to the control group after 7 days of treatment, LEDT increased expression of IL-10 (interleukin 10), a known anti-inflammatory cytokine. On the 7th and 14th days there was an increase in the expression of collagen types I and III, showing that LEDT was beneficial to tendon healing.

Using the previous model of Achilles tendon injury in rats by injected collagenase, Torres-Silva et al.[14] investigated the effects of LLLT (660 nm, 100 mW, 1 J and 3 J) on the inflammatory markers in Achilles tendons in rats. Two hours after induction of tendinitis, the animals were sacrificed in order to quantify the gene expression of COX-2, IL-10, IL-6, and TNF-α. Compared to the control group and the group treated with intramuscular diclofenac, the authors reported a significant reduction in the gene expression of IL-6 and TNF-α in the 3-J LLLT group.

Da Re Guerra et al.[15] also investigated the effects of PBM on inflammatory markers in Achilles tendons of rats after surgically induced tendinitis. LLLT (830 nm, 40 mW, 4 J/cm^2, continuous wave or pulsed at 20 Hz) was applied once a day for 1, 4, 8, and 15 days after the surgery. Compared to the continuous-wave LLLT and tendinitis groups, on the 4th day pulsed LLLT significantly decreased levels of TNF-α. On the 8th day, pulsed LLLT increased TGF-β1 and at the 15th day increased NO (nitric oxide) levels, all suggesting better tendon healing with pulsed LLLT.

Going beyond inflammatory markers and content of different types of collagen in tendon healing, Da Re Guerra et al.[2] analyzed different regimens of PBM on glycosaminoglycans and on functional responses in rats with injury surgically induced in Achilles tendons in rats. LLLT (830 nm, 40 mW, 4 J/cm^2) was applied in continuous or pulsed modes (20 Hz and 2 KHz) once a day for 8 to 15 days. This study reported increases in the concentration of sulfated glycosaminoglycans in the LLLT groups at 8 and 15 days, suggesting an improved healing process. In addition, the performance on the functional test (CatWalk) was improved with pulsed LLLT after 8 days of treatment compared to the control and continuous-wave LLLT groups.

Another study investigated the number of mast cells during the tendon healing process because mast cells can play an important role in the tendon healing process as they may be responsible for increases in protein synthesis and improved vascularization.[16] Therefore, the authors investigated the effects of LLLT (830 nm, 80 mW, 1.12 J) on mast cells during a time course of 6 h, 12 h, 24 h, 2 days, and 3 days after PBM compared to a sham group. The results showed an increased number of mast cells in the LLLT group at 6 h, 12 h, 24 h, and 2 days after tendon injury when compared to the sham group. With similar overall goals, Ferreira et al.[17] investigated the vascularization of Achilles tendons in rats at the proximal, medial, and distal regions. These authors applied LLLT (830 nm or 660 nm, 60 mW, 1.1 J) over 4 days, once a day, starting immediately after a blunt trauma injury to the Achilles tendon. However, compared to the control group, LLLT (830 nm or 660 nm) was not able to increase blood vessels in any region of the tendons studied.

Tendon injury can be a consequence of overuse in excessive exercise, Ng and Chung[9] induced an Achilles tendon injury in rats by overuse after 8 weeks of daily bipedal downhill running. Different treatments were performed after each running session, totaling 56 treatments of LLLT (660 nm, 8.8 mW, 10 kHz, 0.44 J), passive stretching, combined LLLT and stretching, or no treatment (control). The authors compared the tendon stiffness, the force required to rupture, and the load on the tendon among all of the groups. The only significant difference was the force required to rupture in the LLLT group and the combined LLLT and stretching group compared to the stretching and untreated groups, suggesting positive effects of LLLT in the treatment of tendon injury by overuse in exercise.

14.3.1 Achilles tendon healing in diabetic rats

Tendon healing is impaired in individuals diagnosed with diabetes mellitus. In order to verify the possible benefit of PBM on tendons in induced diabetic rats, Nouruzian et al.[18] induced diabetes in rats by administering streptozotocin and applied LLLT (632.8 nm, 7.2 mW, 2.9, 4.3, and 11.5 J/cm^2) to the Achilles tendons during ten consecutive days and then performed biomechanical analysis. LLLT with a dose of 2.9 J/cm^2 improved the maximum stress (resistance to stretching) when compared to the control group.

Using the same parameters of LLLT and the same methodology to induce diabetes in rats as the previous study,[18] Aliodoust et al.[19] showed a significant reduction of inflammation following 5–10 days of treatment with LLLT. In addition, the authors quantified the gene expression of TGF-β1 (a known marker of tendon healing), which enhances tendon repair during the fibrosis period, both *in vitro* and *in vivo*, increasing the cell proliferation, migration, and synthesis of both collagen and proteoglycans. Compared to the control group, LLLT was able to increase the gene expression of TGF-β1, suggesting better tendon repair.

14.4 Tendon Healing in Clinical Trials

There are a few review articles with and without meta-analysis that have reported the effects of PBM in the management of tendinopathies in human clinical studies.[10,20–22] Stasinopoulos and Johnson[20] did not find positive effects of PBM using LLLT in the management of lateral elbow tendinopathy in their study review. However, the authors suggested that further studies, using different parameters of LLLT, could produce positive effects because PBM is known to be a therapy with a clear biphasic dose response. As mentioned in Chapter 13, the World Association for Laser Therapy (WALT) has published recommendations to help clinicians choose the parameters for several types of treatment.[25]

Conversely, Bjordal et al.[21] also investigated the effects of PBM on patients with lateral elbow tendinopathy in a systematic review with procedural assessments. The authors analyzed the pain intensity, global status, pain-free grip strength, pain pressure threshold, sick leave (days), and bias of each study. As results, the authors suggested that PBM using LLLT is a safe and effective therapy that acts with a dose-dependent response. LLLT (904 nm and 632 nm) with light energy doses ranging from 0.5 to 7.2 J, in conjunction with other therapies or used alone, provided short-term pain relief and led to less disability caused by lateral elbow tendinopathy. These results were confirmed by Eslamian et al.[23] in a clinical trial that combined LLLT (830 nm, 100 mW, 4 J/cm^2) with conventional physiotherapy in patients with rotator-cuff tendinitis. In addition, Tumilty et al.[22] in another systematic review with meta-analyses covered several types of tendinopathies (rotator cuff, Achilles tendinopathy, De Quervain's tenosynovitis, and epicondylitis) and concluded that LLLT can be effective to treat tendinopathies if the WALT dosage recommendation are used, in agreement with Bjordal et al.[21]

Finally, Tumilty et al.[8] conducted a randomized controlled clinical trial to investigate the effectiveness of PBM using LLLT (810 nm, 100 mW, 3 J per site of irradiation, totaling 18 J per session) as an adjunct therapy in the treatment of Achilles tendon injuries combined with an eccentric exercise program for 12 weeks. The treatment with LLLT was performed three times a week but did not provide any significant added benefits regarding pain. Bjordal and Lopes-Martins[24] disagreed with the LLLT parameters used by Tumilty et al.[8] and reinforced the advisability of using the WALT recommendations.

References

1. M. Xavier et al., "Low-level light-emitting diode therapy increases mRNA expressions of IL-10 and type I and III collagens on Achilles tendinitis in rats," *Lasers Med. Sci.* **29**(1), 85–90 (2014) [doi: 10.1007/s10103-013-1280-y].

2. W. C. Tsai et al., "Low-level laser irradiation stimulates tenocyte proliferation in association with increased NO synthesis and upregulation of PCNA and cyclins," *Lasers Med. Sci.* **29**(4), 1377–1384 (2014) [doi: 10.1007/s10103-014-1528-1].

3. M. H. Chen, Y. C. Huang, J. S. Sun, and Y. H. Chao, "Second messengers mediating the proliferation and collagen synthesis of tenocytes induced by low-level laser irradiation," *Lasers Med. Sci.* **30**(1), 263–272 (2015) [doi: 10.1007/s10103-014-1658-5].

4. M. A. Neves et al., "Different power settings of LLLT on the repair of the calcaneal tendon," *Photomed. Laser Surg.* **29**(10), 663–668 (2011) [doi: 10.1089/pho.2010.2919].

5. R. L. Marcos et al., "Low-level laser therapy in collagenase-induced Achilles tendinitis in rats: analyses of biochemical and biomechanical aspects," *J. Orthop. Res.* **30**(12), 1945–1951 (2012) [doi: 10.1002/jor.22156].

6. R. L. Marcos et al., "Biomechanical and biochemical protective effect of low-level laser therapy for Achilles tendinitis," *J. Mech. Behavior Biomed. Materials* **29**, 272–285 (2014) [doi: 10.1016/j.jmbbm.2013.08.028].

7. J. F. de Jesus et al., "Low-level laser therapy in IL-1beta, COX-2, and PGE2 modulation in partially injured Achilles tendon," *Lasers Med. Sci.* **30**(1), 153–158 (2014) [doi: 10.1007/s10103-014-1636-y].

8. J. F. de Jesus et al., "Low-level laser therapy on tissue repair of partially injured achilles tendon in rats," *Photomed. Laser Surg.* **32**(6), 345–350 (2014) [doi: 10.1089/pho.2013.3694].

9. H. L. Casalechi et al., "Analysis of the effect of phototherapy in model with traumatic Achilles tendon injury in rats," *Lasers Med. Sci.* **29**(3), 1075–1081 (2014) [doi: 10.1007/s10103-013-1468-1].

10. R. Torres-Silva et al., "The low-level laser therapy (LLLT) operating in 660 nm reduce gene expression of inflammatory mediators in the

experimental model of collagenase-induced rat tendinitis," *Lasers Med. Sci.* **30**(7), 1985–1990 (2015) [doi: 10.1007/s10103-014-1676-3].

11. F. Da Ré Guerra et al., "Low-level laser therapy modulates proinflammatory cytokines after partial tenotomy," *Lasers Med. Sci.* **31**(4), 759–766 (2016) [doi: 10.1007/s10103-016-1918-7].

12. F. Da Ré Guerra et al., "Pulsed LLLT improves tendon healing in rats: a biochemical, organizational, and functional evaluation," *Lasers Med. Sci.* **29**(2), 805–811 (2014) [doi: 10.1007/s10103-013-1406-2].

13. C. E. Pinfildi et al., "Mast cell curve-response in partial Achilles tendon rupture after 830 nm phototherapy," *Photomed. Laser Surg.* **32**(2), 88–92 (2014) [doi: 10.1089/pho.2013.3638].

14. R. Ferreira et al., "Achilles tendon vascularization of proximal, medial, and distal portion before and after partial lesion in rats treated with phototherapy," *Photomed. Laser Surg.* **33**(12), 579–584 (2015) [doi: 10.1089/pho.2015.3974].

15. G. Y. Ng and P. Y. Chung, "Effects of a therapeutic laser and passive stretching program for treating tendon overuse," *Photomed. Laser Surg.* **30**(3), 155–159 (2012) [doi: 10.1089/pho.2011.3095].

16. M. Nouruzian, M. Alidoust, M. Bayat, and M. Akbari, "Effect of low-level laser therapy on healing of tenotomized Achilles tendon in streptozotocin-induced diabetic rats," *Lasers Med. Sci.* **28**(2), 399–405 (2013) [doi: 10.1007/s10103-012-1074-7].

17. M. Aliodoust et al., "Evaluating the effect of low-level laser therapy on healing of tentomized Achilles tendon in streptozotocin-induced diabetic rats by light microscopical and gene expression examinations," *Lasers Med. Sci.* **29**(4), 1495–1503 (2014) [doi: 10.1007/s10103-014-1561-0].

18. J. M. Bjordal et al., "A systematic review with procedural assessments and meta-analysis of low level laser therapy in lateral elbow tendinopathy (tennis elbow)," *BMC Musculoskelet. Disord.* **9**(75) (2008) [doi: 10.1186/1471-2474-9-75].

19. F. Eslamian, S. K. Shakouri, M. Ghojazadeh, O. E. Nobari, and B. Eftekharsadat, "Effects of low-level laser therapy in combination with physiotherapy in the management of rotator cuff tendinitis," *Lasers Med. Sci.* **27**(5), 951–958 (2012) [doi: 10.1007/s10103-011-1001-3].

20. S. Tumilty, S. McDonough, D. A. Hurley, and G. D. Baxter, "Clinical effectiveness of low-level laser therapy as an adjunct to eccentric exercise for the treatment of Achilles' tendinopathy: a randomized controlled trial," *Arch. Phys. Med. Rehabil.* **93**(5), 733–739 (2012) [doi: 10.1016/j.apmr.2011.08.049].

Chapter 15

Dermatology and Aesthetic Medicine Applications*

15.1 Effects of LLLT on Skin

15.1.1 Skin rejuvenation

Skin aging is a process that can present itself relatively early on in life, sometimes even as soon as 20–30 years of age. Common signs and symptoms associated with skin aging include skin wrinkling, skin dyspigmentation, telangiectasia, and reduced tissue elasticity. At the histological and molecular level, common noticeable features include a reduction in collagen content, fragmentation of collagen fibers, elastotic degeneration of elastic fibers, the appearance of dilated and tortuous dermal vessels, disorientation and atrophy of the epidermis, and up-regulation of matrix metalloproteinases (MMPs), especially MMP-1 and MMP-2.[1,2] Skin aging can be influenced by both time (normal aging) and environmental factors, but the single most influential factor responsible for accelerated skin aging is believed to be ultraviolet (UV) radiation-induced photodamage.[2]

A wide range of therapeutic modalities has been developed to address the aesthetically undesirable effects associated with skin aging. Most therapeutic modalities depend on some form of controlled epidermal removal and skin wounding to promote collagen biosynthesis, and dermal matrix remodeling, as a preliminary means to address the problems associated with skin aging. Some commonly used modalities include topical ointments containing vitamin A derivatives such as retinoic acid, dermabrasion, chemical peels, and ablative laser resurfacing technologies [most commonly utilizing carbon dioxide (CO_2) or erbium: yttrium-aluminum-garnet (Er:YAG) lasers], or, some combined form of therapy.[3–5] These techniques are limited by restrictions such as intensive post-treatment care, prolonged downtime, and other complications, including long-lasting erythema, pain, infections, bleeding, oozing, burns,

---

*Based on material first printed in M. R. Hamblin, M. V. P. de Sousa, and T. Agarwal, Eds., *Handbook of Low-Level Laser Therapy*, Pan Stanford Publishing, Singapore (2016).

hyper- or hypopigmentation, and scarring.[6,7] These limitations have facilitated the development of technologies such as non-ablative laser resurfacing, which can transcend the restrictions of conventional modalities and provide safe and efficacious treatment.[8,9] Unlike ablative laser resurfacing, non-ablative laser resurfacing technologies provide aesthetic improvement of aged skin without inducing epidermal destruction; it requires little to no downtime, thus providing a suitable alternative to traditional therapeutic modalities.[8,9] Additionally, intense pulsed light (IPL) sources [532-nm potassium-titanyl-phosphate (KTP) lasers] and high-dose (585/595 nm) pulsed dye lasers (PDLs) can be used to treat irregular pigmentation and telangiectasia, whereas low-dose (589/595 nm) PDLs, neodymium: yttrium-aluminum-garnet (Nd:YAG) lasers (1064 and 1320 nm), diode lasers (1450 nm), and erbium glass lasers (1540 nm) mainly address skin wrinkle reduction and skin tightening via thermal injury to the dermis (photothermolysis).[10] Treatments combining KTP lasers (532 nm) with Nd:YAG lasers (1064 nm) have been shown to possess synergistic effects for photorejuvenation.[11] Although ablative and non-ablative modalities provide a means for the treatment of photodamaged skin, they are not without their limitations. Ablative laser modalities pose the risk for dyspigmentation, scarring, post-operative erythema, and prolonged downtime, whereas non-ablative modalities suffer from reduced efficacy. Fractional photothermolysis (FPT) is a modality that bridges the gap between the ablative and non-ablative versions, and it has been gaining popularity due to its desirable profile of effects, reduced recovery time, and efficacious results.[12] FPT utilizes water as a target tissue chromophore for the laser and results in the creation of an array of thermal micro-lesions. These micro-lesions have an amazingly rapid rate of healing compared to the lesions induced by using traditional laser resurfacing modalities, resulting in controlled resurfacing of small areas of the skin, without any damage to the basement membrane. Consequently, reduced post-operative problems and increased patient comfort are observed.[12]

Low-level light therapy (LLLT) is a novel treatment option available for non-thermal and non-ablative skin rejuvenation, which has been shown to be effective for improving skin conditions such as wrinkles and skin laxity.[13–18] A wide range of light sources have been used to deliver light for these treatments, particularly to the face, and some are shown in Fig. 15.1. LLLT provides increased rates of wound healing while also reducing post-operative pain, edema, and several types of inflammation, making it a highly desirable modality.[19,20] Early studies reported increases in the production of pro-collagen, collagen, basic fibroblast growth factor (bFGF), and proliferation of fibroblasts, following low-energy laser irradiation in different settings.[21,22] The use of LLLT sources with wavelengths of 633 nm and 830 nm is most common in cases of clinical applications involving wound healing and skin rejuvenation. LLLT is now also used for the treatment of chronic, non-healing

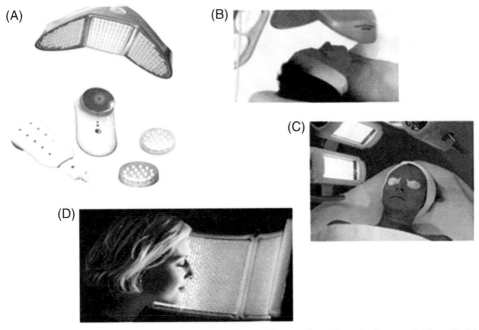

Figure 15.1 LLLT devices used for skin rejuvenation and treatment of acne: (a) handheld devices from various manufacturers; (b) Omnilux Revive, Phototherapeutics London, UK; (c) Dermaclear Blue and Red LED Acne Light Therapy, Britebox, Steubenville, OH; (d) Gentlewaves, Virginia Beach, VA.

wounds via the restoration of imbalances in collagenesis/collagenase, which allows for rapid and enhanced wound healing in general.[20]

A study conducted by Lee et al.[10] investigated the histological and ultrastructural alterations that followed a series of light treatments, utilizing LEDs with the following parameters: 830 nm, 55 mW/cm^2, and 66 J/cm^2; and 633 nm, 105 mW/cm^2, and 126 J/cm^2. Alterations to the levels of MMPs and tissue inhibitors of metalloproteinases (TIMPs) were reported. Increased mRNA levels of interleukin-1 beta (IL-1ß), tumor necrosis factor alpha (TNF-α), intercellular adhesion molecule 1 (ICAM-1), and connexin 43 (Cx43) were also reported following LED phototherapy, whereas the IL-6 levels were reported to be decreased.[10] Additionally, a well-marked increase in the amount of collagen was reported in the post-treatment specimens. In fractional-laser resurfacing, the deliberate development of microscopic, photothermally-induced wounds is believed to be responsible for the recruitment of pro-inflammatory cytokines IL-1ß and TNF-α to the site of injury, which contributes to tissue repair.[10] The generation of such a wound-healing cascade thus contributes to new collagen synthesis. LLLT can also induce wound healing through the non-thermal and non-traumatic induction of a subclinical "quasi-wound" without inflicting thermal injury, thus avoiding the complications seen with other therapeutic laser modalities.[10] Furthermore, because TIMPs are known to inhibit the activities of MMPs, increased collagen synthesis via the induction of TIMPs may also contribute to the effects associated with LLLT. The findings collectively suggest that the increased production of IL-1ß and TNF-α may be responsible for the stimulation of MMP activity (as an early response to light treatment), which might contribute to the removal of photodamaged collagen fragments, and facilitate new collagen biosynthesis. Furthermore, as a result of therapy, increased concentrations of TIMPs may be observed, which would protect newly synthesized collagen against proteolytic degradation by MMPs.[10] The heightened expression of Cx43 might also be responsible for enhanced cell-to-cell communication between dermal components (especially fibroblasts), resulting in greater synchrony between cellular responses following photo-biostimulation.[10]

A clinical study by Weiss et al.[23] demonstrated the benefits of LLLT over traditional thermal-based rejuvenation modalities. A group of 300 patients was administered LLLT (590 nm, 0.10 J/cm^2) alone, and another group of 600 patients received LLLT in association with a thermal-based photo-rejuvenation procedure. Of the patients who received only light treatment, 90% reported an observable softening of skin textures, as well as a reduction in skin coarseness and fine lines.[23] Patients who received some form of LLLT ($n = 152$) reported a noticeable reduction in post-treatment erythema and an overall impression of increased efficacy when compared to the patients that received treatment via a thermal photorejuvenation laser or light source lacking any form of LLLT photomodulation.[23,24] The reduction in post-treatment erythema can most likely be attributed to the anti-inflammatory effects of LLLT.[13] Using various pulse sequence parameters, a multicenter clinical trial was conducted, wherein 90 patients received eight LLLT treatments over 4 weeks.[17,25–27] The study displayed good overall results, with more than 90% of patients improving by at least one Fitzpatrick photoaging category, and 65% of the patients displaying global improvements in facial texture, fine lines, background erythema, and pigmentation, with results peaking at 4–6 months following the eight treatments. A noticeable increase in papillary dermal collagen and a reduction in MMP-1 were generally observed. A study conducted by Barolet et al.[13] also supported the aforementioned results. The study used a 3D model of tissue-engineered human reconstructed skin (HRS) to investigate the potential of LLLT (660 nm, 50 mW/cm^2, 4 J/cm^2) for collagen and MMP-1 modulation. The results showed an up-regulation of collagen and down-regulation of MMP-1, *in vitro*. A split-face, single-blind clinical study was then conducted to assess the results of this treatment on skin texture and the appearance of individuals with aged/photoaged skin. Profilometric quantification demonstrated that more than 90% of individuals had a reduction in rhytid depth and surface roughness, and 87% of individuals reported a reduction in the Fitzpatrick wrinkling severity score after 12 LLLT treatments.[13]

15.1.2 Acne

Acne vulgaris is a relatively common skin disorder with a reported prevalence of up to 90% among adolescents. Some studies have reported a comedone prevalence nearing 100% for both male and female sexes during adolescence.[28] Although typical acne is neither a serious nor a contagious condition, it can greatly impact the emotional and social aspects of an individual's life. The pathogenesis of acne is not completely understood, but the current consensus is that it involves four major events: follicular hyperconification, increased sebum production, colonization of *Propionibacterium acnes* (*P. acnes*), and inflammation.[29] *P. acnes* plays a major role in the development of acne by acting on triglycerides and releasing cytokines, which results in inflammatory reactions, and alters infundibular keratinization.[29] Current therapeutic options for acne vulgaris include topical antibiotics (e.g., clindamycin and erythromycin), topical retinoids (e.g., tretinoin and adapalene), benzoyl peroxide, alpha hydroxy acids (AHA), salicylic acid, and azelaic acid. In severe cases, the administration of antibiotics (e.g., tetracycline, doxycycline), oral retinoids, and certain hormonal treatments is recommended.[30] Most medications work by counteracting microcomedone formation, sebum production, *P. acnes*, and inflammation.[30] Despite the many treatment options currently available, several patients still show an inadequate response to the treatment, whereas others suffer from actual adverse effects.

Phototherapy offers an alternative mode of treatment for acne vulgaris with a suitable profile of side effects.[31] Sunlight exposure has often been reported to have a significant impact on the treatment of acne, with a high efficacy of up to 70%. More recently, techniques utilizing broad-spectrum visible light (LLLT) are currently being employed for the treatment of acne.[32] One mechanism of action of phototherapy is via the excitation of porphyrins generated by *P. acnes* as part of its normal metabolism. These porphyrins act as endogenous photosensitizers, absorbing light (specifically blue light, and to a lesser extent, red light) and stimulating photochemical reactions that generate reactive free radicals and singlet oxygen species, which are toxic for *P. acnes* (Fig. 15.2).[29,33] Red light has been demonstrated to have a greater penetration depth when compared to that of blue light.[30] Infrared (IR) light has been proposed to destroy sebaceous glands and thus reduce acne lesions.[34] Red light is believed to stimulate cytokine release from various cells (including macrophages) and reduce inflammation.[31,35]

Several studies have demonstrated the efficacy of red to near-infrared light (NIR) (spectral range 630 nm to 1000 nm, and non-thermal power less than 200 mW) for the treatment of acne vulgaris. Red light can be used alone or in combination with other modalities (in particular, blue light).[29,32,35–37] One study demonstrated a significant reduction in active acne lesions after 12 sessions of treatment using 630-nm red-spectrum LLLT with a fluence of 12 J/cm^2 twice a week for 12 sessions, in conjunction with 2% topical

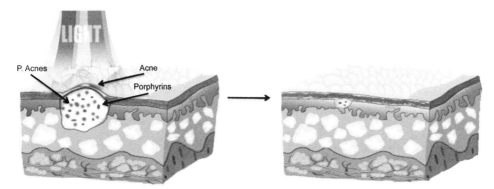

Figure 15.2 Acne treatment with red and blue light. The sebaceous gland is colonized by the bacteria, which can be killed by blue light due to the endogenous porphyrins they produce, acting as photosensitizers and forming reactive oxygen species. Red light can reduce inflammation and stimulate healing with minimal scarring.

clindamycin.[30] However, the study showed no significant effects when an 890-nm laser was used.[30] Other studies have reported that the use of blue light and red light in combination results in synergistic effects for the treatment of acne.[29,35,36,38] It has been proposed that the enhanced effects of mixed light are due to a synergy between the anti-bacterial and anti-inflammatory effects of blue light and red light, respectively (Fig. 15.2).[29,38] In several studies, improvements in inflammatory lesions were reported to be greater than the improvements in comedones.[29,38]

Additionally, fractional laser therapy can be used to treat post-acne scars with the best results obtained for the treatment of macular, superficial, and medium-depth scars. Deep scars and ice-pick scars show only marginal improvement with the use of fractional laser treatment, although severe scarring can be treated in combination with other modalities, such as chemical peels, surgical dermabrasion, derma-roller, and trichloroacetic acid chemical peel (CROSS) techniques. Furthermore, fractional laser treatment provides a suitable means for the treatment of scars in individuals with darker skin tones and has also shown remarkable pore improvement.[12] As with any therapeutic modality, proper counseling and evaluation should be conducted to minimize the probability of adverse effects.

15.1.3 Herpes virus infections

Herpes simplex virus (HSV) infections are some of the most common types of infections in the present age and are a bane to patients due to the lifelong persistence of the virus within the host's body. Two strains of this virus most commonly infect humans: HSV-1 and HSV-2. The former is primarily responsible for infections of the mouth, throat, face, eye(s), and central nervous system, whereas the latter primarily causes anogenital infections; however, each may cause infections in any of the mentioned systems.

Following the initial infection and resolution of lesions, the virus traverses across nerve endings of the affected nerve and establishes a state of latency in the sensory ganglia of the nerve (usually the trigeminal nerve).[39] Several cues can trigger reactivation and migration of the virus to the skin and mucosa (via the sensory nerves), leading to reactivation of the virus, especially on the basal epithelium of the lips and perioral areas. These cues may be physical or emotional, e.g., fever, exposure to UV light, and immune suppression.[39] Manifestations of viral infection can vary from cold sores in immunocompetent individuals to severe complications in immunocompromised patients. Up to 60% of all patients (both immunocompetent and immunocompromised) experience a prodromal period after which outbreaks develop through the stages of erythema, papule, vesicle, ulcer, and crust, until finally healing is achieved. This prodromal period is accompanied by pain, burning, itching, or tingling at the site of future blister formation, causing great discomfort to the patients. Immune responses to viral infection encompass the action of macrophages, Langerhans cells, natural killer cells, lymphocyte-mediated delayed-type hypersensitivity, and cytotoxicity.[40]

Although a variety of anti-viral drugs (e.g., acyclovir and valacyclovir) are available for managing outbreaks, they can only operate within a narrow time window to accomplish any patient benefit at all, and even then only limited effects are observed with regard to the healing time of the viral lesions.[39] Additionally, drug resistant strains of the herpes virus pose an ever-increasing risk of severe, unmanageable infections, especially for immunocompromised patients.[40] Thus, new treatment modalities that can reduce the frequency of recurrent episodes, as well as address the issue of undesirable effects of current treatment modalities, are desirable.

LLLT serves as a suitable alternative to current therapeutic modalities, providing accelerated healing, reduced symptoms, and managing the recurrence of outbreaks.[39,41,42] One study reported that when LLLT was administered to a group of 50 patients suffering from recurrent perioral HSV infections during an outbreak-free period (wavelength: 690 nm, intensity: 80 mW/cm^2, and dosage: 48 J/cm^2), a reduction in the frequency of recurrence of herpes labialis episodes was observed.[43] In another study with similar irradiation parameters (intensity: 50 mW/cm^2, fluence: 4.5 J/cm^2, and wavelength: 647 nm), it was reported that intervals of remission were prolonged from 30 days to 73 days in patients with recurrent HSV infections.[44] Intriguingly, the treatment proved more effective in patients suffering from herpes labialis than in those with genital infections. LLLT treatment, however, did not affect established HSV latency in a murine model.[45] The mechanism of action of LLLT in inducing anti-viral effects is not known; however, it can be hypothesized that LLLT acts in an indirect manner, influencing the cellular and humoral components of the immune system, as opposed to through a mechanism involving direct viral inactivation.[46] In one particular instance, a study conducted by Inoue et al.[47] investigating suppressed tuberculin reactions in guinea pigs suggested that the application of LLLT through the use of a low power laser (fluence of 3.6 J/cm^2) was responsible for a systemic inhibitory effect on delayed hypersensitivity. The activation and proliferation of lymphocytes[48–51] and macrophages,[52] as well as the synthesis and expression of cytokines[53,54] accompanying exposure to low intensities of red and NIR light, have been reported on several occasions. Whether or not these findings are actually influential against HSV infection remains to be seen.

15.1.4 Vitiligo

Vitiligo is an acquired pigmentary disorder characterized by depigmentation of the skin and hair. The underlying mechanism of how functional melanocytes are lost from the affected skin is still under investigation; however, current findings suggest that melanocytes, melanoblasts, keratinocytes, and fibroblasts may be involved in the repigmentation process of vitiligo[55–60] Thus, stimulation of such cells may offer a possible mode of treatment, but due to the obscure pathogenesis of the condition, treatment outcomes have generally been unsatisfactory. Topical corticosteroids, phototherapy, and photochemotherapy are some current therapeutic modalities that have shown varying degrees of repigmentation in vitiligo patients.[57] In 1982, a group of investigators looked into the effect of LLLT on the defective biosynthesis of catecholamines (involved in melanin biosynthesis) and discovered that it was able to influence conditions such as vitiligo and scleroderma.[61,62] Later on, one of the investigators from the same group reported that, following 6–8 months of low-energy HeNe laser (632 nm, 25 mW/cm^2) therapy, there was a noticeable degree of repigmentation in 64% of the patients belonging to a group of 18 individuals, whereas follicular repigmentation was observed in another 34% of the patients.[62] Thus, LLLT has been suggested as a suitable modality for the treatment of vitiligo.[56,57,59]

A certain type of vitiligo (segmental type) is linked to sympathetic nerve dysfunction in affected areas of the skin and has proved to be resistant to several conventional forms of treatment.[59] Pre-existing studies report that LLLT improves nerve injury[63–65] and also generates responses to promote repigmentation.[66,67] Thus, existing data suggests that LLLT may serve as a potential therapeutic modality for this treatment-resistant form of vitiligo. Upon local administration of a low-powered HeNe laser (3 J/cm^2, 1.0 mW, 632.8 nm), it was observed that 60% of the patients showed noticeable perilesional and perifollicular repigmentation with successive treatments. In the same study, upon irradiation of keratinocytes and fibroblasts with a HeNe laser (0.5–1.5 J/cm^2), significant increases in the amount of NGF released from keratinocytes were observed. Significant increases in the bFGF released from keratinocytes and fibroblasts have also been reported.[57] NGF and bFGF are known to stimulate the migration of melanocytes and might contribute to the repigmentation process of vitiligo.[60,68,69] Furthermore, the medium that was irradiated with the HeNe laser (along with the keratinocytes) led to the stimulation of deoxythymidine uptake and proliferation of cultured melanocytes. Finally, enhanced melanocyte migration was observed, which is thought to have arisen either from the direct action of the HeNe laser or indirectly due to some effect induced by the laser-irradiated medium. Another study showed that LLLT could lead to the enhanced expression of $\alpha_2\beta_1$ integrins and stimulate melanocyte proliferation.[56] LLLT also demonstrated the ability to induce melanocyte growth through the up-regulated expression of phosphorylated cyclic-AMP response element binding protein (CREB), an important melanocyte growth regulator.[56] Components of the ECM also operate as regulators of factors such as morphology, migration, tyrosinase activity, and proliferation of pigment cells, and are thus important to the pigmentation process.[70–72] Type-IV collagen is an ECM component present in the basement membranes of tissues and is known to have intricate associations with melanocytes in the epidermis, such as promoting melanocyte mobility.[57] LLLT has been shown to greatly promote melanocyte attachment to type-IV collagen and thus modulate the physiological functioning of melanocytes.[56] Fibronectin, among other ECM elements, has been shown to have significant effects on differentiation and the migration of cultured melanoblasts and melanocytes.[73,74] An *in vivo* study conducted by Gibson et al.[75] demonstrated that the physical distribution of fibronectin was closely associated with the migration path undertaken by melanoblasts during the repigmentation process of vitiligo. Based on the findings of Lan et al.,[57] a significant decrease in fibronectin binding was displayed by immature melanoblast cell lines (NCCmelb4), whereas a more differentiated melanoblast cell line (NCCmclan5) showed an increase in attachment to fibronectin by ~20% following LLLT (1 J/cm^2, 10-mW HeNe laser). Lastly, the expression of integrin $\alpha_5\beta_1$ on NCCmelb4 cells was observed to be enhanced, which is responsible for regulating the locomotion of pigmented cells.[57]

15.1.5 Pigmented lesions

Several studies, especially for vitiligo, show that LLLT exhibits stimulatory effects on pigmentation. Despite these studies, which are supportive of the pigmentation-promoting abilities of LLLT, one study showed that the effects of blue light (415 + 5 nm, irradiance 40 mW/cm^2, 48 J/cm^2) and red light (633 + 6 nm, 80 mW/cm^2, 96 J/cm^2) in combination yielded results where an overall decrease in melanin was observed.[29] The results showed that melanin levels increased by 6.7 arbitrary units in individuals after blue light irradiation without a statistical significance (P value > 0.1), whereas they decreased by 15.5 arbitrary units, with a statistical significance (P value < 0.005), following red light irradiation. These findings may be associated with the ability of the laser to brighten the skin tone of the irradiated area, which was reported by 14 out of 24 subjects after the treatment period. Until now, however, no other studies have shown similar results. Considering the differences in parameters used for vitiligo and acne treatments, the different effects of LLLT on the same tissue could be attributed to the biphasic dose response of LLLT.[76]

15.1.6 Hypertrophic scars and keloids

Hypertrophic scars and keloids are benign fibrotic skin lesions that usually arise following surgery, trauma, or acne, and are difficult to remove. Fibroblastic proliferation and excess collagen deposition are the main characteristics of these lesions,[77] and imbalances between rates of collagen biosynthesis and degradation, superimposed on the individual's genetic predisposition, have been implicated in the pathogenesis of keloids and hypertrophic scars. A broad range of surgical (e.g., cryotherapy and excision), non-surgical (e.g., pharmacological administration, mechanical pressure, and silicone gel dressings), and laser-based therapies (CO_2, pulsed dye, fractional ablative, and non-ablative lasers) have been tested with variable success; however, the optimal method of treating these lesions remains undefined.[78-80] It has been recently suggested that poor regulation of the transforming growth factor beta-I (TGF-βI) expression and interleukin 6 (IL-6) signaling pathways has a significant role in this process, and thus inhibition of the IL-6 pathway and/or TGF-βI expression could serve as a potential therapeutic target.[78,80-83] Reports indicating the effects of LLLT on the reduction of IL-6 mRNA levels,[10] modulation of platelet-derived growth factor (PDGF), TGF-β, interleukins such as IL-13 and IL-15, and MMPs (all of which are associated with abnormal wound repair[84,85]) have led to the proposal of LLLT as an alternative to the currently available therapeutic options. A new promising treatment modality involves pulsed dye lasers (PDLs) with a wavelength of 585 nm, believed to act through the induction of capillary destruction and alteration of local collagen formation.[86] Moreover, PDL appears to stimulate the up-regulation of MMPs, which also helps to improve keloids and hypertrophic scars.[86] Recommended protocols call for non-overlapping pulse doses of fluences between 6.0 to 7.5 J/cm^2 for 7-mm spots, and 4.5–5.5 J/cm^2 for 10-mm spots; however, results that definitively indicate the efficacy of PDL for clinical use are lacking.[86] PDL treatments can have mild side effects, generally purpura; however, in certain instances reactivation of the keloids has been observed.[86] In some cases, prolonged hyperpigmentation is observed, particularly in the case of individuals possessing darker pigmented skin, but it can be managed with low fluences. The 1064-nm Nd:YAG laser has been suggested as a means for improving hypertrophic scars and keloids because the Nd:YAG laser has a greater penetration depth than PDLs and would allow for treatment of thicker scars, but it might be limited by decreased efficacy associated with the increased penetration depth.[86] The use of LLLT as a prophylactic to avoid and impair the formation of hypertrophic scars or keloids has been investigated by Barolet and Boucher.[84] They examined three different cases wherein a single scar was treated by the patient at home on a daily basis with a NIR LED (805 nm, 30 mW/cm^2, 27 J/cm^2), following scar revision by surgery or CO_2 laser ablation on bilateral areas. The first patient had pre-auricular, linear, bilateral keloids, and a post-face-lift procedure and surgical scar revision/excision had been conducted. The second patient had post-acne, bilateral hypertrophic scars on the chest, and CO_2 laser resurfacing had been performed. For the third patient, CO_2 laser resurfacing had also been used for post-excision, bilateral hypertrophic scars on the back.[84] Collectively, in these studies, it was observed that the NIR-LED-treated scars showed significant improvement over the control scars in all measures of efficacy. Additionally, no adverse effects associated with treatment were reported.[84]

15.1.7 Burns

In a clinical study by Weiss et al.,[27] 10 patients were treated with LLLT (590 nm, 0.10 J/cm^2) for acute sunburn once or twice a day for 3 days, where only half of the affected area was treated. A reduction in redness, swelling, burning, and peeling was reported by the patients post-treatment. In one of the individuals who received treatment twice a day for 3 days, immunofluorescence staining showed that the LLLT treated area exhibited a reduction in MMP-1.[27] Furthermore, the light-treated area also exhibited a decrease in MMP-1 gene activity, both 4 h and 24 h post-UV injury, as shown by reverse transcription–polymerase chain reaction (RT-PCR). Four days after UV exposure, changes in inflammation and the dermal matrix were also reported to be associated with LLLT treatment.[23]

Burns associated with laser treatments themselves are also an issue for patients because these burns cause great discomfort to the patients. Studies support that LLLT facilitates faster healing. In one study, a group of patients ($n = 9$) that had received second-degree burns as a result of non-ablative laser therapy were administered LLLT daily for a week. According to patient and clinician reports, healing of the burns was observed to be substantially faster (50% faster) in patients who received LLLT treatment compared to those who did not.[23] In another study, by Weiss et al.,[23] intentional injury was afflicted on the forearm of a patient, and a CO_2 laser and a computerized pattern generator were used to induce two identical burns on the patient's forearm, one on each side of the forearm. Both sites of injury were given daily dressing changes using a non-stick dressing and Polysporin® ointment, and one of the sites was also treated with LLLT. The injury site that was administered LLLT displayed accelerated tissue re-epithelialization in comparison to the untreated site.[23]

In a study conducted by Schlager et al.,[87] the efficacy of a low-powered laser (670 nm, 250 mW, 2 J/cm^2) was studied using a rat model ($n = 30$ rats).

The rats received burns on their left and right flanks, and one of the burn sites received light treatment, whereas the other site was left untreated. Macroscopic and histological evaluations of the wounded tissue were conducted, but they failed to show any accelerated wound healing in the light treated areas in comparison to the control wounds.[87]

Another study conducted by Ezzati et al.[88] tested the efficacy of LLLT for healing burns. The study used a mouse model with a sample size of 74 mice, and each mouse received two third-degree burns, one proximal (control) and one distal (experimental). The mice were divided into four different groups. The mice in the first group received sham LLLT on the distal burn with the laser powered off, i.e., the placebo group. Mice of the second and third groups were administered a 3000-Hz pulsed IR diode laser at the distal burn with fluences of 2.3 J/cm^2 and 11.7 J/cm^2, respectively. The fourth group was treated with 0.2% nitrofurazone alone.[88] Assessment of the LLLT-treated groups showed a substantial reduction in the incidence of pathogenic infections by microbes such as *Staphylococcus epidermidis*, *Lactobacillus*, and *Corynebacterium diphtheriae* when compared to the baseline.[88] Additionally, the LLLT-treated groups showed enhanced tissue healing over the baseline and nitrofurazone treatment groups. Enhanced healing was reported for the laser with a fluence of 2.3 J/cm^2, but it occurred mostly during the early stages of healing. The most substantial increases in tissue repair were reported for the group that was treated with a fluence of 11.7 J/cm^2.[88] Studies suggest that LLLT is able to effectively stimulate tissue repair, by modulating cellular interactions that are responsible for repair. LLLT can induce the release of growth factors by the stimulation of macrophages and mast cells. Fibroblast, endothelial cell, and keratinocyte proliferation, which are maintained during adverse situations, can also be stimulated by means of LLLT.[88]

Burn scars are problematic to treat because they progressively worsen with hypertrophy and contracture; therefore, with limited treatment options, LLLT may be a potential mode of treatment. In a study consisting of 19 patients with burn scars, the patients were treated with a low-powered light source (400 mW, 670 nm, 4 J/cm^2) twice a week over a period of 8 weeks. Post-treatment, the scars were reported to be softer and more pliable.[89] Additionally, relief from pain and pruritus, and occasional improvements in scar patterns (within mesh grafts) were also reported. These effects were sometimes limited, and thus complete scar disappearances could not be expected. Moreover, better results were obtained following treatment in the cases where the burn scars were not more than 12 months old.[89]

15.1.8 Psoriasis

Psoriasis is a chronic and recurrent inflammatory skin condition that affects about 1–3% of the population.[90,91] Its etiology is not entirely understood; however, psoriasis is known to result from the interactions of systemic, genetic, immunological, and environmental factors.[92] Psoriasis patients present well-demarcated plaques, formed as a result of keratinocyte hyperproliferation, mediated by T-lymphocytes that attack the skin.[93]

The regions of the body that are most commonly affected in psoriasis include the knees, elbows, scalp, nails, and lower back (sacrum); however, the body in its entirety may be affected. The severity of the condition is measured by assessing the total body area involved in the disease (plaque severity). The different variants of psoriasis include chronic plaque psoriasis (psoriasis vulgaris),[93] flexural psoriasis (inverse psoriasis),[94,95] guttate psoriasis,[96] erythrodermic psoriasis,[94] palmar–plantar psoriasis, facial psoriasis, and scalp psoriasis. Almost all the variants result in great morbidity and diminished quality of life for the patient.[97] Some of the therapeutic modalities, implemented for the treatment of psoriasis, include topical agent use, systemic drug administration, photodynamic therapy (PDT), UV phototherapy, and laser therapy.

Psoralen combined with UVA and UVB phototherapy provided a revolutionary means for the treatment of psoriasis when it was initially introduced. However, some later studies suggested that repeated and excessive exposure to UVB radiation put individuals at an increased risk for developing skin cancer. Thus, Psoralen + UVA (PUVA) was introduced as a therapeutic modality with a reduced risk of developing cancer, but its use was still restricted because it did not completely eliminate the risk of cancer.

Studies investigating the use of LLLT for treatment with CO_2 ablative lasers,[98] helium-neon lasers,[99] and red-light photodynamic therapy can be dated to the 1980s.[100] Laser treatment provides a variety of advantages over conventional treatment modalities: it allows for selective treatment of a lesion without affecting the surrounding skin with limited or no systemic effects. It can also be used in combination with other therapeutic modalities, allowing for more effective treatment of resistant lesions. Several studies were conducted using a selective excimer laser of 308-nm wavelength.[101–103] Laser therapy displayed results analogous to those observed in UVB treatment. The laser treatment was effective in that it prevented epidermal cell replication while also suppressing the localized immune responses and thereby reducing the characteristic inflammation observed in psoriasis.[104] However, uncertainty exists regarding the carcinogenic ability of long-term excimer laser exposure. Thus, a PDL with a wavelength of 585 nm was suggested as an alternative. PDLs are commonly used for the treatment of vascular disorders and have proven to be a legitimate treatment modality for psoriasis due to the association of increased vascularity with psoriasis.[105,106] Furthermore, a recent study that investigated the efficacy of a combination of 830-nm (NIR) and 630-nm (visible red light) LLLT for the treatment of recalcitrant psoriasis has facilitated the consideration of LLLT for the treatment of plaques associated with psoriasis. In the study, psoriasis patients resistant to conventional treatment were administered sequential treatments with

830-nm and 630-nm wavelengths for two 20-minute sessions, 48 h apart, for a total of 4 or 5 weeks. The results from the study did not display any adverse effects; rather, the results demonstrated a resolution of psoriasis.[107] Although the study was promising, it was limited by its small sample size; nonetheless, the results of the study provided motivation for future investigations of the applications of LLLT as a therapeutic modality.

15.2 LLLT for Treatment of Hair Loss

15.2.1 Hair and types of hair loss

Hair is amongst the fastest growing tissues of the body, undergoing repetitive and regenerative cyclical changes, with each cycle consisting of telogen (resting), anagen (active), and catagen (physiological involution) stages (see Fig. 15.3).[108] During the transition from telogen to anagen, there is stringent regulation of the activation of epithelial bulge stem cells, while transit amplifying (TA) progeny cells arise from the secondary hair germ cells.[109] Along the period of the anagen phase, the TA cells display resilient proliferation within the epithelial matrix of the hair follicle. As a result, the end product of the hair cycle (i.e., the bulk of the hair filament) is formed through terminal differentiation of the proliferating trichocytes. The prime regulatory element of progenitor cell activation, hair matrix cell proliferation,

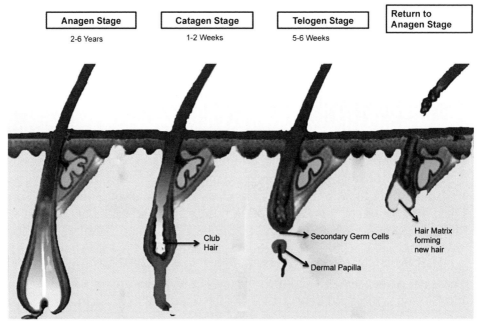

Figure 15.3 The growth cycle of hair follicles: anagen to catagen stage, catagen to telogen stage, and the eventual return to the anagen stage following senescence of the hair at the end of the telogen stage.

and terminal differentiation of trichocytes is believed to be the dermal papilla of the hair follicle.[110] The anagen stage represents the growth stage of the hair cycle and can last 2–6 years. The catagen stage, which generally lasts 1 to 2 weeks, is when the transitioning of club hair is observed as it progresses towards the skin pore and the dermal papilla begins to separate from the hair follicle. The telogen stage which lasts from 5–6 weeks and exhibits a complete dermal papillary separation from the hair follicle. Lastly, the cycle progresses again towards the anagen stage as the dermal papilla joins up with the hair follicle, and the hair matrix starts synthesizing new hair.

Androgenetic alopecia (AGA) is the most common form of hair loss in men, affecting almost 50% of the male population.[111] As the name suggests, AGA refers to hair loss induced in genetically susceptible individuals due to the effects of androgens such as testosterone. Testosterone is a lipophilic hormone that diffuses across the cell membrane to carry out its function. It is converted to a more active form called dihydrotestosterone (DHT), which is responsible for many of the effects observed in AGA. The enzyme responsible for the conversion of testosterone to DHT is 5α-reductase. Two types of 5α-reductase enzymes are found in body tissues: Type 1, which is prevalent in keratinocytes, fibroblasts, sweat glands, and sebocytes; and Type 2, found in skin and the inner root sheath of hair follicles. DHT acts by binding to its nuclear androgen receptor, which is responsible for regulating associated gene expression.[112] Abnormal androgen signaling is responsible for the disruption of epithelial progenitor cell activation and TA cell proliferation, which forms the essential pathophysiological basis for AGA.[113] The exact genes associated with the process of hair loss are not entirely known; however, some genes implicated in hair growth are known and include genes for desmoglein, activin, epidermal growth factor (EGF), fibroblast growth factor (FGF), lymphoid-enhancer factor-1 (LEF-1), and sonic hedgehog.[112] Amongst the treatment options currently available, the most commonly used include minoxidil, finasteride, or surgical hair transplantation.[111] Recently, the United States Food and Drug Administration (FDA) has approved the use of LLLT as a novel treatment modality for hair loss (see Fig. 15.4).[114]

Several other forms of hair loss also exist, such as telogen effluvium (TE), alopecia areata (AA), and alopecia induced via chemotherapy. AA is an autoimmune inflammatory condition that presents with non-scarring alopecia, where histologic characterizations display intra- or peri-follicular lymphocytic infiltrates composed of CD4+ and CD8+ T-cells.[114] AA has two variants: alopecia totalis (complete loss of scalp hair), and alopecia universalis (total loss of body and scalp hair).[114] The most common forms of treatments for alopecia involve intra-lesional corticosteroids; however, other treatment modalities are available, such as topical and systemic corticosteroids, e.g., minoxidil (used in moderate cases) and anthralin. Contact sensitizers are used when more than half of the scalp is affected. PUVA

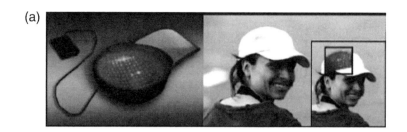

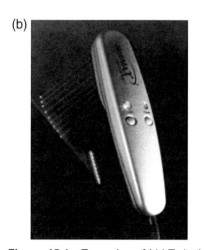

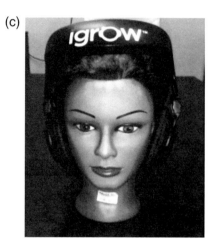

Figure 15.4 Examples of LLLT devices for treating hair loss: (a) Lasercap 660-nm laser diodes, Transdermal Cap, Inc., Cleveland, OH; (b) HairMax LaserComb®, 635-nm laser diodes, Lexington International, Boca Raton, FL; (c) iGrow Helmet, 655-nm laser diodes and LEDs, Apira Science, Inc., Boca Raton, FL.

treatment, cyclosporine, tacrolimus, and biologics such as alefacept, efalizumab, etanercept, infliximab, and adalimumab are also utilized for the treatment of hair loss.[112] TE is a condition where abnormal hair cycling results in excessive loss of telogen hair.[112] Some of the common causes of TE include acute severe illness, surgery, iron-deficiency anemia, thyroid disease, malnutrition, chronic illness, and medications (e.g., contraceptives, lithium, and cimetidine). Chemotherapy functions by acting on fast-growing cancer cells and destroying them, but it also results in the destruction of fast-growing somatic cells in the body, such as those of the hair follicles, thus inducing alopecia. It is usually observed within 1–3 weeks of initiating therapy, where the most profound effects are observed.[115]

15.2.2 Existing treatments

Lasers have recently gathered much attention due to their remarkable ability to cause selective hair removal; however, in some instances it has been observed that lasers can result in undesirable effects on hair growth such as increased hair density, increased color or coarseness, or a combination of these effects.[114,116–118] This phenomenon is known as "paradoxical hyper-trichosis," and its incidence varies from 0.6% to 10%.[114] It has also been reported that low-powered laser irradiation of small vellus hairs can cause them to transform into larger terminal hairs (i.e., terminalization of vellus hair follicles).[119,120]

The idea that lasers are able to induce hair growth is not something new; in the late 1960s, Endre Mester, a Hungarian scientist, conducted a series of experiments to investigate the ability of the newly discovered lasers to cure cancer in mice using a low-powered ruby laser (694 nm). Because the laser had much lower total power than expected, not only did the laser exposure fail to cure cancer on shaved mice, it also seemed to enhance both hair growth and wound healing.[121] This fortuitous observation was the first example of "photobiostimulation" using LLLT, and it opened up a new avenue for the field of medicine.[122]

Different mechanisms have been proposed in an attempt to explain the effects of LLLT. In one particular study, the ability of lasers to promote hair growth was attributed to a side effect of polycystic ovarian syndrome (PCOS) present in 5 out of 49 women undergoing IPL laser treatment for facial hirsutism.[116] Another study suggested that although lasers were responsible for the heat-generating effects in tissues, the heat produced was insufficient to induce hair follicle thermolysis; however, it may be sufficient to stimulate follicular stem cell proliferation and differentiation by increasing the levels of heat shock proteins (HSPs) such as HSP27, which influence the regulation of cell growth and differentiation.[114] Some form of sub-therapeutic injury could potentially cause the release of certain factors that could induce follicular angiogenesis and influence the cycling of cells.[120]

In 2007, the FDA approved LLLT as a possible treatment modality for hair loss.[114] Some of the devices that are used for LLLT in hair regrowth are shown in Fig. 15.4. It is believed that LLLT can stimulate the re-entry of telogen hair follicles into the anagen stage, bring about greater rates of proliferation in active anagen follicles, prevent the development of a premature catagen stage, and extend the duration of the anagen phase.[114,123] Although the exact underlying mechanism regarding how LLLT promotes hair growth is not known, several hypotheses have been proposed. Current data suggests that the action of LLLT on mitochondria leads to increased ATP production, modulation of ROS, and stimulation of transcription factors. These transcription factors, in turn, are responsible for the synthesis of proteins that cause certain downstream responses that lead to the enhanced proliferation and migration of cells; the modulation of cytokine levels, growth factors, and mediators of inflammation; and increased tissue oxygenation.[124]

In one study, the backs of Sprague Dawley rats were irradiated using a linearly polarized IR laser, and an up-regulation of hepatocyte growth factor (HGF) and HGF activator was observed.[125] Another study reported increases in temperature of the skin as well as improved blood flow around areas of the stellate ganglion following LLLT.[126]

Minoxidil is another therapeutic modality available for the treatment of hair loss. The exact mechanism of action of minoxidil is not completely understood, but it is known that minoxidil contains NO, which is an important cellular signaling molecule and vasodilator[127] that influences a variety of physiological and pathological processes.[128] Furthermore, NO regulates the opening of ATP-dependent potassium (K^+) channels and thus is responsible for the hyperpolarization of cell membranes.[129] It has been suggested that ATP-sensitive K^+ channels of the mitochondria and elevated levels of NO might be involved in the mechanism of action of LLLT[130–132] in areas of the brain and heart.[131,133,134] Thus, given the dependency of both minoxidil and LLLT on the aforementioned factors, there is possibly some mechanistic overlap between the two modalities. Other studies have demonstrated that LLLT is able to modulate 5α-reductase, the enzyme responsible for the conversion of testosterone to DTH, as well as alter the genetic expression of vascular endothelial growth factor (VEGF), which plays an influential role in hair follicle growth (and thus LLLT can stimulate hair growth).[18,135,136] Furthermore, it has been demonstrated that LLLT can stimulate hair growth through the modulation of inflammatory processes and immunological responses.[137] A study conducted on C_3H/HeJ AA mice models, wherein the mice were exposed to a LaserComb®, supported this assumption, and it was observed that treatment led to an increase in the quantity of hair follicles, i.e., the majority of the follicles in the anagen phase were seen to have decreased inflammatory infiltrates. Taking into account the disruptive effect that inflammatory infiltrates have on hair follicles, along with the notion that several cytokines such as interferon gamma (IFN-γ), IL-1α and -β, TNF-α and Fas-antigen, and macrophage migration inhibitory factor are all involved in cyclical hair growth and the pathogenesis of alopecia areata (AA), LLLT might be able to play a significant role in the treatment of AA due to its modulating effects on inflammation.[114]

15.2.3 Androgenetic alopecia

The effects of a HeNe laser (632 nm) on cyclical hair follicle growth in Swiss albino mice were studied at doses of 1 and 5 J/cm^2 at 24-h intervals for 5 days, with and without the administration of testosterone.[138] The mice that received HeNe laser treatment at a dosage of 1 J/cm^2 showed greater proportions of hair follicles in the anagen phase when compared to those of the control group, which received no testosterone or HeNe laser. Furthermore, exposure of the mice to a dose of 5 J/cm^2 showed a decrease in the proportion of hair follicles in the anagen phase when compared to the control group, which could be due to the biphasic dose response of LLLT.[124,138] It was also noted that treatment with testosterone caused an inhibition of hair growth with respect to the control group, which was shown by a significant reduction in the proportion of catagen hair follicles. Despite this finding, mice that were treated with a HeNe laser at 1 J/cm^2 and with testosterone still showed an increase in the percentage of anagen-stage follicles when compared to testosterone alone. However, when testosterone-treated mice were exposed to a HeNe laser dose of 5 J/cm^2, a twofold increase in the amount of anagen-stage hair follicles was observed. These results showed that the hair-promoting ability of LLLT (1-J/cm^2 HeNe laser) was higher in combination with testosterone; thus, it can be proposed that cells possessing slow rates of growth or undergoing stressful conditions respond better to the stimulatory effects of LLLT.

Another noteworthy finding of the study was that in the skin irradiated by the HeNe laser (1 J/cm^2), some of the anagen follicles possessed a different orientation and appeared to arise from a greater depth within the skin.[138] Such follicles are characteristic of the late anagen phase of the hair growth cycle, and the observation suggests that LLLT may act by prolonging the anagen phase of the hair cycle.[139,140] In the HeNe (1 J/cm^2) irradiated skin that received testosterone treatment, it was observed that the hair follicles originated from the middle of the dermis, and this type of follicles is generally seen during the early anagen phase.[138] Thus, when considering the aforementioned observations, it can be concluded that LLLT can stimulate the re-entry of telogen and catagen follicles into the anagen phase. In another study, 24 male androgenetic alopecia (AGA) patients were evaluated via global photography and phototrichogram using 655-nm red light and 780-nm IR light, once a day for a period of 10 minutes. Following 14 weeks of treatment, significant increases in hair density and anagen were observed; telogen ratios were observed at both the vertex and occiput, with 83% patients reporting that the treatment resulted in satisfactory results.[141]

A study was performed to investigate the efficacy of LLLT on hair growth and tensile strength involving 28 male and 7 female AGA patients. Each patient was given a 655-nm HairMax LaserComb® to use at home for a period of 6 months, applying it for 5–10 minutes per day on alternate days. The results showed improvements in hair growth in all treated areas for both men and women; however, in the case of men the greatest improvements were observed in the vertex area, whereas for women the best improvements were seen in the temporal areas. All treated areas of both sexes showed an improvement in hair count, but the vertex area showed the greatest improvement in the male patients.[142] In a double-blind, sham-device-controlled, multi-center, randomized 26-week trial, the same device was tested on 110 male AGA patients who used the device three times a week for 15 minutes for a total period of 26 weeks. Noticeable increases in the mean terminal density of hair were observed in the treatment group when compared to the sham treatment group. Also, subjective assessments of the patients over the 26-week period showed significant improvements in overall hair regrowth, a decreased rate of hair loss, thicker-feeling hair, and improved scalp health and hair shine.[123]

15.2.4 Alopecia areata

A clinical study was carried out to investigate the effect of LLLT on the treatment of AA, consisting of a sample size of 15 patients (6 men and 9 women), utilizing a Super Lizer[TM]—a medical instrument that uses polarized linear light with a high output (1.8 W) of IR radiation (600–1600 nm)—which possesses sufficient penetration depth to reach deep subcutaneous tissues.[143] The patients received a 3-minute laser treatment on the scalp, either once a week or once every 2 weeks, and they were administered additional carpronium chloride 5% twice daily to all lesions.[143] Supplemental oral antihistamines, cepharanthin, and glycyrrhizin (extracts of medicinal Chinese herbs) were prescribed as well. The results of the study showed that 47% of the patients experienced hair growth 1.6 months earlier on areas irradiated with a laser when compared to the areas that were not irradiated.[143] In another study, the hair-growth-stimulating effects of LLLT were studied in a C_3H/HeJ mouse model of AA, where the mice were irradiated using a HairMax LaserComb® (the comb emits nine beams of light at 655 nm while utilizing the attached combs for parting hair and allowing for a better delivery of light to the scalp) for 20 seconds daily, three times a week for a total of 6 weeks (Fig. 15.4). When the treatment was concluded, increased hair regrowth was observed in the mice that were treated, but the sham treatment group showed no difference in hair growth. Histological examination of mouse tissues showed that there was an increase in the content of anagen follicles in the light-treated mice, whereas the sham treatment group exhibited more telogen follicles.[114]

15.2.5 Chemotherapy-induced alopecia

About 65% of the patients that receive chemotherapy for cancer develop alopecia, which can have detrimental effects on the psychological health of the patient.[115] It has been proposed that LLLT may serve as a treatment modality to stimulate and promote hair growth in cases of chemotherapy-induced alopecia. In one study conducted in a rat model, the animals were administered varying regimens of chemotherapy, in conjunction with LLLT, using a device that possessed the components (laser unit and switch, lacking a comb or handle) of the HairMax LaserComb®.[114] In all rats that were given laser treatment, hair regrowth occurred at a faster rate when compared to the sham treatment group; additionally, LLLT did not hinder the efficacy of the chemotherapeutic procedures.[114]

15.3 LLLT for Fat Reduction and Cellulite Treatment

15.3.1 Lipoplasty and liposuction

Charles Dujarier, a French surgeon, first introduced the concept of lipoplasty (also known as liposuction) in the 1920s. Dujarier attempted to perform body sculpting on the knee of one of his patients (a model), but the patient ultimately developed gangrene, leading to the amputation of her affected limb, and thus the concept of lipoplasty suffered a major setback.[144] In 1974, Fischer[145] reintroduced liposuction, using a novel arrangement of oscillating blades within a cannula to chisel away subcutaneous fat. In 1983, Illouz[146] reported his 5-year experience with a new liposuction technique that could use relatively large cannulas along with suction tubing to safely remove fat from several regions of the body. This technique ushered in the modern era of lipoplasty. Over the following decades, the concept of tumescent liposuction allowed for better results and decreased morbidity associated with liposuction.

15.3.2 Fat reduction and cellulite treatment

Neira et al.[147,148] first demonstrated the use of LLLT as a new means for liposuction and successfully utilized it with doses that did not produce any detectable increases in tissue temperature or cause any noticeable macroscopic alterations in tissue structure. Prior investigations concerned with the effects of LLLT on wound healing, pain relief, and edema prevention helped pave the way for this therapeutic application.[149,150] The development of LLLT as a therapeutic modality to augment liposuction while avoiding macroscopic tissue alterations was based on the determination of optimal parameters such as wavelength and power output for use.[151] Evidence suggests that wavelengths suitable for biomodulation range between 630 and 640 nm.[152–157] Several intriguing observations regarding the effects of LLLT on adipocytes were made using a low-level diode laser (635 nm) with a maximal power of 10 mW and energy values ranging from 1.2 to 3.6 J/cm^2.[147] Scanning electron microscopy (SEM) and transmission electron microscopy (TEM) demonstrated that adipocyte plasma membranes exhibit transitory pore formation as a result of irradiation. It was suggested that this behavior enables the release of intracellular lipids from the adipocytes, and thus supplements liposuction because it is expected to reduce the time taken for the procedure, allow for the extraction of greater volumes of fat, and reduce the energy expenditure of the surgeon.

Although the findings associated with LLLT gathered much attention and enthusiasm, an extensively conducted study by Brown et al.[158] put these findings associated with LLLT into question. In their study, cultured human preadipocytes, after 60 minutes of irradiation using an LLLT source (635 nm and 1 J/cm^2), did not show any differences in lipid content when compared to non-irradiated cells. Furthermore, histological examination of human lipoaspirates and lipoaspirates from a porcine model, treated with LLLT for 30 minutes, failed to demonstrate transitory pores in adipocytes when analyzed using SEM.[158] Additional data raised questions regarding the ability of red light (635 nm) to effectively penetrate below the skin, into the sub-dermal tissues.[159] Since the data reported by Brown et al.,[158] there have been several instances of literature that have supported the efficacy of LLLT in lipolysis.[160–162] Some of the devices that are used for fat reduction are shown in Fig. 15.5.

15.3.3 Combination treatments including LLLT

The efficacy of LLLT in combination with vibration therapy for the reduction of local adiposities has also been studied. The study consisted of a total number of 33 patients including men and women aged 18–64 years, where the patients were divided into groups depending on whether treatment was to take place in the abdomen and/or the flanks, thighs, or buttocks. The parameters for the treatment of localized adiposities were as follows: 6 Hz (frequency of oscillating platform) with LLLT (635 nm) for 10 minutes; 9 Hz with LLLT (635 nm) for 2 minutes; 16 Hz with LLLT (635 nm) for 5 minutes; and 7 Hz with LLLT (635 nm) for 2 minutes. These parameters varied depending on the

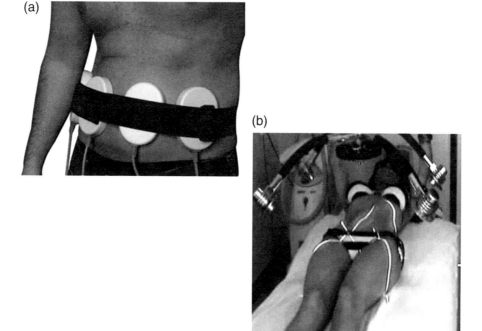

Figure 15.5 Examples of external LLLT devices used for fat reduction and cellulite treatment: (a) iLipo, 650-nm laser diodes (Chromogenex US, Inc. Howell, MI), and (b) Zerona Laser Scanner, 635-nm laser diodes (Erchonia, McKinney, TX).

area being treated, but none of the treatments exceeded a total time period of 28 minutes to maximize patient comfort and avoid unnecessary exertion. Several means of analysis were employed to gauge the effect of LLLT on fat reduction, including histological and echographic evaluation. The treatment brought about a significant reduction in the median fat by 6.83 cm for the abdomen and flanks, 3.42 cm for thighs, and 6.16 cm for buttocks. The greatest results were seen with the abdominal/flank regions, whereas the thighs showed the least response to treatment.[163] Thus, studies such as the aforementioned have attempted to describe the mechanistic functioning of LLLT, but the topic remains somewhat controversial.

15.3.4 LLLT for treating cellulite

Cellulite is a condition observed in ~85% of post-pubertal women that poses a major cosmetic concern for such women, where affected individuals display a characteristic "orange peel" dimpling of the skin, most commonly in areas of the thighs and buttocks. The underlying mechanism regarding the patho-physiology of cellulite is still under investigation, but it is suspected that the enlargement of adipocytes, weakening of connective tissue, and decrease in microcirculation are possible triggering factors, which helps to initiate the condition.[164] Several devices and topical treatment agents are available for managing the condition, but they are limited by their ability to generate only temporary effects. Considering the stimulatory effects of LLLT on circulation, collagen formation, and fat reduction, it may provide an alternative to current treatment modalities. In a study conducted with 83 subjects possessing mild to moderate cellulite, administration of a dual-wavelength (650 nm and 915 nm) laser, in combination with a massage device, was carried out to test the efficacy of LLLT on cellulite. The results demonstrated an improvement in cellulite appearance, as well as a 71% reduction in the circumference of patient thighs that were treated, as compared to a 53% reduction in the circumference of the thighs belonging to the control group.[164]

Topical phosphotidylcholine-based anticellulite gels have also been used, along with LED arrays (660 nm and 950 nm), as an experimental modality for the reduction of cellulite.[165] The results of the study were intriguing as LLLT alone failed to generate improvement in cellulite, but in combination with the topical anti-cellulite gel it could bring about a remarkable cellulite reduction.[165] Eight out of nine patients were reported to have experienced a reduction in cellulite of the thighs when LLLT was used in combination with the anti-cellulite gel.[165] Further clinical examinations, measurements, and ultrasound evaluations showed a noticeable reduction in hypodermal thickness, and supported the results.[165] However, 18 months following treatment, it was reported that five of the improved thighs had reverted back to their original grade of cellulite, and only three remained with their improved status. Such studies have shown that LLLT can be a promising treatment modality as an alternative to current treatment modalities, especially when used in combination with other existing modalities. Current literature suggests that LLLT may have a broad range of applications with a relatively small profile of adverse effects; however, the full extent of its potential remains unknown.

15.4 Conclusion

LLLT has been investigated as a novel therapeutic modality for the treatment and management of several dermatological conditions. The majority of the applications of LLLT have been concerned with some form of skin rejuvenation (mostly, the reversal of chronic photodamage). Several studies have demonstrated the use of LLLT for photorejuvenation, photoprotection, and the treatment of conditions such as acne and vitiligo. More recent data demonstrates its potential for the treatment of cosmetic conditions such as alopecia, cellulite, and adiposities. Furthermore, LLLT is a modality that provides a patient-friendly treatment approach with its noninvasive mode of action, mild side effects, and convenience of use. LLLT shows promise for future applications as a novel treatment modality that not only works well on its own but also in association with other therapeutic modalities. With growing acceptance and continuing research in the field of photomedicine, it can be concluded that LLLT, among other phototherapeutic modalities, will continue to grow and emerge as a versatile tool in the field of dermatology.

References

1. L. H. Kligman, "Photoaging. Manifestations, prevention, and treatment," *Clin. Geriatr. Med.* **5**(1), 235–251 (1989).
2. Y. Takema, Y. Yorimoto, M. Kawai, and G. Imokawa, "Age-related changes in the elastic properties and thickness of human facial skin," *Br. J. Dermatol.* **131**(5), 641–648 (1994).
3. L. E. Airan and G. Hruza, "Current lasers in skin resurfacing," *Facial Plast. Surg. Clin. North Am.* **13**(1), 127–139 (2005).
4. G. H. Branham and J. R. Thomas, "Rejuvenation of the skin surface: chemical peel and dermabrasion," *Facial Plast. Surg.* **12**(2), 125–133 (1996).
5. U. Paasch and M. Haedersdal, "Laser systems for ablative fractional resurfacing," *Expert Rev. Med. Devices* **8**(1), 67–83 (2011).
6. C. A. Nanni and T. S. Alster, "Complications of carbon dioxide laser resurfacing. An evaluation of 500 patients," *Dermatol. Surg.* **24**(3), 315–320 (1998).
7. S. Sriprachya-Anunt, R. E. Fitzpatrick, M. P. Goldman, and S. R. Smith, "Infections complicating pulsed carbon dioxide laser resurfacing for

photoaged facial skin," *Dermatol. Surg.* **23**(7), 527–535; discussion 535–526 (1997).

8. C. A. Hardaway and E. V. Ross, "Nonablative laser skin remodeling," *Dermatol. Clin.* **20**(1), 97–111, ix (2002).

9. R. A. Weiss, D. H. McDaniel, and R. Geronemus, "Review of nonablative photorejuvenation: reversal of the aging effects of the sun and environmental damage using laser and light sources," *Semin. Cutan. Med. Surg.* **22**(2), 93–106 (2003).

10. S. Y. Lee, K. H. Park, J. W. Choi, J. K. Kwon, D. R. Lee, M. S. Shin, J. S. Lee, C. E. You, and M. Y. Park, "A prospective, randomized, placebo-controlled, double-blinded, and split-face clinical study on LED phototherapy for skin rejuvenation: clinical, profilometric, histologic, ultrastructural, and biochemical evaluations and comparison of three different treatment settings," *J. Photochem. Photobiol. B* **88**(1), 51–67 (2007a).

11. M. W. Lee, "Combination visible and infrared lasers for skin rejuvenation," *Semin. Cutan. Med. Surg.* **21**(4), 288–300 (2002).

12. A. Goel, D. S. Krupashankar, S. Aurangabadkar, K. C. Nischal, H. M. Omprakash, and V. Mysore, "Fractional lasers in dermatology–current status and recommendations," *Indian J. Dermatol. Venereol. Leprol.* **77**(3), 369–379 (2011).

13. D. Barolet, C. J. Roberge, F. A. Auger, A. Boucher, and L. Germain, "Regulation of skin collagen metabolism in vitro using a pulsed 660 nm LED light source: clinical correlation with a single-blinded study," *J. Invest. Dermatol.* **129**(12), 2751–2759 (2009).

14. J. Bhat, J. Birch, C. Whitehurst, and S. W. Lanigan, "A single-blinded randomised controlled study to determine the efficacy of Omnilux Revive facial treatment in skin rejuvenation," *Lasers Med. Sci.* **20**(1), 6–10 (2005).

15. C. C. Dierickx and R. R. Anderson, "Visible light treatment of photoaging," *Dermatol. Ther.* **18**(3), 191–208 (2005).

16. B. A. Russell, N. Kellett, and L. R. Reilly, "A study to determine the efficacy of combination LED light therapy (633 nm and 830 nm) in facial skin rejuvenation," *J. Cosmet. Laser Ther.* **7**(3-4), 196–200 (2005).

17. R. A. Weiss, M. A. Weiss, R. Geronemus, and D. H. McDaniel, "A novel non-thermal non-ablative full panel LED photomodulation device for reversal of photoaging: digital microscopic and clinical results in various skin types," *J. Drugs Dermatol.* **3**(6), 605–610 (2004).

18. R. A. Weiss, D. H. McDaniel, R. Geronemus, and M. A. Weiss, "LED photomodulation induced hair growth stimulation," *Lasers Surg. Med.* **36**: Supplement 16, 27 (Abstract) (2005)

19. R. G. Calderhead, J. Kubota, M. A. Trelles, and T. Ohshiro, "One mechanism behind LED phototherapy for wound healing and skin

rejuvenation: key role of the mast cell," *Laser Therapy* **17**, 141–148 (2008).

20. W. S. Kim and R. G. Calderhead, "Is light-emitting diode phototherapy (LED-LLLT) really effective?," *Laser Ther.* **20**(3), 205–215 (2011).

21. R. P. Abergel, R. F. Lyons, J. C. Castel, R. M. Dwyer, and J. Uitto, "Biostimulation of wound healing by lasers: experimental approaches in animal models and in fibroblast cultures," *J. Dermatol. Surg. Oncol.* **13**(2), 127–133 (1987).

22. W. Yu, J. O. Naim, and R. J. Lanzafame, "The effect of laser irradiation on the release of bFGF from 3T3 fibroblasts," *Photochem. Photobiol.* **59**(2), 167–170 (1994).

23. R. A. Weiss, D. H. McDaniel, R. Geronemus, M. A. Weiss, K. L. Beasley, G. M. Munavalli, and S. G. Bellew, "Clinical experience with light-emitting diode (LED) photomodulation," *Dermatol. Surg.* **31**, 1199–1205 (2005b).

24. B. B. Kucuk, K. Oral, N. A. Selcuk, T. Toklu, and O. G. Civi, "The anti-inflammatory effect of low-level laser therapy on experimentally induced inflammation of rabbit temporomandibular joint retrodiscal tissues," *J. Orofac. Pain.* **24**(3), 293–297 (2010).

25. R. Geronemus, R. A. Weiss, M. A. Weiss, D. H. McDaniel, and J. Newman, "Non-ablative LED photomodulation light activated fibroblast stimulation clinical trial," *Lasers Surg. Med.* **25**, 22 (2003).

26. D. H. McDaniel, J. Newman, R. Geronemus, R. A. Weiss, and M. A. Weiss, "Non-ablative non-thermal LED photomodulation—a multicenter clinical photoaging trial," *Lasers Surg. Med.* **15**, 22 (2003).

27. R. A. Weiss, D. H. McDaniel, R. Geronemus, and M. A. Weiss, "Clinical trial of a novel non-thermal LED array for reversal of photoaging: clinical, histologic, and surface profilometric results," *Lasers Surg. Med.* **36**, 85–91 (2005a).

28. V. Stathakis, M. Kilkenny, and R. Marks, "Descriptive epidemiology of acne vulgaris in the community," *Australas J. Dermatol.* **38**(3), 115–123 (1997).

29. S. Y. Lee, C. E. You, and M. Y. Park, "Blue and red light combination LED phototherapy for acne vulgaris in patients with skin phototype IV," *Lasers Surg. Med.* **39**(2), 180–188 (2007b).

30. M. H. Aziz-Jalali, S. M. Tabaie, and G. E. Djavid, "Comparison of Red and Infrared Low-level Laser Therapy in the Treatment of Acne Vulgaris," *Indian J. Dermatol.* **57**(2), 128–130 (2012).

31. A. M. Rotunda, A. R. Bhupathy, and T. E. Rohrer, "The new age of acne therapy: light, lasers, and radiofrequency," *J. Cosmet. Laser Ther.* **6**(4), 191–200 (2004).

32. W. J. Cunliffe and V. Goulden, "Phototherapy and acne vulgaris," *Br. J. Dermatol.* **142**(5), 855–856 (2000).

33. E. V. Ross, "Optical treatments for acne," *Dermatol. Ther.* **18**(3), 253–266 (2005).

34. J. R. Lloyd and M. Mirkov, "Selective photothermolysis of the sebaceous glands for acne treatment," *Lasers Surg. Med.* **31**(2), 115–120 (2002).

35. N. S. Sadick, "Handheld LED array device in the treatment of acne vulgaris," *J. Drugs Dermatol.* **7**(4), 347–350 (2008).

36. D. J. Goldberg and B. A. Russell, "Combination blue (415 nm) and red (633 nm) LED phototherapy in the treatment of mild to severe acne vulgaris," *J. Cosmet. Laser Ther.* **8**(2), 71–75 (2006).

37. W. Posten, D. A. Wrone, J. S. Dover, K. A. Arndt, S. Silapunt, and M. Alam, "Low-level laser therapy for wound healing: mechanism and efficacy," *Dermatol. Surg.* **31**(3), 334–340 (2005).

38. P. Papageorgiou, A. Katsambas, and A. Chu, "Phototherapy with blue (415 nm) and red (660 nm) light in the treatment of acne vulgaris," *Br. J. Dermatol.* **142**(5), 973–978 (2000).

39. C. de Paula Eduardo, L. M. Bezinelli, F. de Paula Eduardo, R. Marques da Graca Lopes, K. M. Ramalho, M. Stella Bello-Silva, and M. Esteves-Oliveira, "Prevention of recurrent herpes labialis outbreaks through low-intensity laser therapy: a clinical protocol with 3-year follow-up," *Lasers Med. Sci.* **27**(5), 1077–83 (2012).

40. R. J. Whitley, D. W. Kimberlin, and B. Roizman, "Herpes simplex viruses," *Clin. Infect. Dis.* **26**(3), 541–553; quiz 554–545 (1998).

41. M. S. Bello-Silva, P. M. de Freitas, A. C. Aranha, J. L. Lage-Marques, A. Simoes, and C. de Paula Eduardo, "Low- and high-intensity lasers in the treatment of herpes simplex virus 1 infection," *Photomed. Laser Surg.* **28**(1), 135–139 (2010).

42. P. J. Munoz Sanchez, J. L. Capote Femenias, A. Diaz Tejeda, and J. Tuner, "The effect of 670-nm low laser therapy on herpes simplex type 1," *Photomed. Laser Surg.* **30**(1), 37–40 (2012).

43. A. Schindl and R. Neumann, "Low-intensity laser therapy is an effective treatment for recurrent herpes simplex infection. Results from a randomized double-blind placebo-controlled study," *J. Invest. Dermatol.* **113**(2), 221–223 (1999).

44. M. Landthaler, D. Haina, and W. Waidelich, "Treatment of zoster, post-zoster pain and herpes simplex recidivans in loco with laser light," *Fortschr. Med.* **101**(22), 1039–1041 (1983).

45. D. Perrin, J. R. Jolivald, H. Triki, A. Garbarg-Chenon, B. Lamotte D'incamps, B. Lefevre, G. Malka, L. Miro, and J. C. Nicolas, "Effect of laser irradiation on latency of herpes simplex virus in a mouse model," *Pathol. Biol. (Paris).* **45**(1), 24–27 (1997).

46. R. Korner, F. Bahmer, and R. Wigand, "The effect of infrared laser rays on herpes simplex virus and the functions of human immunocompetent cells," *Hautarzt.* **40**(6), 350–354 (1989).

47. K. Inoue, J. Nishioka, and S. Hukuda, "Altered lymphocyte proliferation by low dosage laser irradiation," *Clin. Exp. Rheumatol.* **7**(5), 521–523 (1989a).

48. V. Manteifel, L. Bakeeva, and T. Karu, "Ultrastructural changes in chondriome of human lymphocytes after irradiation with He-Ne laser: appearance of giant mitochondria," *J. Photochem. Photobiol. B.* **38**(1), 25–30 (1997).

49. L. Schindl, M. Schindl, L. Polo, G. Jori, S. Perl, and A. Schindl, "Effects of low power laser-irradiation on differential blood count and body temperature in endotoxin-preimmunized rabbits," *Life Sci.* **60**(19), 1669–1677 (1997).

50. W. Yu, L. H. Chi, J. O. Naim, and R. J. Lanzafame, "Improvement of host response to sepsis by photobiomodulation," *Lasers Surg. Med.* **21**(3), 262–268 (1997).

51. K. Inoue, J. Nishioka, and S. Hukuda, "Suppressed tuberculin reaction in guinea pigs following laser irradiation," *Lasers Surg. Med.* **9**(3), 271–275 (1989b).

52. P. Bolton, S. Young, and M. Dyson, "Macrophage responsiveness to light therapy: a dose response study," *Laser Ther.* **2**, 101–106 (1990).

53. J. O. Funk, A. Kruse, and H. Kirchner, "Cytokine production after helium-neon laser irradiation in cultures of human peripheral blood mononuclear cells," *J. Photochem. Photobiol. B.* **16**(3-4), 347–355 (1992).

54. H. S. Yu, K. L. Chang, C. L. Yu, J. W. Chen, and G. S. Chen, "Low-energy helium-neon laser irradiation stimulates interleukin-1 alpha and interleukin-8 release from cultured human keratinocytes," *J. Invest. Dermatol.* **107**(4), 593–596 (1996).

55. R. Kitamura, K. Tsukamoto, K. Harada, A. Shimizu, S. Shimada, T. Kobayashi, and G. Imokawa, "Mechanisms underlying the dysfunction of melanocytes in vitiligo epidermis: role of SCF/KIT protein interactions and the downstream effector, MITF-M," *J. Pathol.* **202**(4), 463–475 (2004).

56. C. C. Lan, C. S. Wu, M. H. Chiou, T. Y. Chiang, and H. S. Yu, "Low-energy helium-neon laser induces melanocyte proliferation via interaction with type IV collagen: visible light as a therapeutic option for vitiligo," *Br. J. Dermatol.* **161**(2), 273–280 (2009).

57. C. C. Lan, C. S. Wu, M. H. Chiou, P. C. Hsieh, and H. S. Yu, "Low-energy helium-neon laser induces locomotion of the immature melanoblasts and promotes melanogenesis of the more differentiated melanoblasts: recapitulation of vitiligo repigmentation in vitro," *J. Invest. Dermatol.* **126**(9), 2119–2126 (2006).

58. A. Y. Lee, "Role of keratinocytes in the development of vitiligo," *Ann. Dermatol.* **24**(2), 115–125 (2012).

59. H. S. Yu, C. S. Wu, C. L. Yu, Y. H. Kao, and M. H. Chiou, "Helium-neon laser irradiation stimulates migration and proliferation in

melanocytes and induces repigmentation in segmental-type vitiligo," *J. Invest. Dermatol.* **120**(1), 56–64 (2003).

60. R. Yu, Y. Huang, X. Zhang, and Y. Zhou, "Potential role of neurogenic inflammatory factors in the pathogenesis of vitiligo," *J. Cutan. Med. Surg.* **16**(4), 230–244 (2012).

61. A. Mandel and L. P. Dunaeva, "Effect of laser therapy on blood levels of serotonin and dopamine scleroderma patients," *Vestn. Dermatol. Venerol.* **8**, 13–17 (1982).

62. A. S. Mandel, H. F. Haberman, D. Pawlowski, and E. Goldstein, "Non PUVA nonsurgical therapies for vitiligo," *Clin. Dermatol.* **15**(6), 907–919 (1997).

63. J. J. Anders, R. C. Borke, S. K. Woolery, and W. P. Van de Merwe, "Low power laser irradiation alters the rate of regeneration of the rat facial nerve," *Lasers Surg. Med.* **13**(1), 72–82 (1993).

64. S. M. Khullar, P. Brodin, P. Barkvoll, and H. R. Haanaes, "Preliminary study of low-level laser for treatment of long-standing sensory aberrations in the inferior alveolar nerve," *J. Oral. Maxillofac. Surg.* **54**(1), 2–7; discussion 7–8 (1996).

65. S. Rochkind, M. Rousso, M. Nissan, M. Villarreal, L. Barr-Nea, and D. G. Rees, "Systemic effects of low-power laser irradiation on the peripheral and central nervous system, cutaneous wounds, and burns," *Lasers Surg. Med.* **9**(2), 174–182 (1989).

66. A. Mandel, "Skin repigmentation after laser therapy," *Vestn. Dermatol. Venerol.* **9**, 26–29 (1984).

67. H. S. Yu, "Treatment of vitiligo vulgaris with helium-neon laser," *MB Derma.* **35**(13-18), (2000).

68. M. Peacocke, M. Yaar, C. P. Mansur, M. V. Chao, and B. A. Gilchrest, "Induction of nerve growth factor receptors on cultured human melanocytes," *Proc. Natl. Acad. Sci. U S A.* **85**(14), 5282–5286 (1988).

69. C. S. Wu, C. C. Lan, M. H. Chiou, and H. S. Yu, "Basic fibroblast growth factor promotes melanocyte migration via increased expression of p125 (FAK) on melanocytes," *Acta. Derm. Venereol.* **86**(6), 498–502 (2006).

70. S. J. Hedley, M. Wagner, S. Bielby, L. Smith-Thomas, D. J. Gawkrodger, and S. MacNeil, "The influence of extracellular matrix proteins on cutaneous and uveal melanocytes," *Pigment Cell Res.* **10**(1-2), 54–59 (1997).

71. H. J. Ma, W. Y. Zhu, D. G. Wang, X. Z. Yue, and C. R. Li, "Endothelin-1 combined with extracellular matrix proteins promotes the adhesion and chemotaxis of amelanotic melanocytes from human hair follicles in vitro," *Cell Biol. Int.* **30**(12), 999–1006 (2006).

72. J. G. Morelli, J. J. Yohn, T. Zekman, and D. A. Norris, "Melanocyte movement in vitro: role of matrix proteins and integrin receptors," *J. Invest. Dermatol.* **101**(4), 605–608 (1993).

73. R. Ideta, T. Soma, M. Tsunenaga, and O. Ifuku, "Cultured human dermal papilla cells secrete a chemotactic factor for melanocytes," *J. Dermatol. Sci.* **28**(1), 48–59 (2002).

74. N. Takano, T. Kawakami, Y. Kawa, M. Asano, H. Watabe, M. Ito, Y. Soma, Y. Kubota, and M. Mizoguchi, "Fibronectin combined with stem cell factor plays an important role in melanocyte proliferation, differentiation and migration in cultured mouse neural crest cells," *Pigment Cell Res.* **15**(3), 192–200 (2002).

75. W. T. Gibson, J. R. Couchman, and A. C. Weaver, "Fibronectin distribution during the development of fetal rat skin," *J. Invest. Dermatol.* **81**(6), 480–485 (1983).

76. Y. Y. Huang, A. C. Chen, J. D. Carroll, and M. R. Hamblin, "Biphasic dose response in low level light therapy," *Dose Response* **7**, 358–83 (2009).

77. J. Uitto and D. Kouba, "Cytokine modulation of extracellular matrix gene expression: relevance to fibrotic skin diseases," *J. Dermatol. Sci.* **24**: Suppl 1, S60–69 (2000).

78. N. Bouzari, S. C. Davis, and K. Nouri, "Laser treatment of keloids and hypertrophic scars," *Int. J. Dermatol.* **46**(1), 80–88 (2007).

79. L. Louw, "The keloid phenomenon: progress toward a solution," *Clin. Anat.* **20**(1), 3–14 (2007).

80. D. Wolfram, A. Tzankov, P. Pulzl, and H. Piza-Katzer, "Hypertrophic scars and keloids–a review of their pathophysiology, risk factors, and therapeutic management," *Dermatol. Surg.* **35**(2), 171–181 (2009).

81. M. Ghazizadeh, M. Tosa, H. Shimizu, H. Hyakusoku, and O. Kawanami, "Functional implications of the IL-6 signaling pathway in keloid pathogenesis," *J. Invest. Dermatol.* **127**(1), 98–105 (2007).

82. W. Liu, D. R. Wang, and Y. L. Cao, "TGF-beta: a fibrotic factor in wound scarring and a potential target for anti-scarring gene therapy," *Curr. Gene. Ther.* **4**(1), 123–136 (2004).

83. J. Uitto, "IL-6 signaling pathway in keloids: a target for pharmacologic intervention?," *J. Invest. Dermatol.* **127**(1), 6–8 (2007).

84. D. Barolet and A. Boucher, "Prophylactic low-level light therapy for the treatment of hypertrophic scars and keloids: a case series," *Lasers Surg. Med.* **42**(6), 597–601 (2010).

85. M. R. Hamblin and T. N. Demidova, "Mechanisms of low level light therapy," *Proc. SPIE* **6140**(61001), 1–12 (2006).

86. G. G. Gauglitz, "Management of keloids and hypertrophic scars: current and emerging options," *Clin. Cosmet. Investig. Dermatol.* **6**, 103–114 (2013).

87. A. Schlager, K. Oehler, K. U. Huebner, M. Schmuth, and L. Spoetl, "Healing of burns after treatment with 670-nanometer low-power laser light," *Plast. Reconstr. Surg.* **105**(5), 1635–1639 (2000).

88. A. Ezzati, M. Bayat, S. Taheri, and Z. Mohsenifar, "Low-level laser therapy with pulsed infrared laser accelerates third-degree burn healing process in rats," *J. Rehabil. Res. Dev.* **46**(4), 543–554 (2009).

89. K. Gaida, R. Koller, C. Isler, O. Aytekin, M. Al-Awami, G. Meissl, and M. Frey, "Low Level Laser Therapy–a conservative approach to the burn scar?," *Burns.* **30**(4), 362–367 (2004).

90. J. M. Gelfand, R. Weinstein, S. B. Porter, A. L. Neimann, J. A. Berlin, and D. J. Margolis, "Prevalence and treatment of psoriasis in the United Kingdom: a population-based study," *Arch. Dermatol.* **141**(12), 1537–1541 (2005).

91. R. S. Stern, T. Nijsten, S. R. Feldman, D. J. Margolis, and T. Rolstad, "Psoriasis is common, carries a substantial burden even when not extensive, and is associated with widespread treatment dissatisfaction," *J. Investig. Dermatol. Symp. Proc.* **9**(2), 136–139 (2004).

92. X. Zhang, "Genome-wide association study of skin complex diseases," *J. Dermatol. Sci.* **66**(2), 89–97.

93. C. E. Griffiths and J. N. Barker, "Pathogenesis and clinical features of psoriasis," *Lancet.* **370**(9583), 263–271 (2007).

94. P. M. Laws and H. S. Young, "Topical treatment of psoriasis," *Expert Opin. Pharmacother.* **11**(12), 1999–2009 (2010).

95. P. C. van de Kerkhof, G. M. Murphy, J. Austad, A. Ljungberg, F. Cambazard, and L. B. Duvold, "Psoriasis of the face and flexures," *J. Dermatolog. Treat.* **18**(6), 351–360 (2007).

96. K. Krishnamurthy, A. Walker, C. A. Gropper, and C. Hoffman, "To treat or not to treat? Management of guttate psoriasis and pityriasis rosea in patients with evidence of group A Streptococcal infection," *J. Drugs Dermatol.* **9**(3), 241–250 (2010).

97. A. Y. Finlay, G. K. Khan, D. K. Luscombe, and M. S. Salek, "Validation of Sickness Impact Profile and Psoriasis Disability Index in Psoriasis,"
Br. J. Dermatol. **123**(6), 751–756 (1990).

98. Z. Bekassy and B. Astedt, "Laser surgery for psoriasis," *Lancet.* **2**(8457), 725 (1985).

99. G. B. Colver, G. W. Cherry, and T. J. Ryan, "Lasers, psoriasis and the public," *Br. J. Dermatol.* **111**(2), 243–244 (1984).

100. M. W. Berns, M. Rettenmaier, J. McCullough, J. Coffey, A. Wile, M. Berman, P. DiSaia, and G. Weinstein, "Response of psoriasis to red laser light (630 nm) following systemic injection of hematoporphyrin derivative," *Lasers Surg. Med.* **4**(1), 73–77 (1984).

101. P. Asawanonda, R. R. Anderson, Y. Chang, and C. R. Taylor, "308-nm excimer laser for the treatment of psoriasis: a dose-response study," *Arch. Dermatol.* **136**(5), 619–624 (2000).

102. S. Gattu, R. M. Rashid, and J. J. Wu, "308-nm excimer laser in psoriasis vulgaris, scalp psoriasis, and palmoplantar psoriasis," *J. Eur. Acad. Dermatol. Venereol.* **23**(1), 36–41 (2009).

103. M. Trehan and C. R. Taylor, "Medium-dose 308-nm excimer laser for the treatment of psoriasis," *J. Am. Acad. Dermatol.* **47**(5), 701–708 (2002).

104. D. Railan and T. S. Alster, "Laser treatment of acne, psoriasis, leukoderma, and scars," *Semin. Cutan. Med. Surg.* **27**(4), 285–291 (2008).

105. J. De Leeuw, R. G. Van Lingen, H. Both, B. Tank, T. Nijsten, and H. A. Martino Neumann, "A comparative study on the efficacy of treatment with 585 nm pulsed dye laser and ultraviolet B-TL01 in plaque type psoriasis," *Dermatol. Surg.* **35**(1), 80–91 (2009).

106. T. Ilknur, S. Akarsu, S. Aktan, and S. Ozkan, "Comparison of the effects of pulsed dye laser, pulsed dye laser + salicylic acid, and clobetasole propionate + salicylic acid on psoriatic plaques," *Dermatol. Surg.* **32**(1), 49–55 (2006).

107. G. Ablon, "Combination 830-nm and 633-nm light-emitting diode phototherapy shows promise in the treatment of recalcitrant psoriasis: preliminary findings," *Photomed. Laser Surg.* **28**(1), 141–146 (2010).

108. R. Paus and K. Foitzik, "In search of the "hair cycle clock": a guided tour," *Differentiation* **72**(9-10), 489–511 (2004).

109. S. Tiede, J. E. Kloepper, E. Bodo, S. Tiwari, C. Kruse, and R. Paus, "Hair follicle stem cells: walking the maze," *Eur. J. Cell Biol.* **86**(7), 355–376 (2007).

110. M. V. Plikus, J. P. Sundberg, and C. M. Chuong, Mouse skin ectodermal organs. *The mouse in biomedical research*. J. G. Fox and M. Davisson (eds). New York, Academic Press: 691–694 (2006).

111. N. Otberg, A. M. Finner, and J. Shapiro, "Androgenetic alopecia," *Endocrinol. Metab. Clin. North Am.* **36**(2), 379–398 (2007).

112. M. Ghanaat, "Types of hair loss and treatment options, including the novel low-level light therapy and its proposed mechanism," *South Med. J.* **103**(9), 917–921 (2010).

113. S. Itami and S. Inui, "Role of androgen in mesenchymal epithelial interactions in human hair follicle," *J. Investig. Dermatol. Symp. Proc.* **10**(3), 209–211 (2005).

114. T. C. Wikramanayake, R. Rodriguez, S. Choudhary, L. M. Mauro, K. Nouri, L. A. Schachner, and J. J. Jimenez, "Effects of the Lexington LaserComb on hair regrowth in the C3H/HeJ mouse model of alopecia areata," *Lasers Med. Sci.* **27**(2), 431–436 (2012).

115. R. M. Trueb, "Chemotherapy-induced alopecia," *Semin. Cutan. Med. Surg.* **28**(1), 11–14 (2009).

116. G. Moreno-Arias, C. Castelo-Branco, and J. Ferrando, "Paradoxical effect after IPL photoepilation," *Dermatol. Surg.* **28**(11), 1013–1016; discussion 1016 (2002a).

117. G. A. Moreno-Arias, C. Castelo-Branco, and J. Ferrando, "Side-effects after IPL photodepilation," *Dermatol. Surg.* **28**(12), 1131–1134 (2002b).

118. S. P. Vlachos and P. P. Kontoes, "Development of terminal hair following skin lesion treatments with an intense pulsed light source," *Aesthetic Plast. Surg.* **26**(4), 303–307 (2002).

119. E. F. Bernstein, "Hair growth induced by diode laser treatment," *Dermatol. Surg.* **31**(5), 584–586 (2005).

120. N. Bouzari and A. R. Firooz, "Lasers may induce terminal hair growth," *Dermatol. Surg.* **32**(3), 460 (2006).

121. E. Mester, G. Ludany, M. Sellyei, B. Szende, G. Gyenes, and G. J. Tota, "Studies on the inhibiting and activating effects of laser beams," *Langenbecks Arch. Chir.* **322**, 1022–1027 (1968).

122. D. Barolet and A. Boucher, "LED photoprevention: reduced MED response following multiple LED exposures," *Lasers Surg. Med.* **40**(2), 106–112 (2008).

123. M. Leavitt, G. Charles, E. Heyman, and D. Michaels, "HairMax LaserComb laser phototherapy device in the treatment of male androgenetic alopecia: A randomized, double-blind, sham device-controlled, multicentre trial," *Clin. Drug Investig.* **29**(5), 283–292 (2009).

124. H. Chung, T. Dai, S. K. Sharma, Y. Y. Huang, J. D. Carroll, and M. R. Hamblin, "The nuts and bolts of low-level laser (light) therapy," *Ann. Biomed. Eng.* **40**(2), 516–533 (2012).

125. Y. Miura, M. Yamazaki, R. Tsuboi, and H. Ogawa, "Promotion of rat hair growth by irradiation using Super LizerTM," *Jpn. J. Dermatol.* **109**(13), 2149–2152 (1999).

126. Z. Wajima, T. Shitara, T. Inoue, and R. Ogawa, "Linear polarized light irradiation around the stellate ganglion area increases skin temperature and blood flow," *Masui.* **45**(4), 433–438 (1996).

127. P. H. Proctor, "Endothelium-derived relaxing factor and minoxidil: active mechanisms in hair growth," *Arch. Dermatol.* **125**(8), 1146 (1989).

128. Y. C. Hou, A. Janczuk, and P. G. Wang, "Current trends in the development of nitric oxide donors," *Curr. Pharm. Des.* **5**(6), 417–441 (1999).

129. A. Rossi, C. Cantisani, L. Melis, A. Iorio, E. Scali, and S. Calvieri, "Minoxidil use in dermatology, side effects and recent patents," *Recent Pat. Inflamm. Allergy Drug Discov.* **6**(2), 130–136 (2012).

130. T. I. Karu, L. V. Pyatibrat, and N. I. Afanasyeva, "Cellular effects of low power laser therapy can be mediated by nitric oxide," *Lasers Surg. Med.* **36**(4), 307–314 (2005).

131. T. I. Karu, "Mitochondrial signaling in mammalian cells activated by red and near-IR radiation," *Photochem. Photobiol.* **84**(5), 1091–1099 (2008).

132. H. Tuby, L. Maltz, and U. Oron, "Modulations of VEGF and iNOS in the rat heart by low level laser therapy are associated with

cardioprotection and enhanced angiogenesis," *Lasers Surg. Med.* **38**(7), 682–688 (2006).

133. T. I. Karu, L. V. Pyatibrat, and N. I. Afanasyeva, "A novel mitochondrial signaling pathway activated by visible-to-near infrared radiation," *Photochem. Photobiol.* **80**(2), 366–372 (2004).

134. Y. D. Ignatov, A. I. Vislobokov, T. D. Vlasov, M. E. Kolpakova, K. N. Mel'nikov, and I. N. Petrishchev, "Effects of helium-neon laser irradiation and local anesthetics on potassium channels in pond snail neurons," *Neurosci. Behav. Physiol.* **35**, 871–875 (2005).

135. K. Yano, L. F. Brown, and M. Detmar, "Control of hair growth and follicle size by VEGF-mediated angiogenesis," *J. Clin. Invest.* **107**, 409–417 (2001).

136. N. Castex-Rizzi, S. Lachgar, M. Charveron, and Y. Gall, "Implication of VEGF, steroid hormones and neuropeptides in hair follicle cell responses," *Ann. Dermatol. Venereol.* **129**(5 Pt 2), 783–786 (2002).

137. D. T. Meneguzzo, L. A. Lopes, R. Pallota, L. Soares-Ferreira, R. A. Lopes-Martins, and M. S. Ribeiro, "Prevention and treatment of mice paw edema by near-infrared low-level laser therapy on lymph nodes," *Lasers Med. Sci.* **28**(3), 973–80 (2013).

138. S. Shukla, K. Sahu, Y. Verma, K. D. Rao, A. Dube, and P. K. Gupta, "Effect of helium-neon laser irradiation on hair follicle growth cycle of Swiss albino mice," *Skin Pharmacol. Physiol.* **23**(2), 79–85 (2010).

139. S. Muller-Rover, B. Handjiski, C. van der Veen, S. Eichmuller, K. Foitzik, I. A. McKay, K. S. Stenn, and R. Paus, "A comprehensive guide for the accurate classification of murine hair follicles in distinct hair cycle stages," *J. Invest. Dermatol.* **117**(1), 3–15 (2001).

140. D. Philp, M. Nguyen, B. Scheremeta, S. St-Surin, A. M. Villa, A. Orgel, H. K. Kleinman, and M. Elkin, "Thymosin beta4 increases hair growth by activation of hair follicle stem cells," *FASEB J.* **18**(2), 385–387 (2004).

141. S. S. Kim, M. W. Park, and C. J. Lee, "Phototherapy of androgenetic alopecia with low level narrow band 655-nm red light and 780-nm infrared light," *J. Am. Acad. Dermatolog., American Academy of Dermatology 65th Annual Meeting* **56**, AB112 (2007).

142. J. L. Satino and M. Markou, "Hair Regrowth and Increased Hair Tensile Strenght Using the HairMax LaserComb for Low-Level Laser Therapy," *Int. J. Cos. Surg. Aest. Dermatol.* **5**, 113–117 (2003).

143. M. Yamazaki, Y. Miura, R. Tsuboi, and H. Ogawa, "Linear polarized infrared irradiation using Super Lizer is an effective treatment for multiple-type alopecia areata," *Int. J. Dermatol.* **42**(9), 738–740 (2003).

144. M. Thorek, "Plastic reconstruction of the female breasts and abdomen," *Am. J. Surg.* **43**(2), 268–278 (1939).

145. G. Fischer, "Liposculpture: the "correct" history of liposuction. Part I," *J. Dermatol. Surg. Oncol.* **16**(12), 1087–1089 (1990).

146. Y. G. Illouz, "Body contouring by lipolysis: a 5-year experience with over 3000 cases," *Plast. Reconstr. Surg.* **72**(5), 591–597 (1983).

147. R. Neira, J. Arroyave, H. Ramirez, C. L. Ortiz, E. Solarte, F. Sequeda, and M. I. Gutierrez, "Fat liquefaction: effect of low-level laser energy on adipose tissue," *Plast. Reconstr. Surg.* **110**(3), 912–922; Discussion 923–915 (2002).

148. R. Neira, E. Solarte, M. A. Reyes et al., Low-level laser-assisted lipoplasty: A new techique. *Proceedings of the World Congress on Liposuction*, Dearborn, Michigan (2000).

149. G. D. Baxter, A. J. Bell, J. M. Allen, and J. Ravey, "LowLevelLaser Therapy: Current Clinical Practice in Northern Ireland," *Physiotherapy.* **77**(3), 171–178 (1991).

150. P. R. King, "Low level laser therapy: A review," *Laser Med. Sci.* **4**(3), 141–150 (1989).

151. J. L. Oschman Structural Integration (Rolfing), osteopathic, chiropractic, Feldenkrais, Alexander, myofascial release, and related methods. In *Energy Medicine: The Scientific Basis.* J. L. Oschman (ed). Edinburgh: Churchill Livingston. (2000).

152. F. Al-Watban and X. Y. Zang, "Comparison of the effects of laser therapy on wound healing using different laser wavelengths," *Laser Ther.* **1996**(8), 127–135 (1996).

153. H. Frohlich, "Long-range coherence and energy storage in biological systems," *Int. J. Quantum Chem.* **2**(5), 641–649 (1968).

154. H. Frohlich, "Long range coherence and the action of enzymes," *Nature.* **228**(5276), 1093 (1970).

155. H. Frohlich, "The extraordinary dielectric properties of biological materials and the action of enzymes," *Proc. Natl. Acad. Sci. U S A.* **72**(11), 4211–4215 (1975).

156. R. Sroka, C. Fuchs, M. Schaffer, U. Schrader-Reichardt, M. Busch, T. Pongratz, and R. Baumgartner, "Biomodulation effects on cell mitosis after laser irradiation using different wavelenghts," *Laser Surg. Med. Supplement* **21**(9), 6 (Abstract) (1997).

157. H. H. van Breugel and P. R. Bar, "Power density and exposure time of He-Ne laser irradiation are more important than total energy dose in photo-biomodulation of human fibroblasts in vitro," *Lasers Surg. Med.* **12**(5), 528–537 (1992).

158. S. A. Brown, R. J. Rohrich, J. Kenkel, V. L. Young, J. Hoopman, and M. Coimbra, "Effect of low-level laser therapy on abdominal adipocytes before lipoplasty procedures," *Plast. Reconstr. Surg.* **113**(6), 1796–1804; discussion 1805–1796 (2004).

159. P. J. Kolari and O. Airaksinen, "Poor penetration of infra-red and helium neon low power laser light into the dermal tissue," *Acupunct. Electrother. Res.* **18**(1), 17–21 (1993).

160. M. K. Caruso-Davis, T. S. Guillot, V. K. Podichetty, N. Mashtalir, N. V. Dhurandhar, O. Dubuisson, Y. Yu, and F. L. Greenway, "Efficacy of low-level laser therapy for body contouring and spot fat reduction," *Obes. Surg.* **21**(6), 722–729 (2011).

161. R. S. Mulholland, M. D. Paul, and C. Chalfoun, "Noninvasive body contouring with radiofrequency, ultrasound, cryolipolysis, and low-level laser therapy," *Clin. Plast. Surg.* **38**(3), 503–520, vii–iii (2011).

162. M. S. Nestor, J. Newburger, and M. B. Zarraga, "Body contouring using 635-nm low level laser therapy," *Semin. Cutan. Med. Surg.* **32**(1), 35–40 (2013).

163. A. Savoia, S. Landi, F. Vannini, and A. Baldi, "Low-level laser therapy and vibration therapy for the treatment of localized adiposity and fibrous cellulite," *Dermatol. Ther. (Heidelb).* **3**(1), 41–52 (2013).

164. M. H. Gold, K. A. Khatri, K. Hails, R. A. Weiss, and N. Fournier, "Reduction in thigh circumference and improvement in the appearance of cellulite with dual-wavelength, low-level laser energy and massage," *J. Cosmet. Laser Ther.* **13**(1), 13–20 (2011).

165. G. H. Sasaki, K. Oberg, B. Tucker, and M. Gaston, "The effectiveness and safety of topical PhotoActif phosphatidylcholine-based anti-cellulite gel and LED (red and near-infrared) light on Grade II-III thigh cellulite: a randomized, double-blinded study," *J. Cosmet. Laser. Ther.* **9**(2), 87–96 (2007).

Bibliography

Chen, A. C., P. R. Arany, Y. Y. Huang, E. M. Tomkinson, S. K. Sharma, G. B. Kharkwal, T. Saleem, D. Mooney, F. E. Yull, T. S. Blackwell, and M. R. Hamblin, "Low-Level Laser Therapy Activates NF-κB via Generation of Reactive Oxygen Species in Mouse Embryonic Fibroblasts," *PLoS One* **6**(7), e22453 (2011).

Geiger, P. G., W. Korytowski, and A. W. Girotti, "Photodynamically generated 3-beta-hydroxy-5 alpha-cholest-6-ene-5-hydroperoxide: toxic reactivity in membranes and susceptibility to enzymatic detoxification," *Photochem. Photobiol.* **62**(3), 580–587 (1995).

Gupta, A., P. Avci, M. Sadasivam, R. Chandran, N. Parizotto, D. Vecchio, W. C. de Melo, T. Dai, L. Y. Chiang, and M. R. Hamblin, "Shining light on nanotechnology to help repair and regeneration," *Biotechnol. Adv.* (2012).

Honnor, R. C., G. S. Dhillon, and C. Londos, "cAMP-dependent protein kinase and lipolysis in rat adipocytes. II. Definition of steady-state relationship with lipolytic and antilipolytic modulators," *J. Biol. Chem.* **260**(28), 15130–15138 (1985).

Karu, T. I., "Primary and secondary mechanisms of action of visible to near-IR radiation on cells," *J. Photochem. Photobiol. B.* **49**(1), 1–17 (1999).

Karu, T. I., V. V. Lobko, G. G. Lukpanova, I. M. Parkhomenko, and L. Chirkov, "Effect of irradiation with monochromatic visible light on the cAMP content in mammalian cells," *Dokl. Akad. Nauk SSSR.* **281**(5), 1242–1244 (1985).

Nestor, M. S., M. B. Zarraga, and H. Park, "Effect of 635nm Low-level Laser Therapy on Upper Arm Circumference Reduction: A Double-blind, Randomized, Sham-controlled Trial," *J. Clin. Aesthet. Dermatol.* **5**(2), 42–48 (2012).

Sachdev, M., S. Hameed, and V. Mysore, "Nonablative lasers and nonlaser systems in dermatology: current status," *Indian J. Dermatol. Venereol. Leprol.* **77**(3), 380–388 (2011).

Tafur, J., and P. J. Mills, "Low-intensity light therapy: exploring the role of redox mechanisms," *Photomed. Laser Surg.* **26**(4), 323–328 (2008).

Wasserman, D., D. A. Guzman-Sanchez, K. Scott, and A. McMichael, "Alopecia areata," *Int. J. Dermatol.* **46**(2), 121–131 (2007).

Weiss, R. A., D. H. McDaniel, R. Geronemus, M. A. Weiss, and J. Newman, "Non-ablative, non-thermal light emitting diode (LED) phototherapy of photoaged skin," *Laser Surg. Med.* **34**: Supplement 16, 31 (Abstract) (2004).

Wikramanayake, T. C., A. C. Villasante, L. M. Mauro, K. Nouri, L. A. Schachner, C. I. Perez, and J. J. Jimenez, "Low-level laser treatment accelerated hair regrowth in a rat model of chemotherapy-induced alopecia (CIA)," *Lasers Med. Sci.* **28**(3), 701–6 (2013).

Chapter 16
Dental Applications*

There is a wide variety of PBM applications in general dentistry and dental subspecialties (periodontics, orthodontics, prosthodontics, maxillofacial, endodontics, oral medicine). PBM has important applications in pediatric dentistry, restorative dentistry, chronic dental pain, and can benefit other disorders that dentists deal with, such as disturbed sleep and headaches. Painful conditions include musculoskeletal pain, such as temporal mandibular joint (TMJ) dysfunction; neuropathic pain, such as trigeminal neuralgia; post-surgical pain, such as tooth extraction; infections, such as *Herpes simplex* virus and periodontitis; cancer therapy side effects. such as oral mucositis and xerostomia; wound-healing indications, such as post-surgical and diabetic wounds; and nerve regeneration, such as iatrogenic surgical injury, headaches, and burning-mouth syndrome.

The same principles for choosing a wavelength and the optimum dosimetry apply in and around the oral cavity as for PBM applied elsewhere on the body.

16.1 Musculoskeletal Pain: Temporal Mandibular Joint Disorder

A quick search of the PBM literature on PubMed retrieves 19 RCTs on PBM/LLLT for TMJ pain. Systematic reviews disagree on its efficacy: Petrucci et al.[1] found only six RCTs and concluded that changes in pain from the baseline produced a mean difference of 7.77 mm (95% CI, –2.49 to 18.02), which was not statistically significant, but the pain scores were quite variable in those six studies. Medlicott et al.[2] found 11 papers and noted that the studies exhibited methodological differences, especially with regard to the number of sessions, anatomic sites, duration of laser irradiation, and the irradiation parameters. These authors concluded that the dose and ideal parameters for this promising field of research needed to be standardized in

---

*Based on material first printed in Y. Y. Huang, M. R. Hamblin, and L. De Taboada, "Low-level laser therapy for stroke and central nervous system disorders," in *Advanced Biophotonics*, V. V. Tuchin, Ed., Taylor and Francis, Boca Raton, FL (2010).

order to benefit individuals with TMJ. This important point was highlighted by Bjordal et al.,[3] who pointed out that when performing systematic reviews, the data must be stratified to identify different doses and treatment locations. Successful PBM depends on the specific irradiation parameters, dose, number of treatments, and location for the treatment to be optimally successful. TMJ pain is a complex multifactorial pathology that may include joint inflammation, myofascial trigger points, and central sensitization of the nervous system; therefore, a comprehensive approach is necessary for success.

Ahwrari et al.[4] focused their trial on patients with myogenic TMD. In this RCT, treatment was only applied to painful muscles three times a week for four weeks. There was a significant increase in mouth opening and a significant reduction of pain at one month follow-up in the laser group ($p < 0.05$) when compared with the placebo group. The researchers concluded that LLLT could produce a significant reduction in pain and mouth opening in patients affected with myogenic TMD.

16.2 Neuropathic Pain

There appear to be only two controlled studies for neuropathic pain of the head and neck region.[5,6] There was also a 100-patient case report.[7] Neurogenic facial pain is a particularly difficult condition to treat with conventional drug-based therapies, but PBM seems to provide benefit where these drugs have failed.

Eckerdal and Bastian[8] applied PBM (or placebo) to 30 patients with trigeminal neuralgia. Patients were divided into two groups (16 treatment, 14 placebo) and treated once a week for five weeks. Of the 16 patients treated with active laser, ten were free from pain after completing the treatment, and another two had noticeably less pain, whereas in the remaining four there was little or no change. After a one-year follow-up, six patients remained entirely free from pain. In the group treated with the placebo, only one was free from pain, four had less pain, and the remaining nine patients had little or no relief. After one year, only one patient in the placebo group was still completely free from pain.

Walker et al.[9] conducted a trial with 18 patients with trigeminal neuralgia who received laser PBM to the painful areas and to the nerve trunks supplying the painful region. Seventeen patients received a placebo laser treatment three times a week for ten weeks. Subjects in the active treatment group displayed a statistically significant reduction in the intensity of pain ($p < 0.002$) and a reduction in the number of painful episodes.

Moore et al.[10] reviewed 18 patients with cranial post-herpetic neuralgia (PHN) treated with PBM. The patients showed a mean improvement of 61% in the monitored parameters compared with baseline. At 1-year follow-up, pain relief was maintained in 66% of cases, and more than 50% of patients with recurring pain achieved good pain relief following a second course of treatment. Moore mentioned that cephalic PHN was notoriously difficult to treat successfully and that laser therapy has been proved to be a valuable adjunct to therapy, particularly when conventional methods of treatment have failed.

16.3 Post-extraction Pain, Swelling, and Trismus

A quick search on PubMed retrieves 15 randomized and controlled clinical trials. In 2015, He et al.[11] performed a systematic review and meta-analysis on the efficacy of PBM in the management of mandibular third molar extraction. They found that the use of PBM versus placebo controls led to a significant reduction of pain on the first day as measured by a visual analog scale (VAS) (mean difference (MD) = –2.63, 95% confidence interval (CI) –4.46 to –0.79, $p = 0.005$). The superiority of LLLT in pain control persisted on the second day (MD = –2.34, 95% CI –4.61 to –0.06, $p = 0.04$) and the third day (MD = –3.40, 95% CI –4.12 to –2.68, $p < 0.00001$). Moreover, LLLT reduced an average of 4.94 mm on the VAS (MD = 4.94, 95% CI 1.53 to 8.34, $p = 0.004$) for trismus compared with placebo laser irradiation in the first three days. On the seventh day, the superiority of LLLT also persisted (MD = 3.24, 95% CI 0.37 to 6.12, $p = 0.03$). In the first three days after surgery, extraoral irradiation alone (MD = –0.69, 95% CI –1.30 to –0.08, $p = 0.03$) and intraoral irradiation combined with extraoral irradiation (MD = –0.65, 95% CI –1.15 to –0.15, $p = 0.01$) reduced facial swelling significantly. On the seventh day, the intraoral combined with extraoral irradiation group (MD = –0.32, 95% CI –0.59 to –0.06, $p = 0.02$) still showed a benefit in relieving facial swelling. However, due to the heterogeneity of the intervention and different methods of assessing outcomes and the risk of bias, the overall evidence for efficacy is considered to be limited. In the future, well-designed RCTs with larger sample sizes will be required to provide clearer recommendations.[11]

Treatment of post-operative pain, when performed early, usually only requires a single or double treatment so long as it is performed pre-operatively and immediately post-operatively.

16.4 Nerve Injuries

A systematic review by Veitz-Keenan et al. in 2015[12] found just two RCT, both considered to have a high risk of bias, reporting data from 26 analyzed patients. Both studies compared the use of an active laser to a placebo to treat an inferior alveolar sensory deficit as a result of iatrogenic injury. There was evidence of an improvement in the subjective assessment of neurosensory deficits in the chin of 8.40 cm (95% CI 3.67 to 13.13) and a difference in mean change in neurosensory deficit of the lip of 21.79 cm (95% CI 5.29 to 38.29) though the quality of the evidence was considered very low. Despite the cautious conclusion of this study, the importance of this approach must not be overlooked, as there are no other options for these patients.

16.5 Orthodontic Pain

A systematic review with meta-analysis on the effectiveness of PBM for orthodontic pain was published by Ren et al.[13] They found 14 RCTs, including a total of 659 participants. There was a "moderate risk of bias" in three studies and a "high risk of bias" in the remaining 11 studies. The methodological weaknesses were mainly due to issues with "blinding" and "allocation concealment." The meta-analysis showed that PBM significantly reduced orthodontic pain by 39% in comparison with placebo groups ($p = 0.02$). PBM significantly reduced the maximum pain intensity among parallel-design studies ($p = 0.003$ versus placebo groups, $p = 0.000$ versus control groups). However, no significant effects were shown for split-mouth-design studies ($p = 0.38$ versus placebo groups). The use of diode LLLT for orthodontic pain appears promising. Seasoned PBM researchers are aware of the systemic effects of the treatment, so treating only one side of the mouth may well improve healing of another part of the mouth.

Another systematic review and meta-analysis by Shi et al.[14] asked whether PBM could reduce pain caused by the use of the orthodontic separators designed to encourage tooth movement. Pain during orthodontic treatment can affect patient compliance and even force them to terminate treatments. Six studies met their criteria. Overall, the PBM groups had significantly less pain compared to the placebo groups. The statistically significant benefit was most pronounced at 6 hours, 1 day, 2 days, and 3 days after the placement of separators. A 4d and 5d after the placement, the results tend to support PBM, but were not statistically significant.

16.6 Orthodontic Tooth Movement

A systematic review and meta-analysis was published in 2014 by Ge et al.[15] on the efficacy of PBM for accelerating tooth movement during orthodontic treatment. They found six RCTs and three "quasi-RCTs," involving 211 patients. Five were assessed as having a moderate risk of bias, whereas the rest were assessed as high risk of bias. The mean difference and the 95% CI of cumulative distance moved of treated teeth were observed among all of the studies. The results showed that PBM could accelerate orthodontic tooth movement (OTM) measured at 7 days (MD = 0.19, 95% CI 0.02 to 0.37, $p = 0.03$) and at 2 months (MD = 1.08, 95% CI 0.16 to 2.01, $p = 0.02$). These authors noted that a fluence of 5–8 J/cm^2 was more effective than fluences

>20 J/cm^2. Other systematic reviews were less convincing, probably because they did not stratify the results by dose.

Another systematic review and meta-analysis by Seifi et al.[16] studied the efficacy of PBM for orthodontic tooth movement. Five clinical studies met their criteria, and four of these used an 810-/820-nm laser, whereas the other one used a 660-nm laser. Four out of the five studies reported improvements in the rate of movement and total distance moved, whereas the study that used 810 nm saw no difference.

16.7 Dentine Hypersensitivity

A systematic review and meta-analysis published by He in 2011[17] looked at the efficacy of PBM for treating dentine hypersensitivity. They compared PBM with topical desensitizing agents (toothpastes). A secondary objective sought to determine the safety of laser application according to the relevant studies. A total of eight trials were included that met the inclusion criteria involving 234 participants. Based on the "quality" of evidence, one study was classified as "A level," five as "B level," and two as "C level." Due to the heterogeneity of the studies, a meta-analysis was not performed. Half of the included studies compared a GaAlAs laser with topical desensitizing agents, but the findings were conflicting. The remaining studies involved a Nd:YAG laser, Er:YAG laser, and CO$_2$ laser, and together they showed that the three types of lasers were each superior to topical desensitizing agents, but the superiority was only slight. A systematic review of the literature indicated the likelihood that laser therapy has a slight clinical advantage over topical medicaments in the treatment of dentine hypersensitivity. This review could have been more useful if they had calculated the doses in the individual trials. The GaAlAs lasers were only 15 mW and 30 mW in total power, and the energy delivered per treatment was just 0.5–3.5 J, compared with the Nd:YAG, Er:YAG, and CO$_2$ lasers, where energy levels of 10–120 J were used.

Another review by Al-Sabbagh et al.[18] looked at the efficacy of PBM for dental hypersensitivity. Most of these studies used various dental lasers, including the carbon dioxide laser. These authors found four positive studies and one negative study. The best study reported that 97% of subjects achieved complete relief. Moreover, several other studies reported that PBM or laser treatment could be advantageously combined with other treatments, such as coating the teeth with a fluoride-containing varnish or using dentine-bonding agents.

16.8 Herpes Simplex Infection

A nonsystematic review and meta-analysis was published by de Paula Eduardo in 2013[19] on the efficacy of PBM in treating recurrent herpes labialis infections. The review was performed to identify the effects of PBM on healing time, pain relief, duration of viral shedding, viral inactivation, and interval of recurrence. No trials could completely eliminate the virus or totally prevent its recurrence; however, one PBM protocol appeared to strongly decrease the pain and extend the interval between recurrences. Although these results suggest a potential beneficial use for lasers in the management of recurrent herpes labialis, they are based on a limited number of published clinical trials and case reports. The literature still lacks double-blind, well-controlled clinical trials to verify these effects.

16.9 Cancer Therapy Side Effects

Up to the present, there have been 32 separate controlled clinical trials and seven systematic reviews reporting on PBM for oral mucositis, and a substantial overview paper reviewing PBM treatments in general for cancer therapy side effects, including oral mucositis, radiation dermatitis, dysphagia, xerostomia, hyposalivation, dysgeusia, trismus, osteonecrosis of the jaw, and head and neck lymphedema.[20]

There are therefore high levels of evidence for the PBM treatment of oral mucositis. A statement from the Multinational Association of Supportive Care in Cancer (MASCC) recommended using PBM on patients receiving hematopoietic stem-cell transplantation who had been conditioned with high-dose chemotherapy, with or without total body irradiation.

16.10 Post-operative Wound Healing

There have been no systematic reviews on wound healing in dentistry, but there are 9 RCTs, 8 of which reported improved wound healing compared with placebo controls. Significant improvement in the predictability and stability of root coverage was found for "coronally advanced flap" (CAF) and "semilunar coronally advanced flap" (SCAF) surgery,[21,22] and another study reported no scar tissue.[23] In addition, a reduction in pain and swelling has been frequently reported.[24]

16.11 Endodontics

A review article by Mohammadi[25] discussed all the ways PBM and laser therapy could be employed in endodontics. Most of the studies reported concerned the use of high-power dental lasers in the root canal cavity and the observation of better effects compared with traditional mechanical or chemical procedures. These better effects may be due to PBM effects occurring at the periphery of the high-power-laser-treated region where the power density is much lower than at the laser focus. For instance, devitalization of vital pulp (pulpotomy) carried out by CO_2, Er:YAG, or Nd:YAG lasers was superior to chemical devitalization using formocresol or calcium hydroxide. Similar considerations apply in the case of laser disinfection of the root canal system, preparation of the root canal dentine walls, root canal shaping, root canal obturation, and peri-radicular surgery.

16.12 Analgesia

A study by Kawakami et al[26] reported on the efficacy of PBM for analgesia in dentistry. They used a GaAlAs semiconductor laser called "semi laser nanoX" with a wavelength of the total power of 30 mW and an exposure time between 30 s and 180 s per treatment. The results were as follows: for dentin hypersensitivity, the treatment was not effective in two cases of grade III, but with all grade I or II (35 cases) the pain decreased immediately after irradiation. The treatment was effective in all cases with pain after root canal filling and after tooth extraction. It was also effective in all cases with gingivitis, stomatitis, and gingival ulcers that developed after the injection of local anesthesia, etc. Another report of a trial of PBM for post-operative pain and swelling[27] used a 40-mW, 830-nm "Biophoton" laser. Twenty-five healthy adults with bilateral, identically impacted, lower third molars were selected for this study. The teeth were removed in two separate operations. Laser treatment was compared to a placebo laser. However, there was no significant difference between groups with regard to swelling, trismus, and pain after third-molar surgery.

Many children develop a fear of dentists partly due to the painful nature of injections of local anesthetics into the oral mucosa. PBM may represent an alternative for dental analgesia in pediatric patients. A review by Kotlow[28] suggests that PBM using a focused laser spot at relatively low power could replace injected local anesthetics.

16.13 Lichen Planus

Oral lichen planus (OLP) is a relatively common chronic inflammatory disease of unknown etiology, often occurring in the oral mucosa. It rarely undergoes spontaneous remission and is considered potentially pre-malignant. OLP mostly affects women between the fifth and sixth decades. The pathogenesis involves a cell-mediated immune response to antigenic changes in the oral mucosa that is marked by predominant T-lymphocyte infiltration. Elshenawy et al. reported a clinical trial[29] of the efficacy of PBM for OLP. Ten patients with symptomatic OLP ranging in age from 45 to 60 years and who were unresponsive to topical steroids were recruited. Patients were treated with a diode laser (970-nm wavelength) in a noncontact mode with a 320-μm-diameter fiber directed at the affected areas of oral mucous membrane. A total output power of 3 W, a pulsed frequency of 30 Hz, a total energy of 180 J, and over 8 minutes divided into four sessions of 2 minutes, with one minute rest in between to allow for tissue relaxation. There was a statistically significant decrease in pain scores through all 8 weeks of the course of treatment. Most patients reported immediate pain relief after the second session, and all of them reported a complete resolution of symptoms at the end of the course, while a few lesions showed only a partial clinical response.

16.14 Stem Cells

Over the past decade, dentistry has benefited from recent findings in stem-cell biology and tissue engineering that led to the elaboration of novel ideas and concepts for the regeneration of dental tissues or entire new teeth. Stem-cell-based regenerative approaches aim at the fully functional restoration of lost or damaged tissues. Stem cells have the potential to self-renew and produce a variety of cell types that ensure tissue repair and regeneration throughout life. Several adult stem-cell populations have been isolated from dental and periodontal tissues, and then characterized and tested for their potential applications in regenerative dentistry.[30] The most important applications of stem cells in dentistry have been proposed for the revitalization and regeneration of dental pulp, regeneration of periodontal ligaments and even the regeneration of new teeth.[31] A systematic review and meta-analysis by Ginani et al.[32] discussed the efficacy of PBM for stimulating proliferation of mesenchymal stem cells (MSCs). Out of 463 references identified by their search strategy, only 19 papers met their criteria and were included in the analysis. The studies varied considerably in the source of the MSC, such as bone marrow, dental pulp, periodontal ligaments, and adipose tissue. The PBM parameters also varied widely with differences in wavelength, power density, total energy, irradiation time, light polarization, and pulse structure. Most studies demonstrated an increase in the proliferation rate of the irradiated MSC.

References

1. A. Petrucci, F. Sgolastra, R. Gatto, A. Mattei, and A. Monaco, "Effectiveness of low-level laser therapy in temporomandibular disorders: a systematic review and meta-analysis," *J. Orofac. Pain.* **25**(4), 298–307 (2011).
2. C. M. Herpich et al., "Analysis of laser therapy and assessment methods in the rehabilitation of temporomandibular disorder: a systematic review of the literature," *J. Phys. Therapy Sci.* **27**(1), 295–301 (2015).
3. J. M. Bjordal, C. Couppe, R. T. Chow, J. Tuner, and E. A. Ljunggren, "A systematic review of low level laser therapy with location-specific doses for pain from chronic joint disorders," *Aust. J. Physiotherapy* **49**(2), 107–116 (2003).

4. F. Ahrari, A. S. Madani, Z. S. Ghafouri, and J. Tuner, "The efficacy of low-level laser therapy for the treatment of myogenous temporomandibular joint disorder," *Laser. Med. Sci.* **29**(2), 551–557 (2014).

5. H. Yoneyama and R. Katsumata, "Antibiotic resistance in bacteria and its future for novel antibiotic development," *Biosci., Biotechnol., and Biochem.* **70**(5), 1060–1075 (2006).

6. J. Walker et al., "Laser therapy for pain of trigeminal neuralgia," *Clin. J. Pain* **3**, 183–187 (1988).

7. K. C. Moore, "Laser Therapy: From Fantasy to Fact – A Decade of Change," *Laser Therapy* **10**(2), 53–54 (1998).

8. A. Eckerdal and H. L. Bastian, "Can low reactive-level laser therapy be used in the treatment of neurogenic facial pain? A double-blind, placebo controlled investigation of patients with trigeminal neuralgia?" *Laser Therapy* **8**(4), 247–252 (1996).

9. F. Falaki, A. H. Nejat, and Z. Dalirsani, "The Effect of Low-level Laser Therapy on Trigeminal Neuralgia: A Review of Literature," *J. Dental Res., Dental Clinics, Dental Prospects* **8**(1), 1–5 (2014).

10. K. C. Moore, H. Naru, S. K. Parswanath, S. J. Copparam, and O. Toshio, "A double blind crossover traialof low level laser therapy in the treatment of post herpetic neuralgia," *Laser Therapy* **1**, 7–9 (1989).

11. W. L. He, F. Y. Yu, C. J. Li, J. Pan, R. Zhuang, and P. J. Duan, "A systematic review and meta-analysis on the efficacy of low-level laser therapy in the management of complication after mandibular third molar surgery," *Lasers Med. Sci.* **30**(6), 1779–1788 (2015).

12. A. Veitz-Keenan and J. R. Keenan, "Trials needed to identify best management of iatrogenic inferior alveolar and lingual nerve injuries," *Evidence-Based Dentistry* **16**(1), 29 (2015).

13. C. Ren, C. McGrath, and Y. Yang, "The effectiveness of low-level diode laser therapy on orthodontic pain management: a systematic review and meta-analysis," *J. Lasers Med. Sci.* **30**(7), 1881–1893 (2015).

14. Q. Shi, S. Yang, F. Jia, and J. Xu, "Does low level laser therapy relieve the pain caused by the placement of the orthodontic separators? A meta-analysis," *Head & Face Med.* **11**, 28 (2015).

15. M. K. Ge et al., "Efficacy of low-level laser therapy for accelerating tooth movement during orthodontic treatment: a systematic review and meta-analysis," *J. Lasers Med. Sci.* **30**(5), 1609–1618 (2015).

16. M. Seifi and E. Vahid-Dastjerdi, "Tooth movement alterations by different low level laser protocols: a literature review," *J. Lasers Med. Sci.* **6**(1), 1–5 (2015).

17. S. He, Y. Wang, X. Li, and D. Hu, "Effectiveness of laser therapy and topical desensitising agents in treating dentine hypersensitivity: a systematic review," *J. Oral Rehabilitation* **38**(5), 348–358 (2011).

18. M. Al-Sabbagh, A. Brown, and M. V. Thomas, "In-office treatment of dentinal hypersensitivity," *Dental Clinics North America* **53**(1), 47–60 (2009).

19. C. de Paula Eduardo et al., "Laser treatment of recurrent herpes labialis: a literature review," *Lasers Med. Sci.* **29**(4), 1517–1529 (2014).

20. J. A. Zecha et al., "Low-level laser therapy/photobiomodulation in the management of side effects of chemoradiation therapy in head and neck cancer, part 2: proposed applications and treatment protocols," *Support Care Cancer* **24**(6), 2793–2805 (2016).

21. S. Ozturan, S. A. Durukan, O. Ozcelik, G. Seydaoglu, and M. C. Haytac, "Coronally advanced flap adjunct with low intensity laser therapy: a randomized controlled clinical pilot study," *J. Clin. Periodontology* **38**(11), 1055–1062 (2011).

22. N. Singh, A. Uppoor, and D. Naik, "Semilunar coronally advanced flap with or without low level laser therapy in treatment of human maxillary multiple adjacent facial gingival recessions: a clinical study," *J. Esthetic and Restorative Dentistry* **27**(6), 355–366 (2015).

23. S. B. Dias et al., "Effect of GaAIAs low-level laser therapy on the healing of human palate mucosa after connective tissue graft harvesting: randomized clinical trial," *J. Lasers Med. Sci.* **30**(6), 1695–1702 (2015).

24. G. Batinjan et al., "Thermographic monitoring of wound healing and oral health-related quality of life in patients treated with laser (aPDT) after impacted mandibular third molar removal," *Internat. J. Oral and Maxillofacial Surgery* **43**(12), 1503–1508 (2014).

25. Z. Mohammadi, "Laser applications in endodontics: an update review," *Internat. Dental J.* **59**(1), 35–46 (2009).

26. T. Kawakami et al., "The effectiveness of GaAlAs semiconductor laser treatment to decrease pain after irradiation," *Higashi Nippon Shigaku Zasshi* **8**, 57–62 (1989).

27. A. K. Roynesdal, T. Bjornland, P. Barkvoll, and H. R. Haanaes, "The effect of soft-laser application on postoperative pain and swelling. A double-blind, crossover study," *Internat. J. Oral and Maxillofacial Surgery* **22**(4), 242–245 (1993).

28. L. Kotlow, "Lasers and pediatric dental care," *General Dentistry* **56**(7), 618–627 (2008).

29. H. M. Elshenawy, A. M. Eldin, and M. A. Abdelmonem, "Clinical assessment of the efficiency of low level laser therapy in the treatment of oral lichen planus," *Open Access Macedonian J. Med. Sci.* **3**(4), 717–721 (2015).

30. S. Miran, T. A. Mitsiadis, and P. Pagella, "Innovative Dental stem cell-based research approaches: the future of dentistry," *Stem Cells Int.* **2016**, 7231038 (2016).

31. P. R. Arany et al., "Photoactivation of endogenous latent transforming growth factor-beta1 directs dental stem cell differentiation for regeneration," *Sci. Translational Med.* **6**(238), 238–269 (2014).

32. F. Ginani, D. M. Soares, M. P. Barreto, and C. A. Barboza, "Effect of low-level laser therapy on mesenchymal stem cell proliferation: a systematic review," *J. Lasers Med. Sci.* **30**(8), 2189–2194 (2015).

Chapter 17
LLLT Treatment of Pain: Clinical Applications*

Roberta Chow

17.1 Background

Low-level laser therapy (LLLT) has been used to treat a wide spectrum of painful clinical conditions, commencing within a decade of its production by Maiman[1] in 1960. Initial clinical use outstripped comprehension of the mechanisms of its effects. Further confusion arose with the concurrent use of lasers in acupuncture, a different paradigm. Over subsequent decades, as research focused on understanding the direct effects of light on tissue, several mechanisms underlying LLLT analgesia were proposed.[2–4] These mechanisms include anti-inflammatory effects, neural blockade, stimulation of lymphatic activity, tissue repair, and reduction of muscle spasm. Each of these mechanisms has been studied from subcellular levels to clinical application. The translation and application of these mechanisms from the laboratory to clinical practice is critical to successful outcomes with LLLT. This chapter outlines the painful conditions in which LLLT is used, the mechanisms for its effects, and practical considerations.

17.2 Pain

To successfully apply LLLT in this context, one must first understand the nature of pain. Pain is defined by the International Association for the Study of Pain (IASP) as "an unpleasant sensory and emotional experience associated with actual or potential tissue damage, or described in terms of such damage."[5] Although this definition encompasses the complexity of the phenomenon of pain, it can be extended beyond the activation of nociceptors

---

*Based on material first published in M. K. Sawhney and M. R. Hamblin, "Low Level Laser (Light) Therapy (LLLT) for Cosmetic Medicine and Dermatology," http://photobiology.info/Sawhney.html.

to the broader concept of a person's emotional response to pain and the social context in which it occurs, i.e., the immune cells, nociceptors, lymphatics, and muscles, where LLLT exerts its primary action in modulating pain.

17.3 Types of Pain and Mechanisms

Pain can be divided into three different types based on the underlying mechanism. The first two are nociceptive and neuropathic pain, both of which can be modulated by LLLT. The third is central pain, which arises from damage to the CNS, such as due to stroke, and is not currently treated with LLLT.

Nociceptive pain is the most common form of pain and arises from activation of nociceptors, the small-diameter, thinly myelinated $A\delta$ and unmyelinated C afferent nerve fibers, which are found in skin and deeper tissues. When tissue damage occurs, an inflammatory soup of chemical mediators and proinflammatory cytokines, such as prostaglandins E_2 (PGE_2) and substance P, is released by injury or inflammation, which sensitize nociceptors. Many musculoskeletal conditions are examples of nociceptive pain: osteoarthritis, rheumatoid arthritis, crystallopathies (such as gout), and trauma, including surgery, whiplash injury, and tendinopathies.

Neuropathic pain, a second form of pain, arises from damage to nerves that can occur with infection, e.g., herpes zoster causing post-herpetic neuralgia or compression with inflammation, which occurs with disc prolapse onto nerve roots, as in sciatica. Other examples are trigeminal neuralgia and carpal tunnel syndrome. Both nociceptive and neuropathic pain can occur concurrently in the same patient, for example, back pain with sciatica. In this and other clinical scenarios, patients may describe two different types of pain: the lancinating or burning pain of neuropathic pain and the dull ache of nociceptive pain.

In recent years, the importance of relieving pain whatever its origin has been recognized as a clinical imperative, with pain now regarded as a disease in its own right.[6] Not only is this good management important from a patient's comfort perspective but it is also understood that reducing the severity of acute pain can prevent pain from becoming chronic.

The underlying pathophysiology of this situation is the phenomenon of "wind up" in the spinal cord leading to long-term potentiation of pain.[7] These changes occur initially in the dorsal horn and result in central sensitization,[8] which causes increased sensitivity of nociceptors. Clinically, this is manifest as hyperalgesia (increased sensitivity to sensation that is not normally painful) and allodynia (pain with activity that is not normally painful). Whiplash-associated disorder (WAD) is a common example in which these symptoms are seen. These changes occur as a result of neuroplasticity in the dorsal horn, which is the capacity of neurons in both the peripheral and central nervous systems to be modulated by increased or decreased afferent activity from the somatosensory nerves. It is neuroplasticity, which underpins the long-term benefits of LLLT.

From a clinical perspective, it is necessary to identify whether the pathophysiology is neuropathic or nociceptive pain because patients with neuropathic pain are often more likely to experience an increase in pain following LLLT.

Complicating the picture in many patients are conditions that appear nociceptive in origin but in which patients experience pain out of proportion to the pathology. WAD, fibromyalgia, and complex regional pain syndrome (CRPS) are examples of conditions where increased sensitization in the "pain matrix" occurs. In these clinical scenarios, central sensitization reduces pain thresholds and patients exhibit hyperalgesia and allodynia. These patients have often been labeled as having psychological problems as a causal factor in their pain, especially if there are no abnormalities on MRI. It is now appreciated that changes in the spinal cord underpin these responses, and what are perceived as abnormal psychological factors are secondary to the pain and limitations it causes. The long-term benefit of LLLT in such patients is to "re-program" their pain matrix and cause long-term depression (LTD) of pain.[9]

17.4 Mechanisms Underlying Pain Relief

17.4.1 Neural blockade

Lasers can relieve nociceptive and neuropathic pain by partially inhibiting nerve conduction and reducing afferent stimulation, mimicking some functions of local anesthetic injections. Demonstrating this anesthetic action is a study by Chan et al.[10] in which a Nd:YAG laser (average power: 1.1 mW, 240 s) applied to the cervical surface of the tooth induced pulpal anesthesia for dental procedures. In other studies, both a 650-nm (35 mW, 30 s) and a 808-nm (400 mW, 30 s) laser, applied at four points to skin over the sciatic nerve, reduced action potentials in the underlying motor and sensory components of the sciatic nerve in rats.[11] A review of the effects of lasers on nerves confirmed the "blockade" effects on nerves in humans as well as animals.[12] When laser light is applied transdermally, not only does it reduce action potentials in underlying nerve trunks but it also inhibits conduction in the superficial peripheral nerve endings of nociceptors in skin and deeper tissues. This behavior translates in the clinical situation to patients reporting a reduction in tenderness and pain, sometimes in association with a sensation of "numbness" during the course of treatment. Importantly, a reduction of afferent stimulation by lasers to peripheral nerve endings results in reduced synaptic activity with second-order dorsal horn neurons, which in turn modulates the afferent input to higher centers. Neuroplasticity underlies this capacity of the nervous system to modulate responses to laser-induced neural blockade leading to long-term pain relief.

17.4.2 Reduced inflammation

Another very important mechanism of nociceptive pain relief with LLLT is its anti-inflammatory effect. Inflammation is a physiological response in tissue to injury (for example, trauma or surgery) or pathological conditions (for example, infection, gout, osteoarthritis, and rheumatoid arthritis). It is mediated by the release of a "chemical soup" of proinflammatory peptides released from cells in the injured area. These molecules sensitize peripheral nerve endings of nociceptors causing pain as well as acting as chemotactic stimuli for other cells such as neutrophils to enter the injured area to initiate healing. Peripheral nerve endings in the skin, when sensitized, also contribute to inflammation (so-called neurogenic inflammation) by releasing substance P and other neuropeptides. This behavior leads to further activation of cells involved in inflammation, such as mast cells, and the cascade of pain and inflammation proceeds. The progress and resolution of inflammation is critical to normal healing. Specific anti-inflammatory effects of lasers have been demonstrated in several different experimental models, e.g., suppression of IL-6 following tendon injury in rats (660 nm, 100 mW, 6 J);[13] decreased mRNA expression of kinin receptors and inflammatory cytokines TNFα and IL-1β in carrageenan-induced inflammation in rat paws (660 nm or 684 nm, 30 mW, 7.5 J/cm^2);[14] and reduced COX-2 expression in a similar model using similar laser parameters.[15] In a case series involving human subjects treated with LLLT (830 nm, 1 W, 3 minutes for 10 treatments) for painful conditions, serum PGE$_2$ was significantly lower in patients with successful outcomes than those who did not get pain relief.[16] In conditions where inflammation is central to the pathophysiology, LLLT can effectively reduce pain, which in some studies is equivalent to anti-inflammatory drugs.[17]

17.4.3 Reduced edema

Swelling is a normal physiological response to acute and chronic inflammation. Extravasation of fluid into the interstitial space occurs in response to proinflammatory mediators acting on capillaries and increasing their permeability. Swelling limits the movement of an injured area, thereby splinting a limb and enforcing rest, which is protective during the initial stages of injury. In acute injuries, reducing edema will reduce pain and allow early mobilization, which in turn will activate muscle pump action in limbs. Swelling of limbs also occurs when there is reduced capacity of the lymphatic system to transport fluid due either to genetics (known as primary lymphedema) or as a result of removal, which occurs during the surgical treatment of cancers. Although edema is a physiological response to injury, swelling contributes to pain; when prolonged, it results in pain, pathologically restricts movement, and causes tissue scarring as fibrin in the interstitial fluid becomes organized. LLLT (650 nm, ED: 1 and 2.5 J/cm^2) reduces edema in experimentally induced arthritis[18,19] and in carrageenan-induced inflammation in rat paws (632.8 nm, 2.5 J/cm^2),[20] and improves macromolecular clearance via lymph nodes (CO$_2$ 30 s, 0.5–1.5 W).[21]

Treatment of lymph nodes draining an area of inflammation has edema-reducing effects without local laser treatment (830 nm, 35 J/cm^2, 10 s).[22] In some studies, extraoral LLLT (808 nm, 100 mW, 120 s)[23] and (637 nm, 50 mW, ED: 4 J/cm^2)[24] reduced edema following tooth extraction. LLLT has been demonstrated to activate the motoricity of lymphatic vessels by increasing the motility of endothelial cells, which make up the lymphangion and increase the number of lymphatic channels over time.[25]

17.4.4 Reduced muscle spasm

Muscle spasm is a physiological reflex response that occurs in response to acute injury or chronic strain. Acute whiplash injury and the more chronic WADs are examples of such muscle strain and spasm that can be prolonged. Chronic postural strain that occurs as a result of maintaining nonphysiological positions for long periods of time, for example, sitting at a computer or playing a musical instrument, can also result in muscle spasms that contribute to the clinical pain picture of many chronic musculoskeletal pain conditions. If the spasm persists over weeks, months, and even years, "trigger points" form within the muscle,[26] causing myofascial pain syndrome (MPS).[27] Although MPS as a diagnosis has been controversial, there is now greater understanding of the pathophysiology[28] that is addressed by the effects of laser on muscles LLLT (see Section 17.5.2.9). After an acute injury resolves or strain is relieved, these changes revert to normal in most, though not all, clinical situations, and normal function resumes. In patients with chronic conditions, LLLT can facilitate more effective rehabilitation if they did not respond to physiotherapy prior to LLLT.

17.4.5 Tissue repair

Trauma and inflammation are associated with tissue damage, which initiates a cascade of physiological events leading to tissue healing. The long-term benefits of LLLT result from its capacity to promote tissue repair, especially in clinical situations where there has been delayed healing. Much of the research in this area relates to chronic wound healing, such as chronic venous ulceration, one of the earliest applications of LLLT.[29] Other clinical scenarios where tissue repair is critically important are tendinopathies, e.g., Achilles tendinopathy, and enthesopathies, e.g., lateral epicondylitis—examples where the immediate anti-inflammatory effects of LLLT will relieve pain, but tissue repair is critical for resumption of normal function. Tissue repair is a complex process, and LLLT acts in multiple ways. Laser stimulates the migration and activation of cells to the injured area,[30] decreases inflammatory cytokine production by neutrophils,[31] increases the phagocytosis of neutrophils, improves microvasculature and endothelial cell proliferation,[32] and increases the production of growth factors[33] and procollagen by fibroblasts.[34]

17.4.6 Release of neurotransmitters

The local and systemic modulation of the release of neuropeptide pain modulators is less studied than many of the aforementioned mechanisms. A number of studies point to significant changes in neuropeptides in response to LLLT, which are important in endogenous pain modulation. These include β-endorphins[35,36] and their precursors,[37] and serotonin,[38,39] all of which are molecules that are the pharmacological basis of drugs used in pain relief. It remains an area for future research.

17.5 Conditions in which LLLT is Used, and Evidence

17.5.1 Reviews of LLLT and pain

Several reviews have been undertaken regarding the efficacy of LLLT in painful conditions. Early reviews stated that there was insufficient evidence to support LLLT in musculoskeletal pain,[40,41] or at best they were equivocal.[42,43] Because the number of randomized controlled trials (RCTs) has increased and there is greater understanding of the mechanisms of action, more recent reviews have found positive outcomes in both chronic and acute pain.[44–46] A common theme among reviewers of LLLT is the need for complete reporting of parameters used in studies, without which no comparison of the doses delivered in trials is possible because the combination and permutation of parameters is almost infinite.[47–49] More sophisticated reviews of LLLT emphasize the importance of finding the appropriate dosage window, which is wavelength specific. The dosage window appropriate for each condition must be found to achieve the best outcome. Later reviews of LLLT painstakingly address this in their analyses.

17.5.2 Evidence for specific conditions

17.5.2.1 Knee osteoarthritis

Knee pain, especially osteoarthritis (OA), is one of the most common forms of arthritis in people over 65 years of age. Weight loss and topical anti-inflammatories are now the recommended first-line treatments according to the NICE UK guidelines.[50] Even Paracetamol, previously recommended as a first-line treatment option, is now being reconsidered due to long-term toxicity. The serious side effect profiles of nonsteroidal anti-inflammatory drugs (NSAIDs) now render them second- and third-line treatments for as short a period of time as possible. At the end of the treatment spectrum, arthroscopy of the knee joint results in more harm than benefit in the long term,[51] and following total knee replacement, approximately 20% of patients experience ongoing pain and disability of some degree, particularly women.[52] The case for LLLT as a mainstream therapy is strong given the limitations of current therapies. Bjordal et al.[53] published a review of studies of osteoarthritis that included an analysis of the doses and application techniques used. They found that there was good evidence for a clinically relevant effect provided the appropriate dose was used (2–12 J for 904 nm and 20–48 J for 830 nm) applied to up to eight points over the joint capsule. Since that review, a number of other studies, each using near-infrared (NIR) lasers (810, 830, and 904 nm), have demonstrated the efficacy of LLLT on knee OA[54–56] supported by animal experiments showing the modulation of inflammation within the knee joint. 810-nm (1, 3, and 6 J) light in experimentally induced rat knee inflammation significantly reduced the number of polymorphonuclear cells at the inflammatory site; COX-1 and -2 gene expression were significantly enhanced by laser irradiation, and PGE_2 production was inhibited.[57] Osteochondral defects were significantly repaired with 890-nm (4.8J/cm^2) light at 8 weeks.[58] A histological study of laser-irradiated (790 nm, 10 mW, 8 minutes daily for 6 days), synovial membrane in patients with rheumatoid arthritis (RA) undergoing total knee replacement demonstrated significantly reduced inflammatory cell density and reduced synovial villi compared with nonirradiated areas of the knee joint.[59]

17.5.2.2 Hand osteoarthritis and rheumatoid arthritis

Studies of effects of laser on both forms of arthritis have been performed. Two reviews[60–62] and an overview of the reviews[60] found moderate evidence of efficacy with caveats on the dosages used. The Ottawa Panel, in particular, pointed out the methodological flaw of using the contralateral hand as a placebo in LLLT trials because of the systemic effects of lasers. One recent study by Meireles et al.[63] found positive but limited effects, although they reported the outcome as negative. The dosages used by Meireles were found to be subtherapeutic, as shown by Tuner and Hode,[64] a common finding among many studies of LLLT.[65,66] The WALT recommendations for Class-3 B wavelengths from 780–860 nm for the treatment of interphalangeal or metacarpophalangeal joints at 1–2 points is 4 J and 2–4 points for the wrist, for a total of 8 J.[67]

17.5.2.3 Gout and other crystallopathies

Crystalline-induced arthropathies include uric acid deposition in gout, calcium pyrophosphate dihydrate (DCPP) in pseudogout, and hydroxyapatite in calcific tendonitis. One small clinical trial suggests the potential of LLLT (904 nm, average power of 40 mW) to reduce pain in acute gouty arthritis.[68] A series of animal experiments provides strong evidence of specific, anti-inflammatory effects of a HeNe laser (632.8 nm, ~5 mW) induced by urate,[68,69] DCPP,[70,71] and hydroxyapatite crystals.[72] In these studies, markers of inflammation such as TNFα, plasma fibrinogen levels, and PGE_2 were reduced to control levels in laser-treated animals. Levels were also found to be equivalent to Meloxicam, an anti-inflammatory NSAID used clinically.

17.5.2.4 Neck pain

Neck pain is one of the most common painful conditions encountered in musculoskeletal medicine, and LLLT is one of the most evidence-based therapies for it.[73] The effectiveness of LLT against neck pain may result from the more superficial nature of the anatomical structures, which are within the penetration depths of most laser wavelengths. Neural blockade will affect the medial branch of the dorsal ramus to the facet joints, the target of radio-frequency ablation, or the occipital nerve at the base of the skull, often the cause of headaches. A reduction in neck-muscle spasms, including the trapezius, will improve mobility. Anti-inflammatory effects will be relevant to enthesitis such as at the insertion of the levator scapulae and facet joints. Guidelines suggest that treating neck pain with infrared diode lasers (780–860 nm) should include up to 12 points overlying the most-affected lateral articular pillars and muscle bellies with tender points, such as trapezius and sternomastoid muscles, with a minimum of 4 J/point. The frequency of treatment can vary from daily to twice a week, depending on the severity of pain, delivered over 3 to 4 weeks.

17.5.2.5 Back pain

Back pain is among the most costly of conditions both economically and in terms of poor quality of life in the individual. In the lumbar region, the anatomical structures that are targets of treatment, such as facet joints and neural foramina, are much deeper than in the neck, and therefore the dose regimes will be different from those of more superficial structures. Entheses around the sacro-iliac joint and the low lumbar region, such as the ilio-lumbar and thoraco-lumbar fascia, are often implicated in chronic back pain and are accessible to LLLT, as are the paravertebral muscles.[74] In back pain associated with failed back surgery, the problem can be conceptualized as a "soft-ware" versus "hard-ware" problem. In this conceptualization of the pathophysiology, LLLT cannot alter the bone structures, but reducing inflammation at entheses and reducing muscle spasm can have a profound effect in pain reduction, even in entrenched painful conditions. The spectrum ranges from acute first presentations of back pain to the end stages of failed-back-surgery syndrome. In acute back pain, two trials have demonstrated efficacy,[75,76] including radicular pain.[77] For chronic low back pain, a case series[78] and several trials[79–87] have demonstrated positive outcomes extending over two decades. The most recent Cochrane review[88] was, however, found to be "inconclusive." Comments by Jan Bjordal were added to the review that recorded his objection to the conclusion given that 5 out of 6 RCTs had acceptable methodology and had partly or fully positive outcomes yet did not merit a positive conclusion. Bjordal et al. have also challenged the negative findings of the conclusions of an overview of systematic reviews of LLLT in back pain by Chou and Huffman.[89] They identified several methodological shortcomings in their analysis, showing that there is indeed moderate evidence of efficacy of LLLT in treating chronic nonspecific back pain.[90] This is illustrative of the widespread problem of handling technological data with which reviewers are unfamiliar when evaluating evidence for nonpharmacological therapies such as LLLT.[91,92] Distilling from the studies, the WALT dose recommendations for the treatment of back pain using a 904-nm laser with a peak pulse output of 1 W, mean output >5 mW, and power density of >5 mW/cm^2 involve treating at least four points, delivering 4 J/point.[93] For wavelengths of class-3 B lasers from 780–860 nm, the recommendation for treatment is eight points, with a minimum of 4 J/point.[67]

17.5.2.6 Shoulder pain

There are fewer studies of LLLT in shoulder conditions, but there is sufficient evidence to initiate a trial of LLLT especially where other treatments have failed or patients do not want to undergo corticosteroid injection, which has limited evidence of efficacy and greater evidence of harm.[94] Conditions for which there are positive outcomes include shoulder tendinitis,[95] adhesive capsulitis,[96] frozen shoulder,[97] and myofascial pain of the shoulder girdle.[98] One study with a negative outcome was found to have administered inadequate dosage due to an inadequately measured device.[65,99]

17.5.2.7 Tendinopathy and enthesitis

A "classical" tendinopathy is Achilles tendinopathy. The pathophysiological basis for tendinopathy has swung from being regarded as inflammatory in origin, and then degenerative, and again to having an inflammatory basis.[100] Bjordal et al.[101] demonstrated unequivocally that tendinopathy, at least in an activated state, has inflammation as a component of the pathophysiology. Evidence of the effectiveness of LLLT in tendinopathies is equivocal on the basis of a substantial number of negative trials. Tumilty's review of the literature demonstrated that positive outcomes in tendinopathy are critically dependent on the power density (<100 mW/cm^2), more so than any other parameter.[102] These findings have now been reflected in the WALT guidelines. Given the dual nature of pathophysiology, it is likely that both anti-inflammatory and tissue-healing mechanisms occur in LLLT in tendinopathy.

17.5.2.8 *Lateral epicondylitis*

Tennis elbow is an enthesitis, which is archetypal of all enthesopathies in that pain arises from the insertion of a muscle to the periosteum at the lateral epicondyle, which is aggravated by use of the forearm. Both tendons and entheses (and teeth) attach to the periosteum by a network of Sharpey's fibers, which are collagen fibers active in the metabolism of the underlying bone that enable the stress of muscle contractions to be transmitted to a limb and movement of a joint.[103] Inflammation can occur as a result of the microtrauma and injury at this junction. As with tendinopathies, both tissue-repair stimulation and anti-inflammatory activity are important mechanisms of LLLT in these conditions. A review of the literature shows a moderate benefit when the appropriate dose guidelines are observed.[104]

17.5.2.9 Trigger point and myofascial pain

Myofascial pain syndrome and associated trigger points are a common cause of widespread musculoskeletal pain,[27] including headache,[105] shoulder pain,[106] groin pain,[107] and back pain.[108] LLLT effects on muscle and trigger points have been demonstrated with both infrared and visible wavelengths. LLLT (632.50 nm, 0.95 mW) decreased pain in patients with neck and back trigger points;[79] NIR (904 nm) reduced pressure-point tenderness in trapezius-muscle trigger points;[109] GaAlAs (780 nm, 25 J/cm^2 and 60 J/cm^2) reduced jaw pain in masseter muscles;[110] 670 nm (cw, 15 mW) improved masseter muscle contraction in patients with orofacial pain;[111] and 808 nm (10 0mW, ED: 70J/cm^2) increased the pressure pain threshold in masseter muscles and remained for 30 days after treatment.[112] The effects of laser on muscle and trigger point activity show several important responses relevant to clinical response: red laser (660 nm, cw, 9 J/cm^2) reduced end-plate noise (EPN) from myofascial trigger points (MTrP) in rabbit skeletal muscle;[113] and 660 nm increased muscle cytochrome c oxidase.[114] Two studies examined the effects of end-plate-potential lasers on the neuromuscular junctions of mouse diaphragms, with 655 nm showing no effect[115] and 830 nm (12 J/cm^2) reducing the amplitudes, suggesting decreased acetylcholine release.[116]

17.5.2.10 Neuropathic pain

Neuropathic pain occurs as a result of injury to an underlying nerve. Conditions such as trigeminal neuralgia, post-herpetic neuralgia, diabetic neuropathy, and carpal tunnel syndrome are examples of neuropathic pain. Even in conditions such as back pain, neuropathic pain is estimated to occur in up to 40% of patients. Those apparently musculoskeletal conditions where hyperalgesia and allodynia are present, such as whiplash-associated disorder (WAD) and fibromyalgia, where central sensitization is present but there is no single identifiable nerve pathology, all have the characteristics of neuropathic pain and need to be treated as such. Neuropathic pain conditions are often very sensitive to lasers and can be easily aggravated by too-aggressive treatment.

There are only two controlled trials for post-herpetic neuralgia, one evaluating long-term effects,[117] and the other investigating the immediate analgesic effect of LLLT on PHN.[118] There are, however, several case series and case reports that provide a guide to treating a condition that is difficult to control, and adjunctive treatment is potentially valuable.[119–128] Visible (632.5 nm) and infrared (830 nm, 904 nm) wavelengths are used in either a scanning or point-by-point treatment over the affected dermatome, repeated on several occasions. Occasional worsening of pain is reported. Age more than 60 years and truncal PHN are poorer prognostic factors. Treatment must have a low dose and short duration with light or minimal pressure.

Trigeminal neuralgia has also been evaluated in several small trials.[129–131] Supporting animal experiments show a suppression of neural activity in the trigeminal nucleus following the application of laser light to the face. This behavior suggests that the neural-blockade effect of laser is operative.[132,133] A small randomized and controlled study of diabetic neuropathy using 905-nm light for 5 minutes approached but did not reach significance for relief of pain.[134] Another study demonstrated improved conduction velocity in peroneal, sural, and tibial nerves affected by diabetic neuropathy, with patients acting as their own control.[135] This study used two wavelengths simultaneously—808 nm and 904 nm—applied over the nerve root exit at L4 to S1 and four points along the sciatic nerve. The study did not assess pain.

Carpal tunnel syndrome is a common neuropathy treated with LLLT. A review of seven studies suggests that LLLT is a promising, cost-effective treatment.[136] Since that review, there have been several additional studies that have favorable outcomes when compared with sham lasers,[137] splinting,[138] surgery,[139] ultrasound and pulsed magnetic fields,[140] and in patients with rheumatoid arthritis.[141] A recent study did not show any functional difference, but LLLT improved median nerve conduction.[142]

17.5.2.11 Lymphedema

Lymphedema is the extravasation of high-protein fluid into tissues, compared to low-protein fluid in acute edema. It can be primary, which is genetic in origin, or secondary, most commonly following surgical dissection and the removal of lymph nodes. Treatment with LLLT of upper-arm lymphedema after mastectomy for breast cancer is effective in reducing limb volume, tissue hardness, and pain.[143] The US FDA has approved a single laser device (LTU-904, 904 nm, 5 mW) for LLLT of lymphedema.[144] Treatment with this wavelength has been found to be cost-effective[143,145] and equivalent to pneumatic compression.[146] A review of five small studies of acceptable methodology has also demonstrated a benefit at a dose of 1–2 J/cm^2 per point applied to several points covering the fibrotic area.[147] A single animal experiment demonstrated the stimulation of lymphatic regeneration where normal structural reorganization occurred in wounds following combined 632.8-nm and 904-nm LLLT compared with controls.[25]

17.5.2.12 Post-operative pain

There is a small but seminal study of post-operative pain following open cholecystectomy. Moore applied a 830-nm, 60-mW cw laser for 6–8 minutes immediately following wound closure, which resulted in significantly decreased post-operative drug use.[148] Dental studies have also demonstrated significant pain relief when administered within two hours of surgery using a HeNe laser (~5 mW, 1.8 J delivered over 3 minutes);[149] 809 nm (7.5 J) for 24 h following endodontic surgery[150] and following a CO_2 laser used for gingivectomy.[151] A recent systematic review found beneficial effects on trismus but not pain in post-operative dental surgery, so confusion around the optimal dosage for post-operative pain relief remains.[152]

17.6 Pre-treatment Pain Relief

Pre-treatment with a laser for surgery can reduce pain. Several examples of such preventative effects are found in both animal and human studies. Pre-treatment reduced orofacial pain in rats following a formalin test,[153] and an Er:YAG laser used before cavity preparation in a pediatric population showed significant reduction in pain during the procedure in two small studies.[154,155] Painful oral mucositis associated with chemotherapy can be prevented by laser pre-treatment.[156]

There are several potential mechanisms underlying effective pre-treatment with LI to reduce pain or diminish the effects of chemotherapy on oral mucosa. LI inhibits the nociceptive response, reducing the release of pro-inflammatory neuropeptides such as substance P, and limits peripheral sensitization, which modulates the inflammatory cascade, prior to a noxious stimulus. Another mechanism may relate to the stabilization of mast cells. Mast-cell degranulation, which occurs with injury, can also be dampened by pre-treatment with LI preventing further sensitization of nociceptors.[157] At a systemic level, pre-irradiation of blood with 830-nm light reduced the pain response in rats by enhancing peripheral endogenous opioids.[36] Honmura et al.[158] found that inflammatory edema was reduced with 780-nm light (10 mW, PD: 31.8 J/cm^2) but only when administered before and after the noxious stimulus.

The range of conditions mentioned in this section is not exhaustive. Many conditions are amenable to a trial of LLLT, even in the absence of high levels of evidence, largely because of the safety profile of LLLT, where no serious events have been reported in any studies.

17.7 Unique Effects of LLLT on Pain

A unique property of LLLT is that all the mechanisms thus described occur concurrently. Conceptually and practically, this behavior is very different from pharmacological therapies, where a drug has a single action on a single molecular target, which affects every cell, often causing multiple side effects while having a limited benefit. For example, COX inhibitors have an inflammatory effect in a target tissue but can equally affect the gut and kidney, thereby mitigating the beneficial effects. Moreover, addressing a single pathophysiological component of a painful condition, for example, inflammation in knee OA, is often of limited benefit as pain can arise from muscles, ligaments, and entheses externally, as well as intra-articular pathology. A modality with several mechanisms of action has many advantages over single-mechanism drug options.

17.8 Practical Considerations

For the successful clinical application of LLLT beyond the confines of randomized, controlled trials, knowledge of the patient will be a large factor in determining the outcomes of pragmatic treatment. LLLT for pain should be administered as part of holistic management following a full clinical evaluation, including differential diagnosis and appropriate investigation. As a corollary, however, MRI or x-ray findings are largely irrelevant to the outcomes of LLLT, apart from excluding potentially serious disease. "Treat the patient and not the x-ray" is a primary tenant of clinical LLLT. The ease of application of LLLT may provide a false sense that everything is amenable to treatment.

17.8.1 Example: treating knee osteoarthritis

The treatment of knee osteoarthritis provides an example of how the full repertoire of mechanisms is operationalized in "real-life" management. In knee pain associated with osteoarthritis, there will be an inflammatory component that involves the synovium and possibly the bursa of the pes anserineus: a mechanical component where both medial and lateral collateral ligaments are often strained due to abnormal forces on the knee; a muscle spasm in hamstring and quadriceps muscles that occurs to protect the joint; enthesitis at the muscle insertions; or a joint effusion. LLLT can modify each of these elements within an osteoarthritic knee. The same principles can also be applied to all joints and most other nociceptive conditions. The anti-inflammatory action of lasers will be effective at the synovial surface as well as at entheses at the insertion of ligaments. The neural-blockade effect will occur at all tender points, causing inhibition in the peripheral endings of nociceptors that are present in the most superficial layers of skin as well as the deep nerve tracts. This action will further dampen inflammation arising from nerve endings, i.e., so-called "neurogenic inflammation." Clinically, the interaction between neural blockade and anti-inflammatory effects will then down-regulate the peripheral sensitization that occurs in injury and inflammation. Treatment of tender points and trigger points in muscle bellies will reduce spasms, thus increasing joint mobility and improving exercise tolerance. The motoricity of lymphatics in the local area will also increase so that interstitial edema and effusions will improve, again improving mobility. This technique can be coupled with treating the inguinal lymphatics to increase lymphatic clearance in the whole limb. The cells involved in tissue repair—including

macrophages, neutrophils and fibroblasts—will be activated. Even chondrocyte activity can be increased so that ultimately some cartilage repair can
occur.[159,160]

Repeated treatment is cumulative so that over a number of treatments the
patient experiences reduced pain, reduced swelling, and improved function.
The patient can resume exercise, lose weight, and reduce medication. If the
joint has an advanced disease, a course of treatment may not control
symptoms permanently, so a "maintenance program" that keeps inflammation, pain, and swelling under control is a reasonable option. Under these
circumstances and in elderly patients in whom surgery is not indicated and in
whom drugs cause serious side effects, the option of seeing patients once every
4–6 weeks is a safe and cost-effective option.

17.8.2 Factors influencing outcomes

The deceptively simple application of LLLT belies the complexity of multiple
factors that influence the clinical outcome. These factors can be divided into
four groups: laser parameters, treatment protocols, and patient and disease
factors and are summarized in Table 17.1.

The interaction of these factors contributes to its complexity and explains
why the outcomes of randomized controlled trials (RCTs) can be so variable.
The response to LLLT will depend on the nature of the problem; the site of
the pathology; the available wavelength; and the sensitivity, tolerance, and
responsiveness of the patient, including the melanin content of the skin.

Table 17.1 Factors affecting treatment outcomes.

Laser Factors	Treatment Protocols	Patient factors		Disease Factors
		Skin pigmentation	More melanin requires larger dose	
		Obesity	More fat means less penetration	
		Age	• Young, healthy	
			• Older, frail	
		Medication	• Steroids	
			• Calcium channel blockers	
Wavelength:	Frequency	Nervous system	• Facilitated mode	Duration of
• Red	of Rx:	state (related to pain)	(e.g., fibromyalgia)	condition:
• NIR	• Daily		• Normal mode	• Acute
	• Twice daily		• Repressed mode	• Subacute
	• Weekly			• Chronic
		Genetics of pain	• Personality traits	
		modulation and	• Anxiety	
		epigenetics of pain	• Catastrophizing	
		Clinical condition	• Acute	
		duration	• Subacute	
			• Chronic	
		Social factors	• "Yellow flags"	
			• Compensation injuries	

17.9 Laser Factors

17.9.1 Wavelength

The evidence strongly suggests that NIR lasers are the most effective at treating musculoskeletal pain, likely because of the greater penetration depth of these lasers and the deeper structures that are the treatment targets in many conditions. Visible lasers with shallower penetration depths are used for more superficial wound healing, anti-inflammatory effects, and tissue repair. Transcutaneous NIR lasers, as well as visible LI, also inhibit underlying nerves causing neural blockade, so the use of both wavelengths in pain management is supported via that mechanism.

17.9.2 Correct dose

What laser therapy has in common with drug therapies is the need for an appropriate "dose" to be delivered to achieve optimal outcomes. The complexity and challenge of the clinical application of laser therapy, whatever the indication, is to achieve the "correct" dose in any one patient for a specific condition. When applying a laser clinically and not within the confines of research, the patient's response to treatment will guide the "dose." But what is the dose? Is it the total number of joules? The energy density? The power density? These questions have been outlined in several papers and continue to be the subject of ongoing discussion.[49] Tendinopathy, for example, appears sensitive to the power density used because more than 100 mW/cm^2 will not be effective. Wound healing is sensitive to energy density, with 1–4 J/cm^2 being most effective and >8 J/cm^2 inhibitory. This biphasic response to LLLT, where small doses of laser are stimulatory and large doses are inhibitory, manifests at a cellular level up to a whole-person level and are relevant across all the clinical applications of LLLT, including pain.[161,162] These limits are very important in research, but a pragmatic approach needs to be adopted in the clinic because the dosage window can be relatively wide. The World Association of Laser Therapy (WALT) has published guidelines for several wavelengths, which are a good starting point. Ultimately, the patient's response is an important guide to dosage.

17.9.3 Application technique

Contact pressure is the degree of pressure applied with the probe in contact with skin. Pressure will temporarily decrease the amount of blood circulating in the target area and reduce the distance between skin and target tissue, especially in obese patients, allowing more photons to reach the site of pathology. This will of course not be an issue in superficial conditions. Several considerations dictate the amount of pressure applied during treatment. If pain is very severe or a very tender area is identified, then pressure should not be so great as to cause pain, which would not only increase the discomfort of the patient but also stimulate nociceptors (the antithesis of what LLLT aims to achieve, i.e., to silence nociceptors). The depth of the target tissue is another consideration because sufficient pressure ensures that enough photons reach the target tissue. Here, a compromise between pain and pressure needs to be reached. Sometimes a tender area will gradually be less painful during the laser application, and that will be an indicator of adequate treatment.

17.9.4 Treatment protocol

The frequency at which laser therapy is given and the duration of each session is dependent on the nature of the condition. As with dose, this aspect is guided to a large extent by patient response. In general, acute conditions can be treated more frequently than chronic conditions. For acute treatments, a rule of thumb is to deliver treatment three times in the first week, twice in the second, and once in the third week, and then once a fortnight, if necessary. When the patient starts to experience fewer symptoms, treatment frequency should decrease. For chronic conditions, treatment can be delivered more slowly: twice a week for the first two weeks, and then once a week for 2–4 weeks, depending on dose.

As tissue approaches "normality," it is possible that too-frequent treatments will have less favorable outcomes with an increase in pain after treatment.

17.9.5 Length of treatment

Patients often want to cease treatment as soon as pain is relieved; however, reduced pain early in treatment does not indicate tissue repair, which may take several weeks for full recovery. Many patients are often very surprised that they can have no or little pain but have widespread tenderness. While there is tissue tenderness patients may easily reactivate the injury and should take care to avoid those activities which activate pain. Achieving pain relief with no tenderness to palpation is the ideal, but it may not be practicable, or indeed possible, to treat patients until all tissue tenderness resolves. Treatment courses can vary; however, between six to ten treatments is suggested as an appropriate course. Follow-up a month after completion is often worthwhile to assess the tissue sensitivity.

17.10 Patient Factors

Evidence now exists that a number of patient factors will alter the laser dose required to achieve a positive outcome, including skin pigmentation, where greater melanin content necessitates a greater dose.[163,164] Similarly, the greater the amount of adipose tissue between the skin and target tissue, the greater the dose required to reach the target. The state of a patient's "pain" setting, i.e., whether they exhibit hyperalgesia and allodynia, may indicate a lowered pain threshold and thus the need for a lighter touch and a lower dose of the initial laser applications.

17.11 Disease Factors

Not all conditions will be responsive to LLLT. Conditions that involve mechanical factors, such as nerve root compression with neurological symptoms, are not likely to respond to LLLT. The presence of hyperalgesia and allodynia is an indicator of central sensitization and underlying changes in the spinal cord, which render the need for treatment at a lower dose and "light touch," as even light touch can aggravate the underlying symptoms. One of the goals of therapy is to reverse these changes by decreasing the nociceptive input over time to induce "long-term depression" (LTD) of pain. In most conditions, after serious disease is excluded, a therapeutic trial with a low threshold for cessation can be considered if there is lack of progress. As a corollary, if a condition is unresponsive to LLLT, it may be regarded as a "red flag" for further investigation.

17.12 Goals of Treatment

In "real-life" practice, where patients present with a variety of conditions of varying severity in different age groups, a pragmatic approach must be taken to outcomes that will be as varied as the patients and conditions. The patient should be aware of the likely outcomes and establish realistic goals. It is the outcome that the patient wants that will identify how to manage the therapeutic process, which should be identified early in the process. Is the patient an athlete who needs to compete after an injury? An elderly patient who wants to have less disturbed sleep? Someone who has an injury and needs to return to the workplace as soon as possible? Each of these individuals will have different therapeutic goals, and LLLT must be tailored to that outcome.

17.12.1 Monotherapy versus adjunctive treatment

The pragmatic approach to using LLLT in clinical applications determines whether it will be a monotherapy or an adjunct to other treatments. "Cure" is desirable but often unachievable in patients with chronic disease. In many circumstances, patients will be satisfied if they can return to a particular activity even if they continue to experience some pain. Patients may not be able to abandon all analgesics, especially opioids or pain-modulators, but their use may be significantly reduced. The use of LLLT as a drug-sparing treatment reduces side effects, costs, and tolerance (particularly to opioids), and can mitigate the development of opioid-induced hyperalgesia. Use of a "home" laser as an interval treatment, where patients continue to use lasers of lower doses to extend the time between treatments or to reinforce the treatment, is also an option for many patients. For some patients, LLLT can facilitate their moving to a more active exercise program and be used for flare-ups as they progress through rehabilitation.

17.13 Patients Unresponsive to LLLT

Patient and disease factors are the most likely reason why patients do not respond to LLLT. This tenet assumes that laser factors have been evaluated and that basic principles, such as checking the output of the laser device, changing wavelengths or increasing (or decreasing) frequency of treatment have been undertaken. The condition may not respond to treatment, or symptoms are too widespread to treat cost effectively. Patients' expectations may exceed the reality of the treatment, and they may not wish to continue with treatment if there is not an immediate response. Drugs may inhibit the response to laser light, including corticosteroids, which have been demonstrated in animal studies to inhibit laser effects. Calcium channel blockers, e.g., nifedipine, have also been demonstrated to interfere with the effects of laser light because laser modulates calcium channel activity and mediates the intracellular response to photons.[165]

17.14 Practice Points

The simplicity of laser application is one of the great advantages of LLLT, but the selection of the appropriate treatment sites is a practical challenge for successful treatment. The aim is to deliver enough photons to the most clinically relevant sites for the condition being treated to initiate a tissue response that will lead to pain relief and healing. In general terms, treatment strategies for all musculoskeletal conditions can be summarized as follows:

- Treat locally at sites of tenderness. Treat the most tender areas first, starting with the most tender points and working systematically around the area. Treat all aspects of the joint or pathology. 1–2 J per point is a safe and reasonable start. Experimental studies indicate that the neural-blockade effect takes approximately 10 minutes; however, for wound healing and tissue repair, delivery of up to 4 J/cm^2 (ED) or up to 100 mW/cm^2 (PD) is a more appropriate way to deliver the correct dose.
- Treat tender structures within the dermatome, myotome, and sclerotome in the nerve root distribution of the primary problem, including three levels above and two below.
- Treat the spine at the level of the nerve root distribution of the pathology, including the spinous processes, where the dorsal branch of the posterior ramus becomes very superficial, and over the nerve root exits.
- Treat the lymphatics, which drain the primary site, when there is significant swelling associated with injury or inflammation or when the

patient complains of tightness or puffiness. Activating the lymphatics will reduce edema.

- Do the "triple test" (T×3) to assess progress during treatment where possible. Test a movement or tenderness to palpation before treatment (T1), treat for an appropriate time (T2), and then test again (T3). If there is a change in the "test," then enough laser has been delivered to that area. This process can be repeated several times during a treatment session.

17.15 "Tip of the Iceberg" Principle

Patients are often surprised to see the extent of tender areas beyond the primary site of pain, where they have no pain. The primary site is "the tip of the iceberg," but a whole limb might exhibit widespread tenderness on examination. The convergence in the dorsal horn of sensory afferents from painful sites synapsing with motor neurons and interneurons results in the enlargement of the receptive field of an injury, so that changes in sensation, lowered pain thresholds, and muscle spasm occur in uninjured areas outside the primary site. The therapeutic consequence of this behavior is the importance of examining the whole dermatome, myotome, and sclerotome of the affected segment. For example, in knee OA or lateral epicondylitis, all of the muscle attachments (at the periosteum) and the muscle bellies should be examined, as well as the joint or the entheses, and the most tender areas should be treated even if the patient is not experiencing pain from these sites.

17.16 Prognostic Factors

Abnormal imaging findings do not preclude a good response to laser therapy unless there are "red flags" that need further investigation. Equally, the severity of pain or dysfunction does not preclude a good response, and a trial of therapy is reasonable. There is no evidence that older patients respond less well to LLLT, but given that there are likely to be other co-morbidities with increasing age, there may be less expectation of complete pain relief. In this scenario, however, LLLT has a place in ongoing maintenance treatment with the goal of keeping analgesic drugs to a minimum, and maintaining mobility is a primary goal. It is the response to treatment that will be the best indicator of positive outcomes. The more rapid response to treatment is a positive prognostic indicator of successful outcome.

17.17 Side Effects of Treatment

The side effects of LLLT are relatively infrequent and minor in nature. When reported, nausea, fatigue, and exacerbation of pain for 1–2 days after treatment are the most common. Kert and Rose have provided a detailed outline of patterns of pain following treatment, which they suggest reflects differing responses to treatment, depending on the type and chronicity of the pain.[166]

17.18 Conclusion

LLLT is a modality with a long history and strong evidence to support its use in pain. It is not a miracle treatment but can achieve good pain relief in a spectrum of conditions, especially where other treatments have failed. It has few side effects and is tolerated well by older patients. It can be used as monotherapy or as adjunctive therapy, where it can play a role in drug sparing or facilitating rehabilitation. The range of conditions able to be treated is wide. It requires some technical expertise and knowledge, but for most doctors, physiotherapists, and allied health professionals it is easy to learn and incorporate in day-to-day practice. Successful outcomes, like all medical management, depend on good clinical skills combined with an understanding of the nature of the pain and mechanisms of laser effects. Laser medicine has the potential to be as well known as laser surgery and become a stand-alone specialty in mainstream medicine.

References

1. T. Maiman, "Stimulated Optical Radiation in Ruby," *Nature* **187**, 493 (1960).
2. M. Belkin, B. Zaturunsky, and S. M., "A critical review of low energy laser bioeffects," *Lasers and Light in Ophthalmology* **2**, 63–71 (1988).
3. L. Navratil and I. Dylevsky, "Mechanisms of the analgesic effect of therapeutic lasers *in vivo*," *Laser Ther.* **9**, 33–39 (1997).
4. A. Schindl, M. Schindl, H. Pernerstorfer-Schon, and L. Schindl, "Low-intensity laser therapy: a review," *J. Investig. Med.* **48**, 312–326 (2000).
5. IASP Task Force on Taxonomy, *Classification of Chronic Pain, Part III: Pain Terms, A Current List with Definitions and Notes on Usage*, IASP Press, Seattle, WA (1994).
6. P. J. Siddall and M. J. Cousins, "Persistent pain as a disease entity: implications for clinical management," *Anesth. Analg.* **99**, 510–520 (2004).
7. R.-R. Ji, T. Kohno, K. A. Moore, and C. J. Cwoolf, "Central sensitisation and LTP: do pain and memory share similar mechanisms?" *Trends in Neuroscience* **26**, 696–706 (2003).
8. L. Arendt-Nielsen and T. Graven-Nielsen, "Central sensitisation in fibromyalgia and other musculoskeletal disorders," *Current Pain and Headache Reports* **7**, 355–361 (2003).

9. X. G. Liu, C. R. Morton, J. J. Azkue, M. Zimmermann, and J. Sandkuhler, "Long-term depression of C-fibre-evoked spinal field potentials by stimulation of primary afferent A delta-fibres in the adult rat," *Eur. J. Neurosci.* **10**, 3069–75 (1998).

10. A. Chan, P. Armati, and A. P. Moorthy, "Pulsed Nd: YAG laser induces pulpal analgesia: a randomized clinical trial," *J. Dent. Res.* **91**, 79S–84S (2012).

11. W. Yan, R. Chow, and P. Armati, "Inhibitory effects of visible 650 nm and infrared 808 nm laser irradiation on somatosensory and motor compound action potentials in rat sciatic nerve: implications for pain modulation by low-level laser therapy," *Journal of the Peripheral Nervous System*, in press (2010).

12. R. Chow, P. Armati, E. L. Laakso, J. M. Bjordal, and G. D. Baxter, "Inhibitory effects of laser irradiation on peripheral mammalian nerves and relevance to analgesic effects: a systematic review," *Photomed. Laser Surg.* **29**, 365–81 (2011).

13. E. M. Laraia et al., "Effect of low-level laser therapy (660 nm) on acute inflammation induced by tenotomy of Achilles tendon in rats," *Photochem. Photobiol.* **88**, 1546–50 (2012).

14. F. Bortone et al., "Low level laser therapy modulates kinin receptors mRNA expression in the subplantar muscle of rat paw subjected to carrageenan-induced inflammation," *Int. Immunopharmacol.* **8**, 206–10 (2008).

15. A. C. Prianti et al., "Low-level laser therapy (LLLT) reduces the COX-2 mRNA expression in both subplantar and total brain tissues in the model of peripheral inflammation induced by administration of carrageenan," *Lasers Med. Sci.* (2014).

16. K. Mizutani et al., "A clinical study on serum Prostaglandin E2 with low-level laser therapy," *Photomedicine and Laser Surgery* **22**, 537–539 (2004).

17. R. Albertini et al., "Effects of different protocol doses of low power gallium–aluminum–arsenate (Ga–Al–As) laser radiation (650 nm) on carrageenan induced rat paw oedema," *Journal of Photochemistry and Photobiology B: Biology* **27**, 101–107 (2004).

18. R. C. Pallotta et al., Infrared (810-nm) low-level laser therapy on rat experimental knee inflammation. *Lasers Med. Sci.* (2011).

19. F. P. Carlos et al., "Protective effect of low-level laser therapy (LLLT) on acute zymosan-induced arthritis," *Lasers Med. Sci.* **29**, 757–63 (2014).

20. D. Ferreira et al., "Analgesic Effect of He-Ne (632.8nm) Low -Level Laser Therapy on Acute Inflammation Pain," *Photomedicine and Laser Surgery* **23**, 177–181 (2005).

21. A. Shimotoyodome et al., "Improvement of macromolecular clearance via lymph flow in hamster gingiva by low-power carbon dioxide laser-irradiation," *Lasers Surg. Med.* **29**, 442–7 (2001).

22. D. Meneguzzo et al., "Prevention and treatment of mice paw edema by near-infrared low-level laser therapy on lymph nodes," *Lasers Med. Sci.* **28**, 973–80 (2013).

23. M. H. Aras and M. Gungormus, "Placebo-controlled randomized clinical trial of the effect two different low-level laser therapies (LLLT)–intraoral and extraoral–on trismus and facial swelling following surgical extraction of the lower third molar," *Lasers Med. Sci.* **25**, 641–5 (2010).

24. A. Markovic and L. Todorovic, "Effectiveness of dexamethasone and low-power laser in minimizing oedema after third molar surgery: a clinical trial," *Int. J. Oral Maxillofac. Surg.* **36**, 226–9 (2007).

25. P. C Lievens, "The effect of a combined HeNe and I.R. laser treatment on the regeneration of the lymphatic system during the process of wound healing," *Lasers in Medical Science* **6**, 193–199 (1991).

26. E. D. Lavelle, W. Lavelle, and H. S. Smith, "Myofascial trigger points," *Med. Clin. North Am.* **91**, 229–39 (2007).

27. R. D. Gerwin, "Diagnosis of Myofascial Pain Syndrome," *Phys. Med. Rehabil. Clin. N. Am.* **25**, 341–355 (2014).

28. D. G. Simons, "New views of myofascial trigger points: etiology and diagnosis," *Arch. Phys. Med. Rehabil.* **89**, 157–9 (2008).

29. E. Mester, B. Szende, T. Spiry, and A. Scher, "Stimulation of Wound Healing by Laser Rays," *Acta Chirurgica Academiae Scientiarum Hungaricae* **13**, 315–324 (1972).

30. N. Hemvani, D. S. Chitinis, and N. S. Bhagwanai, "Effect of Helium-Neon Laser on Cultured Human Macrophages," *Laser Therapy* **10**, 159–164 (1998).

31. A. C. Alves et al., "Effect of low-level laser therapy on the expression of inflammatory mediators and on neutrophils and macrophages in acute joint inflammation," *Arthritis Res. Ther.* **15**, R116 (2013).

32. C. H. Chen, H. S. Hung, and S. H. Hsu, "Low-energy laser irradiation increases endothelial cell proliferation, migration, and eNOS gene expression possibly via PI3K signal pathway," *Lasers Surg. Med.* **40**, 46–54 (2008a).

33. C. A. Damante et al., "Effect of laser phototherapy on the release of fibroblast growth factors by human gingival fibroblasts," *Lasers Med. Sci.* **24**, 885–91 (2009).

34. Y. Yamamoto et al., "Effect of low-power laser irradiation on procollagen synthesis in human fibroblasts," *Journal of Clinical Laser Medicine & Surgery* **14**, 129–132 (1996).

35. A. F. Rico, M. T. L. Manzanares, and M. L. Claros, "ß-Endorphin Response in Blood and Cerebrospinal Fluid after Single and Multiple Irradiation with HeNe and GaAs Low-Power Laser," *Journal of Clinical Laser Medicine and Surgery* **12**, 1–6 (1994).

36. S. Hagiwara, H. Iwasaka, A. Hasegawa, and T. Noguchi, "Pre-Irradiation of blood by gallium aluminum arsenide (830 nm) low-level laser enhances peripheral endogenous opioid analgesia in rats," *Anesth. Analg.* **107**, 1058–63 (2008).

37. E. Laakso, T. Cramond, C. Richardson, and J. Galligan, "Plasma ACTH and Beta-endorphin levels in response to low-level laser therapy (LLLT) for myofascial trigger points," *Laser Ther.* **6**, 133–142 (1994).

38. Y. Ceylan, S. Hizmetli, and Y. Silig, "The effects of infrared laser and medical treatments on pain and serotonin degradation products in patients with myofascial pain syndrome. A controlled trial," *Rheumatol. Int.* **24**, 260–3 (2004).

39. J. Walker, "Relief from chronic pain by low power laser irradiation," *Neurosci. Lett.* **43**, 339–44 (1983).

40. A. Gam, H. Thorsen, and F. Lonneberg, "The effect of low-level laser therapy on musculoskeletal pain: a meta-analysis," *Pain* **52**, 63–66 (1993).

41. R. De bie et al., "Efficacy of 904nm laser therapy in the management of musculoskeletal disorders: a systematic review," *Physical Therapy Reviews* **3**, 59–72 (1998).

42. R. Marks and F. de Palma, "Clinical efficacy of low power laser therapy in osteoarthritis," *Physiotherapy Research International* **4**, 141–157 (1999).

43. A. Schindl, M. Schindl, H. Permerstorfer-Schon, and L. Schindl, "Low-Intensity Laser Therapy: A review," *Journal of Investigative Dermatology* **48**, 312–326 (2000a).

44. C. S. Enwemeka et al., "The Efficacy of low-power lasers in tissue repair and pain control: a meta-analysis study," *Photomed. Laser Surg.* **22**, 323–329 (2004).

45. J. Bjordal, M. Johnson, V. Iverson, F. Aimbire, and R. Lopes-Martins, "Photoradiation in acute pain: A systematic review of possible mechanisms of action and clinical effects in randomized placebo-controlled trials," *Photomed. Laser Surgery* **24**, 158–168 (2006a).

46. H. Jang and H. Lee, "Meta-analysis of pain relief effects by laser irradiation on joint areas," *Photomed. Laser Surg.* **30**, 405–17 (2012).

47. J. Tuner and L. Hode, "It's all in the parameters: a critical analysis of some well-known negative studies on low-level laser therapy," *J. Clin. Laser Med. Surg.* **16**, 245–8 (1998).

48. R. Calderhead, "Watts a Joule: on the Importance of Accurate and Recording of Laser Parameters in Low Reactive-level Laser Therapy and Photobioactivation Research," *Laser Therapy* **3**, 177–182 (1991).

49. P. A. Jenkins and J. D. Carroll, "How to report low-level laser therapy (LLLT)/photomedicine dose and beam parameters in clinical and laboratory studies," *Photomed. Laser Surg.* **29**, 785–7 (2011).

50. National Institute for Health and Care Excellence, Osteoarthritis: the care and management of osteoarthritis in adults. London: National Institute for Health and Care Excellence, (2014).

51. R. Buchbinder and I. A. Harris, "Arthroscopy to treat osteoarthritis of the knee?," *Med. J. Aust.* **199**, 100 (2013).

52. A. D. Beswick et al., "What proportion of patients report long-term pain after total hip or knee replacement for osteoarthritis? A systematic review of prospective studies in unselected patients," *BMJ Open* **2**, e000435 (2012).

53. J. Bjordal, M. I. Johnson, R. A. Lopes-Martins, B. Bogen, R. Chow, and A. E. Ljunggren, "Short-term efficacy of physical interventions in osteoarthritic knee pain. A systematic review and meta-analysis of randomised placebo-controlled trials," *BMC Musculoskel. Dis.* **8**, 51 (2007).

54. B. Hegedus, L. Viharos, M. Gervain, and M. Galfi, "The effect of low-level laser in knee osteoarthritis: a double-blind, randomized, placebo-controlled trial," *Photomed. Laser Surg.* **27**, 577–84 (2009).

55. P. P. Alfredo et al., "Efficacy of low level laser therapy associated with exercises in knee osteoarthritis: a randomized double-blind study," *Clin. Rehabil.* **26**, 523–33 (2012).

56. K. Gworys et al., "Influence of various laser therapy methods on knee joint pain and function in patients with knee osteoarthritis," *Ortop. Traumatol. Rehabil.* **14**, 269–77 (2012).

57. R. C. Pallotta et al., "Infrared (810-nm) low-level laser therapy on rat experimental knee inflammation," *Lasers Med. Sci.* **27**, 71–8 (2012).

58. F. Kamali et al., "The therapeutic effect of low-level laser on repair of osteochondral defects in rabbit knee," *J. Photochem. Photobiol. B.* **88**, 11–5 (2007).

59. A. Amano et al., "Histological studies on the rheumatoid synovial membrane irradiated with a low energy laser," *Lasers Surg. Med.* **15**, 290–4 (1994).

60. A. Christie et al., "Effectiveness of nonpharmacological and nonsurgical interventions for patients with rheumatoid arthritis: an overview of systematic reviews," *Phys. Ther.* **87**, 1697–715 (2007).

61. L. Brosseau et al., "Low level laser therapy (Classes I, II and III) for treating rheumatoid arthritis. [Systematic Review]," Cochrane Musculo-skeletal Group Cochrane Database of Systematic Reviews 2 (2005).

62. Ottawa Panel (2004), "Evidence-based clinical practice guidelines for electrotherapy and thermotherapy interventions in the management of trheumatoid arthritis in adults," *Physical Therapy* **84**, 1016–1043 (2005).

63. S. M. Meireles, A. Jones, and J. Natour, "Low-level laser therapy on hands of patients with rheumatoid arthritis," *Clin. Rheumatol.* **30**, 147–8 (2011).

64. J. Tuner and L. Hode, "Low-level laser therapy for hand arthritis-fact or fiction?," Clin. Rheumatol. **29**, 1075–6 (2010).

65. J. M. Bjordal and G. D. Baxter, "Ineffective dose and lack of laser output testing in laser shoulder and neck studies," *Photomed. Laser Surg.* **24**, 533–4; author reply 534 (2006).

66. C. S. Enwemeka, "Intricacies of dose in laser phototherapy for tissue repair and pain relief," *Photomedicine and Laser Surgery* **27**, 387–393 (2009).

67. World Association of Laser Therapy, Recommended treatment doses for Low Level Laser Therapy: Class 3B 780–860nm (2010b).

68. F. Soriano et al., "Photobiomodulation of pain and inflammation in microcrystalline arthropathies: experimental and clinical results," *Photomed. Laser Surg.* **24**, 140–50 (WALT) (2006).

69. V. Campana et al., "Laser Therapy on Arthritis Induced by Urate Crystals," *Photomedicine and Laser Surgery* **22**, 499–503 (2004).

70. C. R. Rubio et al., "Helium-neon laser reduces the inflammatory process of arthritis," *Photomed. Laser Surg.* **28**, 125–9 (2010).

71. V. Campana et al., "He-Ne laser on microcrystalline arthropathies," *J. Clin. Laser Med. Surg.* **21**, 99–103 (2003).

72. V. Campana et al., "The relative effects of He-Ne laser and meloxicam on experimentally induced inflammation," *Laser Therapy* **11**, 36–42 (1999).

73. R. T. Chow, R. Lopes -Martins, M. Johnson, and J. M. Bjordal, "Efficacy of low-level laser therapy in the management of neck pain: a systematic review and meta-analysis of randomised, placebo and active treatment controlled trials," *Lancet.* **374**, 1897–1908 (2009).

74. M. Benjamin et al., "Where tendons and ligaments meet bone: attachment sites ('entheses') in relation to exercise and/or mechanical load," *J. Anat.* **208**, 471–90 (2006).

75. L. Longo, A. Tamburini, and A. Monti, "Treatment with 904nm and 10600nm laser of acute lumbago," *Journ. Eur. Med. Laser Ass.* **3**, 16–19 (1991).

76. M. Jovicic, L. Konstantinovic, M. Lazovic, and V. Jovicic, "Clinical and functional evaluation of patients with acute low back pain and radiculopathy treated with different energy doses of low level laser therapy," *Vojnosanit Pregl.* **69**, 656–62 (2012).

77. L. Konstantinovic et al., "Acute low back pain with radiculopathy: a double-blind, randomized, placebo-controlled study," *Photomed. Laser Surg.* **28**, 553–60 (2010).

78. T. Ohshiro and Y. Shirono, "Retroactive Study in 524 Patients on the Application of the 830nm GaAlAs Diode Laser in Low Reactive-Level Laser (LLLT) for Lumbago," *Laser Therapy* **4**, 121–126 (1992).

79. L. Snyder-Mackler, A. Barry, A. Perkins, and M. Soucek, "Effects of helium-neon laser irradiation on skin resistance and pain with trigger points in the neck and back," *Physical Therapy* **69**, 336–341 (1989).

80. S. Umegaki, Y. Tanaka, M. Hisakai, and H. Koshimoto, "Effectiveness of low-power laser therapy on low-back pain - Double-blind comparative study to evaluate the analgesic effect of low power laser therapy on low back pain," *Clin. Rep.* **23**, 2838–2846 (1989).

81. S. Toya et al., "Report on a computer-randomised double blind clinical trial to determine the effectiveness of the GaAlAs (830nm) diode laser for pain attenuation in selected pain groups," *Laser Ther.* **6**, 143–148 (1994).

82. F. Soriano and R. Rios, "Gallium Arsenide Laser treatment of chronic low back pain: a prospective, randomized and double blind study," *Laser Therapy* **10**, 175–180 (1998).

83. J. Basford, C. Sheffield, and W. Harmsen, "Laser Therapy: A randomised, controlled trial of the effects of low-intensity Nd:YAG laser irradiation on musculoskeletal back pain," *Archives of Physical Medicine & Rehabilitation* **80**, 647–652 (1999).

84. M. Charlusz et al., "Comparative analysis of analgesic efficacy of selected physiotherapy methods in low back pain patients," *Ortop. Traumatol. Rehabil.* **12**, 225–36 (2010).

85. P. Fiore et al., "Short-term effects of high-intensity laser therapy versus ultrasound therapy in the treatment of low back pain: a randomized controlled trial," *Eur. J. Phys. Rehabil. Med.* **47**, 367–73 (2011).

86. M. Mandic and N. Rancie, "Low power laser in the treatment of the acute low back pain," *Vojnosanit Pregl.* **68**, 57–61 (2011).

87. M. S. Alayat et al., "Long-term effect of high-intensity laser therapy in the treatment of patients with chronic low back pain: a randomized blinded placebo-controlled trial," *Lasers Med. Sci.* (2013).

88. R. Yousefi-Nooraie et al., "Low level laser therapy for nonspecific low-back pain," *Cochrane Database Syst. Rev.* CD005107 (2008).

89. R. Chou and L. H. Huffman, "Medications for acute and chronic low back pain: a review of the evidence for an American Pain Society/ American College of Physicians clinical practice guideline," *Ann. Intern. Med.* **147**, 505–14 (2007).

90. J. M. Bjordal et al., "Overviews and systematic reviews on low back pain," *Ann. Intern. Med.* **148**, 789–90; author reply 791–2 (2008a).

91. J. Bjordal and G. Greve, "What may alter the conclusion of reviews?," *Physical Therapy Reviews* **3**, 121–132 (1998).

92. J. M. Bjordal, R. A. B. Lopes-Martins, and A. Kloving, "Is quality control of Cochrane Reviews in controversial areas sufficient?," *Journal of Alternative and Complementary Medicine* **12**, 181–183 (2006b).

93. World Association of Laser Therapy, Laser dosage table for musculoskeletal disorders using 904 nm laser 2010a.

94. R. Buchbinder, S. Green, and J. M. Youd, "Corticosteroid injections for shoulder pain," *Cochrane Database Syst. Rev.* CD004016 (2003).

95. S. England, A. J. Farrell, J. S. Coppock, G. Struthers, and P. A. Bacon, "Low power laser therapy of shoulder tendonitis," *Scand. J. Rheumatol.* **18**, 427–31 (WALT) (1989).

96. S. Green, R. Buchbinder, and S. Hetrick, "Physiotherapy interventions for shoulder pain," *Cochrane Database Syst. Rev.* CD004258 (2003).

97. M. M. Favejee, B. M. Huisstede, and B. W. Koes, "Frozen shoulder: the effectiveness of conservative and surgical interventions–systematic review," *Br. J. Sports Med.* **45**, 49–56 (2011).

98. S. Rayegani, M. Bahrami, B. Samadi, L. Sedighipour, M. Mokhtarirad, and D. Eliaspoor, "Comparison of the effects of low energy laser and ultrasound in treatment of shoulder myofascial pain syndrome: a randomized single-blinded clinical trial," *Eur. J. Phys. Rehabil. Med.* **47**, 381–9 (2011).

99. U. Bingol, L. Altan, and M. Yurtkuran, "Low-power laser treatment for shoulder pain," *Photomed. Laser Surg.* **23**, 459–64 (2005).

100. J. D. Rees, M. Stride, and A. Scott, "Tendons - time to revisit inflammation," *Br. J. Sports Med.* (2013).

101. J. M. Bjordal, R. A. Lopes-Martins, and V. V. Iversen, "A randomised, placebo controlled trial of low level laser therapy for activated Achilles tendinitis with microdialysis measurement of peritendinous prostaglandin E2 concentrations," *Br. J. Sports Med.* **40**, 76–80; discussion 76–80 (2006c).

102. S. Tumilty, J. Munn, S. McDonough, D. A. Hurley, J. R. Basford, and G. D. Baxter, "Low level laser treatment of tendinopathy: a systematic review with meta-analysis," *Photomed. Laser Surg.* **28**, 3–16 (2010).

103. J. E. Aaron, "Periosteal Sharpey's fibers: a novel bone matrix regulatory system?," *Front Endocrinol (Lausanne)* **3**, 98 (2012).

104. J. M. Bjordal, R. A. Lopes-Martins, J. Joensen, A. E. Ljunggren, C. Couppe, A. Stergioulas, and M. I. Johnson, "A systematic review with procedural assessments and meta-analysis of Low-level laser therapy in lateral elbow tendinopathy (tennis elbow)," *BMC Musculoskel. Dis.* **9**, 75 (2008b).

105. C. Fernandez-de-Las-Penas, D. Simons, M. L. Cuadrado, and J. Pareja, "The role of myofascial trigger points in musculoskeletal pain syndromes of the head and neck," *Curr. Pain Headache Rep.* **11**, 365–72 (2007).

106. F. Alburquerque-Sendin, P. R. Camargo, A. Vieira, and T. F. Salvini, "Bilateral myofascial trigger points and pressure pain thresholds in the shoulder muscles in patients with unilateral shoulder impingement syndrome: a blinded, controlled study," *Clin. J. Pain* **29**, 478–86 (2013).

107. D. S. Kim, T. Y. Jeong, Y. K. Kim, W. H. Chang, J. G. Yoon, and S. C. Lee, "Usefulness of a myofascial trigger point injection for groin pain in patients with chronic prostatitis/chronic pelvic pain syndrome: a pilot study," *Arch. Phys. Med. Rehabil.* **94**, 930–6 (2013).

108. C. K. Chen and A. J. Nizar, "Myofascial pain syndrome in chronic back pain patients," *Korean J. Pain* **24**, 100–4 (2011).
109. O. Airaksinen, P. Rantanen, K. Pertti, and P. Pontinen, "Effects of the infrared laser therapy at treated and non-treated trigger points," *Acupuncture & Electro-therapeutics Research International Journal* **14**, 9–14 (1989).
110. G. C. Venezian, M. A. da Silva, R. G. Mazzetto, and M. O. Mazzetto, "Low level laser effects on pain to palpation and electromyographic activity in TMD patients: a double-blind, randomized, placebo-controlled study," *Cranio.* **28**, 84–91 (2010).
111. J. S. de Medeiros, G. F. Vieira, and P. Y. Nishimura, "Laser application effects on the bite strength of the masseter muscle, as an orofacial pain treatment," *Photomed. Laser Surg.* **23**, 373–6 (2005).
112. M. L. de Moraes Maia, M. A. Ribeiro, L. G. Maia, J. Stuginski-Barbosa, Y. M. Costa, A. L. Porporatti, P. C. Conti, and L. R. Bonjardim, "Evaluation of low-level laser therapy effectiveness on the pain and masticatory performance of patients with myofascial pain," *Lasers Med. Sci.* **29**, 29–35 (2014).
113. K.-H. Chen, C.-Z. Hong, F.-C. P. T. Kuo, H.-C. Hsu, and Y.-L. P. T. Hsieh, "Electrophysiologic Effects of a Therapeutic Laser on Myofascial Trigger Spots of Rabbit Skeletal Muscles," *American Journal of Physical Medicine & Rehabilitation* **87**, 1006–1014 (2008b).
114. C. R. Hayworth, J. C. Rojas, E. Padilla, G. M. Holmes, E. C. Sheridan, and F. Gonzalez-Lima, "In vivo low-level light therapy increases cytochrome oxidase in skeletal muscle," *Photochem. Photobiol.* **86**, 673–80 (2010).
115. R. A. Nicolau, M. S. Martinez, J. Rigau, and J. Tomas, "Effect of Low Power 655nm Diode Laser Irradiation on the Neuromuscular Junctions of the Mouse Diaphragm," *Lasers in Surgery & Medicine* **34**, 277–284 (2004b).
116. R. Nicolau, M. Martinez, J. Rigau, and J. Tomas, "Neurotransmitter release changes induced by low power 830nm diode laser irradiation on the neuromuscular junction," *Lasers in Surgery and Medicine* **35**, 236–241 (2004a).
117. K. Moore, N. Hira, P. Kumar, C. Jayakumar, and T. Ohshiro, "A double blind crossover trial of low level laser therapy in the treatment of postherpetic neuralgia," *Laser Therapy* **1**, 7–9 (1988).
118. O. Kemmotsu, K. Sato, H. Furumido, K. Harada, C. Takigawa, S. Kaseno, S. Yokota, H. Yukari, and T. Yamamura, "Efficacy of low reactive-level laser therapy for pain attenuation of post-herpetic neuralgia," *Laser Therapy* **3**, 71–75 (1991).
119. K. Iijima, N. Shimoyama, M. Shimoyama, T. Yamamoto, T. Shimizu, and T. Mizuguchi, "Effect of repeated irradiation of low-power He-Ne

laser in pain relief from postherpetic neuralgia," *Clin. J. Pain* **5**, 271–4 (1989).

120. K. Iijima, N. Shimoyama, M. Shimoyama, and T. Mizuguchi, "Evaluation of analgesic effect of low-power He:Ne laser on postherpetic neuralgia using VAS and modified McGill pain questionnaire," *J. Clin. Laser Med. Surg.* **9**, 121–6 (1991).

121. L. S. McKibbin and R. Downie, "Treatment of Post-Herpetic Neuralgia Using a 904nm (Infrared) Low Incident Energy Laser: A Clinical Study," *Laser Therapy* **3**, 35–39 (1991).

122. I. Yaksich, L. C. Tan, and V. Previn, "Low energy laser therapy for treatment of post-herpetic neuralgia," *Ann. Acad. Med. Singapore* **22**, 441–2 (1993).

123. H. Yamada and H. Ogawa, "Comparative Study of 60mW Diode Laser Therapy and 150mW Diode Laser Therapy in the Treatment of Postherpetic Neuralgia," *Laser Therapy* **7**, 71–74 (1995).

124. H. Otsuka, R. Numaza, K. Okubo, T. Enya, Y. Saito, and O. Kemmotsu, "Effects of Helium-Neon laser therapy on herpes zoster pain," *Laser Therapy* **7**, 27–32 (1995).

125. R. Namazawa, O. Kemmotsu, H. Otsuka, J. Kakehata, T. Hashimoto, S. Tamagawa, and T. Maumi, "The Role of Laser Therapy in Intensive Pain Management of Postherpetic Neuralgia," *Laser Therapy* **8**, 143–148 (1996).

126. R. R. Mittal, J. S. Jassal, and R. K. Bahl, "Laser therapy in post herpetic neuralgia," *Indian J. Dermatol Venereol Leprol.* **62**, 229–30 (1996).

127. S. S. Mann, S. P. Dewan, A. Kaur, P. Kumar, and A. K. Dhawan, "Role of laser therapy in post herpetic neuralgia," *Indian J. Dermatol Venereol Leprol.* **65**, 134–6 (1999).

128. D. J. Knapp, "Postherpetic neuralgia: case study of class 4 laser therapy intervention," *Clin. J. Pain* **29**, e6–9 (2013).

129. J. Walker, L. Akhanjee, M. Cooney, J. Goldstein, S. Tamayoshi, and F. Segal-gidan, "Laser therapy for pain of trigeminal neuralgia," *The Clinical Journal of Pain* **3**, 183–187 (1988).

130. M. A. Shuster, V. M. Isaev, V. I. Rechitskii, and B. V. Agafonov, "Treatment of trigeminal neuralgia, ganglioneuritis of the pterygopalatine ganglion and other types of prosopalgias by helium-neon laser irradiation of the pterygopalatine ganglion," *Zh Nevropatol Psikhiatr Im S S Korsakova.* **88**, 96–8 (1988).

131. A. Eckerdal and H. Bastian, "Can low reactive level laser therapy be used in the treatment of neurogenic facial pain? A double blind placebo controlled investigation of patients with trigeminal neuralgia," *Laser Therapy* **8**, 247–251 (1996).

132. H. Wakabayashi, M. Hamba, K. Matsumoto, and H. Tachibana, "Effect of irradiation by semiconductor laser on responses evoked in

trigeminal caudal neurons by tooth pulp stimulation," *Laser Surg. Med.* **13**, 605–610 (1993).

133. A. Nelson and M. Friedman, "Somatosensory trigeminal evoked potential amplitudes following low-level laser and sham irradiation over time," *Laser Ther.* **13**, 60–64 (2001).

134. L. H. Zinman, M. Ngo, E. T. Ng, K. T. Nwe, S. Gogov, and V. Bril, "Low-intensity laser therapy for painful symptoms of diabetic sensorimotor polyneuropathy: a controlled trial," *Diabetes Care* **27**, 921–4 (2004).

135. M. E. Khamseh, N. Kazemikho, R. Aghili, B. Forough, M. Lajevardi, F. Hashem Dabaghian, A. Goushegir, and M. Malek, "Diabetic distal symmetric polyneuropathy: effect of low-intensity laser therapy," *Lasers Med. Sci.* **26**, 831–5 (2011).

136. M. A. Naeser, "Photobiomodulation of pain in carpal tunnel syndrome: review of seven laser therapy studies," *Photomedicine and Laser Surgery* **24**, 101–110 (2006).

137. S. M. Shooshtari, V. Badiee, S. H. Taghizadeh, A. H. Nematollahi, A. H. Amanollahi, and M. T. Grami, "The effects of low level laser in clinical outcome and neurophysiological results of carpal tunnel syndrome," *Electromyogr. Clin. Neurophysiol* **48**, 229–31 (2008).

138. I. Yagci, O. Elmas, E. Akcan, I. Ustun, O. H. Gunduz, and Z. Guven, "Comparison of splinting and splinting plus low-level laser therapy in idiopathic carpal tunnel syndrome," *Clin. Rheumatol.* **28**, 1059–65 (2009).

139. T. F. Elwakil, A. Elazzazi, and H. Shokeir, "Treatment of carpal tunnel syndrome by low-level laser versus open carpal tunnel release," *Lasers Med. Sci.* **22**, 265–70 (2007).

140. A. Dakowicz, A. Kuryliszyn-Moskal, B. Kosztyla-Hojna, D. Moskal, and R. Latosiewicz, "Comparison of the long-term effectiveness of physiotherapy programs with low-level laser therapy and pulsed magnetic field in patients with carpal tunnel syndrome," *Adv. Med. Sci.* **56**, 270–4 (2011).

141. A. Ekim, O. Armagan, F. Tascioglu, C. Oner, and M. Colak, "Effect of low level laser therapy in rheumatoid arthritis patients with carpal tunnel syndrome," *Swiss Med. Wkly.* **137**, 347–52 (2007).

142. F. Tascioglu, N. A. Degirmenci, S. Ozkan, and O. Mehmetoglu, "Low-level laser in the treatment of carpal tunnel syndrome: clinical, electrophysiological, and ultrasonographical evaluation," *Rheumatol. Int.* **32**, 409–15 (2012).

143. C. J. Carati, S. N. Anderson, B. J. Gannon, and N. B. Piller, "Treatment of postmastectomy lymphedema with low-level laser therapy: a double-blind, placebo-controlled trial," *Cancer* **98**, 1114–1122 (2003).

144. N. B. Piller and A. Thelander, "Treatment of chronic postmastectomy lymphedema with low level laser therapy: a 2.5 year follow-up," *Lymphology* **31**, 74–86 (1998).

145. N. B. Pillar and A. Thelander, "Treating chronic post-mastectomy lymphoedema with low level laser therapy: a cost effective strategy to reduce severity and improve the quality of survival," *Laser Therapy* **7**, 163–168 (1995).

146. E. Kozanoglu, S. Basaran, S. Paydas, and T. Sarpel, "Efficacy of pneumatic compression and low-level laser therapy in the treatment of postmastectomy lymphoedema: a randomized controlled trial," *Clin. Rehabil.* **23**, 117–24 (2009).

147. M. T. Omar, A. A. Shaheen, and H. Zafar, "A systematic review of the effect of low-level laser therapy in the management of breast cancer-related lymphedema," *Support Care Cancer* (2012).

148. K. C. Moore, N. Hira, I. J. Broome, and J. A. Cruikshank, "The Effect of Infrared Diode Laser Irradiation on the Duration and Severity of Postoperative Pain: A Double Blind Trial," *Laser Therapy* **4**, 145–149 (1992).

149. C. Clokie and E. Al, "The effects of helium-neon laser on post-surgical discomfort: A pilot study," *Canadian Dental Association Journal* **7**, 584–586 (1991).

150. M. B. Kreisler, H. A. Haj, N. Noroozi, and B. Willershausen, "Efficacy of low level laser therapy in reducing postoperative pain after endodontic surgery – a randomized double blind clinical study," *Int. J. Oral Maxillofac. Surg.* **33**, 38–41 (2004).

151. E. ABT, "CO2 laser treatment for gingivectomies reduces hemorrhaging, post-op pain," *Clin. Laser Mon.* **10**, 8 (1992).

152. R. Brignardello-Petersen, A. Carrasco-Labra, I. Araya, N. Yanine, J. Beyene, and P. S. Shah, "Is adjuvant laser therapy effective for preventing pain, swelling, and trismus after surgical removal of impacted mandibular third molars? A systematic review and meta-analysis," *J. Oral Maxillofac. Surg.* **70**, 1789–801 (2012).

153. J. L. Zeredo, K. M. Sasaki, Y. Takeuchi, and K. Toda, "Antinociceptive effect of Er:YAG laser irradiation in the orofacial formalin test," *Brain Res.* **1032**, 149–53 (2005).

154. F. Eren, B. Altinok, F. Ertugral, and I. Tanboga, "The effect of erbium, chromium:yttrium-scandium-gallium-garnet (Er, Cr:YSGG) laser therapy on pain during cavity preparation in paediatric dental patients: a pilot study," *Oral Health Dent. Manag.* **12**, 80–4 (2013).

155. I. Tanboga, F. Eren, B. Altinok, S. Peker, and F. Ertugral, "The effect of low level laser therapy on pain during dental tooth-cavity preparation in children," *Eur. Arch. Paediatr. Dent.* **12**, 93–5 (2011).

156. C. Migliorati, I. Hewson, R. V. Lalla, H. S. Antunes, C. L. Estilo, B. Hodgson, N. N. Lopes, M. M. Schubert, J. Bowen, and S. Elad, "Systematic review of laser and other light therapy for the management of oral mucositis in cancer patients," *Support Care Cancer* (2012).

157. M. Trelles, E. Mayayo, L. Miro, J. Rigau, G. Baudin, and R. Calderhead, "The action of low reactive laser therapy (LLLT) on mast cells: a possible pain relief mechanism examined," *Laser Therapy* **1**, 27–30 (1989).

158. A. Honmura, M. Yanase, J. Obata, and E. Haruki, "Therapeutic effect on GaAlAs Diode Laser Irradiation on Experimentally Induced Inflammation in Rats," *Lasers in Surgery & Medicine* **12**, 441–449 (1992).

159. Y.-L. Jia and Z.-Y. Guo, "Effect of low-power HeNe laser irradiation on rabbit articular chondrocytes in vitro," *Lasers in Surgery & Medicine* **34**, 323–328 (2004).

160. P. K. Holden, C. Li, V. Da Costa, C. H. Sun, S. V. Bryant, D. M. Gardiner, and B. J. Wong, "The effects of laser irradiation of cartilage on chondrocyte gene expression and the collagen matrix," *Lasers Surg. Med.* **41**, 487–91 (2009).

161. A. P. Sommer, A. L. B. Pinheiro, A. R. Mester, R. P. Franke, and H. T. Whelan, "Biostimulatory windows in low-intensity laser activation: lasers, scanners and NASA's light-emitting diode array system," *Journal of Clinical Laser Medicine and Surgery* **19**, 29–33 (2001).

162. Y. Y. Huang, A. C. Chen, J. D. Carroll, and M. R. Hamblin, "Biphasic dose response in low level light therapy," *Dose Response* **7**, 358–83 (2009).

163. E. Nussbaum, J. Van Zuylen, and F. Jing, "Transmission of light through human skin folds during phototherapy: effects of physical characteristics, irradiation wavelength, and skin-diode coupling," *Physiother. Can.* **59**, 194–207 (2007).

164. A. Liebert, G. Waddington, B. T. Bicknell, R. Chow, and R. Adams, *Quantification of the absorption of low-level 904nm super pulsed laser light as a function of skin colour.* In: L., LAAKSO, ed. 9th World Congress of Laser therapy, 2012 Gold Coast, Queensland, Australia. Medimond, 11–15.

165. N. Cohen, R. Lubart, S. Rubinstein, and H. Breitbart, "Light irradiation of mouse spermatozoa: stimulation of in vitro fertilization and calcium signals," *Photochem. Photobiol.* **68**, 407–13 (1998).

166. J. Kert and L. Rose, Clinical Laser Therapy - Low Level Laser Therapy. Copenhagen, Scandinavian Medical Laser Technology (1989).

Chapter 18

Applications to the Central Nervous System*

18.1 Mechanisms of Photobiomodulation in the Central Nervous System

The discussion of transcranial low-level laser therapy has moved past its biological effects into a search for how light energy—specifically, from lasers or LEDs—works at the cellular and organism levels. With a wide range of different applications of photobiomodulation (PBM), it is necessary to find and understand the optimal parameters for each. Heat absorption, one of several unlikely mechanistic explanations underlying PBM, is closely tied to the use of lasers, but the way the light is delivered does not meaningfully raise brain temperature, implying that the photothermal effects from light energy do not play a significant role in explaining the benefits of PBM. Rather, photochemistry is becoming the accepted hypothesis for explaining the biological effects of light absorption in cells and tissues.[1] These effects rely on the absorption of light by chromophores within cells to produce the various biological effects, such as an increase of adenosine triphosphate (ATP), deoxyribonucleic acid (DNA), and ribonucleic acid (RNA); the release of nitric oxide (NO); cytochrome c oxidase activity; the regulation of reactive oxygen species (ROS); and changes to organelle membrane activity in mitochondria.[2–6] In order for the photons to effectively reach their target area, the penetration of the light through the tissue must be maximized by choosing an appropriate wavelength. This "optical window" ranges from 600 nm to 1200 nm and involves almost exclusively infrared and near-infrared light (600 nm to 1100 nm).[7]

Mitochondria are the most important cellular organelle when trying to understand the cellular response of PBM. Conventionally known as the "powerhouse of the cell," mitochondria not only supply the cell with energy but are also involved in cellular signaling, cell differentiation, and cell death,

---

*Based on material first printed in M. R. Hamblin, M. V. P. de Sousa, and T. Agarwal, Eds., *Handbook of Low-Level Laser Therapy*, Pan Stanford Publishing, Singapore (2016).

as well as cellular metabolism and proliferation. Complex IV on the mitochondrial inner membrane, or cytochrome c oxidase (CCO), is considered to be the crucial chromophore in the cellular response to PBM as shown by the action spectra (a plot of the rate of the physiological activity plotted against the wavelength of light).[7,8] Cytochrome c oxidase is a large protein complex with two copper and two iron centers.[9] The way in which light interacts and ultimately affects CCO is not precisely known, but it certainly involves a complex series of interactions that will result in a change in redox states. Transcranial PBM produced a shift towards higher oxidation in the overall cell redox potential[3,10] and briefly increased the creation of ROS.[11] This change in the redox state regulates several transcription factors, including redox factor 1 (Ref-1), cAMP response element (CREB), activator protein 1 (AP-1), p53, nuclear factor kappa B (NF-κB), hypoxia-inducible factor (HIF-1), and HIF-like factor. The activation and regulation of redox sensitive genes and transcription factors are thought to be caused by ROS induced from PBM.[12] An important feature of PBM is its biphasic dose-response curve,[13,14] which can be explained in other terms: a small amount of light can be good, more may lose the beneficial effect, and too much light may be harmful. This effect can be explained by two of the PBM signaling mediators, ROS[4] and NO.[6] Both of these species can have positive effects at low concentration but adverse effects at a high concentration.

Transcranial low-level laser therapy may cause a separation (photodissociation) between NO and CCO.[5,15] Cellular respiration is normally down-regulated when NO binds with CCO and inhibits it binding to the Fe and Cu centers. The NO displaces the oxygen from the CCO, thus decreasing cellular respiration and decreasing the production rate of ATP.[2] Therefore, by breaking NO from CCO, PBM can prevent this inhibition from occurring. In turn, both ATP levels and blood flow increase (NO is a vasodilator).[16] With an increase in blood flow, improved oxygenation is found in damaged areas of the brain. Figure 18.1 depicts the molecular mechanisms and pathways that are thought to occur post-PBM.

When using PBM to treat disorders of the brain, more specific mechanisms need to be closely examined. Brain-specific functional mechanisms of PBM for TBI are illustrated in Fig. 18.2. The cytoprotective effects of PBM are thought to prevent injured neurons from dying and reduce the number of neuronal cells undergoing death, as has been shown for cyanide,[17] tetrodotoxin,[18] and methanol.[19] This protective effect may include several mediators, such as Bcl2, heat-shock proteins,[20] survivin,[21] and superoxide dismutase.[22] The decrease of pro-inflammatory mediators from dendritic cells[23] along with the increase in anti-inflammatory mediators (IL-10 and TGFβ)[24] is thought to cause the anti-inflammatory effect of PBM.[25,26]

Lastly, neurogenesis and neuroplasticity (synaptogenesis) may be other mechanisms that contribute to the beneficial effects of PBM in the brain.[27]

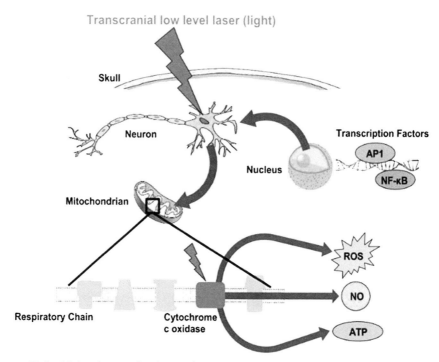

Figure 18.1 Molecular mechanisms of transcranial PBM. Light passes through the scalp and skull, where it is then absorbed by cytochrome c oxidase in the mitochondrial respiratory chain of the cortical neurons. Cell signaling and messenger molecules are up-regulated as a result of stimulated mitochondrial activity, including reactive oxygen species (ROS), nitric oxide (NO), and adenosine triphosphate (ATP). These signaling molecules activate transcription factors, including NF-κB and AP-1, that enter the nucleus and cause transcription of a range of new gene products.

These processes are initiated by the increase in neurotrophin expression, as in brain-derived neurotrophic factor (BDNF) and nerve growth factor (NGF).

18.2 Human-Skull Transmission Measurements

In 1981, Wan et al.[28] reported the transmittance of nonionizing radiation in human tissues. The spectral transmittance of 400–865-nm radiation through various human structures (including the skull with scalp, chest wall, abdominal wall, and scrotum) is presented. There is essentially no visible light of wavelengths shorter than 500 nm transmitted through the chest or the abdominal wall. Transmittance of all tissues increases progressively with wavelengths of 600–814 nm. Tissue thickness, optical absorption, and scattering are major influencing factors.[29] Lychagov et al.[30] presented the recent results of measurements of transmittance of high-power laser irradiation through skull bones and scalp. Figure 18.3 shows the experimental setup of an *ex vivo* human-skull transmission measurement. The character of transmittance was investigated,

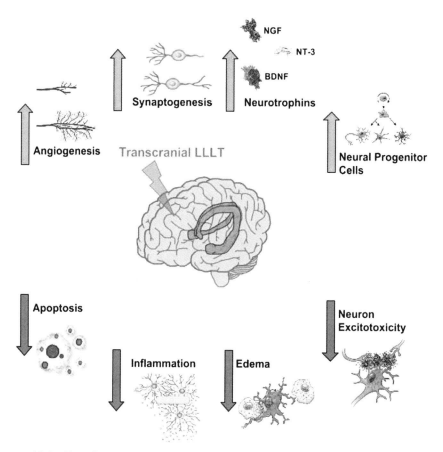

Figure 18.2 Functional mechanisms of transcranial PBM. The gene transcription described in Fig. 18.1 can lead to decreases in neuronal apoptosis, excitotoxicity, and a lessening of inflammation and edema that will help reduce progressive brain damage. Increased angiogenesis, expression of neurotrophins leading to activation of neural progenitor cells, and increased synaptogenesis may all contribute to the brain repairing itself from damage sustained during the trauma.

and the heterogeneous characteristics of the scattering structure of the skull bones were shown. Besides that, the temperature variation of the skull and scalp surfaces under exposure of high-power laser irradiation during experiments was controlled. Experimental results were verified by Monte Carlo simulations. Figure 18.4 shows the transmission of 808-nm NIR light through a fresh human-cadaver brain as measured by an infrared camera.

18.3 PBM for Stroke

18.3.1 Stroke

Stroke is the third leading cause of death in the United States, after heart disease and cancer.[31] Each year, approximately 780,000 people experience a

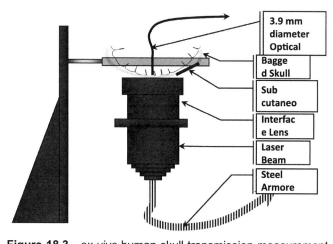

Figure 18.3 *ex vivo* human-skull transmission measurement.

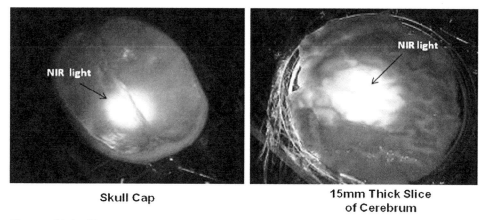

Skull Cap   15mm Thick Slice
                                             of Cerebrum

Figure 18.4 IR camera photos of a fresh human-cadaver brain. 808-nm infrared wavelength transmits through skin, bone, and dura to reach the cortex.

new or recurrent stroke. Approximately 600,000 of these are first attacks, and 180,000 are recurrent attacks.[32] The 3-month mortality rate from ischemic stroke is ~12%. Internationally, millions of people have a new or recurrent stroke each year, and nearly a quarter of these people die. Globally, stroke death rates vary widely; the highest rates are in Portugal, China, Korea, and most of Eastern Europe, and the lowest rates are in Switzerland, Canada, and the United States.

Strokes can be classified into two major categories, ischemic and hemorrhagic. The former account for over 80% of all strokes. The most common cause of ischemic stroke is the blockage of an artery in the brain by a clot, thrombosis, embolism, or stenosis. Hemorrhagic strokes are the result of rupture of a cerebral artery, which can lead to spasm of the artery and various degrees of bleeding. Until recently, care of subjects with ischemic stroke was largely supportive, focusing on prevention and treatment of respiratory and cardiovascular complications. Common acute complications of stroke include pneumonia, urinary tract infection, and pulmonary embolism. Long-term morbidity in survivors of stroke is common, with ambulation difficulty in 20%, need for assistance in activities of daily living in 30%, and vocational disability in 50–70% of patients.

Ischemic stroke is a complex entity with multiple etiologies and variable clinical manifestations. Thrombosis can form in the extracranial and intracranial arteries when the intima is roughened and plaque forms along the injured vessel. The endothelial injury permits platelets to adhere and aggregate, and then coagulation is activated and thrombus develops at the site of plaque. When the compensatory mechanism of collateral circulation fails, perfusion is compromised, leading to decreased perfusion and cell death. During an embolic stroke, a clot travels to the brain through an artery. Cells in the core ischemic zone die within minutes. Ischemia impairs the patient's neurologic function. Cells in the penumbra of the injury remain potentially salvageable for hours.[33] Figure 18.5 shows the physiology of acute ischemic stroke.

When an ischemic stroke occurs, the blood supply to the brain is interrupted, and brain cells are deprived of the glucose and oxygen they need to function. The human brain represents 2% of body weight but requires 20% of total oxygen consumption.[34] The brain requires this large amount of oxygen to generate sufficient ATP by oxidative phosphorylation to maintain and restore ionic gradients. One estimate suggests that the Na+/K+ATPase found on the plasma membrane of neurons consumes 70% of the energy supplied to the brain. This ion pump maintains the high intracellular K+ concentration and the low intracellular Na+ concentrate ion necessary for the propagation of action potentials. After global ischemia, mitochondrial inhibition of ATP synthesis leads to the ATP being consumed within 2 minutes, which causes

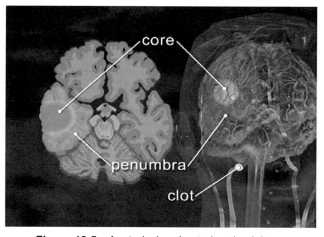

Figure 18.5   Acute ischemic-stroke physiology.

neuronal plasma membrane depolarization, the release of potassium into the extracellular space, and the entry of sodium into cells.[35] Energy failure also prevents the plasma membrane Ca^{2+} ATPase from maintaining the very low concentrations of calcium that are normally present within each cell.

Stroke can manifest as focal injuries (contusions, lacerations, hematomas), diffuse axonal injury (DAI), or a combination thereof. Diffuse axonal injury has been recognized as one of the main consequences of blunt head trauma and blast injuries.[36] Secondary injuries are attributable to further cellular damage that results from follow-on effects of the primary injuries and develop over a period of hours or days following initial traumatic assault. Secondary brain injury is mediated through excitotoxic cell death in which injured neurons depolarize and release glutamate.[37] Neighboring cells are in turn depolarized by the excessive glutamate concentrations, creating a vicious spiral of increasing glutamate concentration. Depolarized neurons suffer a large influx of sodium and calcium but could survive if they had sufficient ATP to power the Na+/K+-ATPase pumps and handle this osmotic load. However, in the setting of metabolic failure they exhibit cytotoxic edema, with an eventual loss of viability.[38] An influx of calcium linked to delayed damage, a decrease in mitochondrial membrane potential, and the increased production of ROS are observed. Other biochemical processes exacerbating stroke include the activation of astrocytes and microglia, leading to increased cytokines contributing to inflammation and characterized by increased prostaglandin E2.[39] Excitotoxic cell death mediated by glutamate also affects glial cells as well as neurons, especially oligodendrocytes.[40] ROS have been implicated as key participants of other acute CNS injuries, such as TBI, spinal-cord injury, and ischemia, as well as chronic neurodegenerative diseases.[41] Stroke causes the physical disruption of neuronal tissue that sets into motion secondary damage resulting in the death of additional tissue. Hypoperfusion and ischemia-induced increases in the formation of superoxide and NO have been reported after stroke, predicting a role for oxidant stress during damage.[42] Cellular protection against these ROS involves an elaborate antioxidant defense system, including that associated with manganese superoxide dismutase (MnSOD).

Thrombolytic therapy is the only intervention of proven and substantial benefit for select patients with acute cerebral ischemia.[43] The evidence basis for thrombolysis therapy includes 21 completed randomized controlled clinical trials enrolling 7,152 patients, using various agents, doses, time windows, and intravenous or intra-arterial modes of administration.[44]

The main agent that has been employed is recombinant tissue plasminogen activator (t-PA),[45] which is produced endogenously by endothelial cells and is relatively fibrin specific. t-PA works by converting the proenzyme plasminogen to the activated enzyme plasmin. Activated plasmin in turn dissolves fibrin clots into low-molecular-weight fibrin degradation products. Other thrombolytics that have been used include streptokinase.[46,47]

Time lost is brain lost in acute cerebral ischemia. In a typical middle-cerebral-artery ischemic stroke, two million nerve cells are lost each minute in which reperfusion has not been achieved.[48] A pooled analysis of all 2,775 patients enrolled in the first six intravenous t-PA trials provided clear and convincing evidence of a time-dependent benefit of thrombolytic therapy.[49]

18.3.2 PBM application

There have been an enormous variety of agents and strategies that have received clinical scrutiny, each justified by a pathophysiological rationale. In all, approximately 165 ongoing or completed clinical trials have been published,[50] as summarized in Fig. 18.6. There has been an almost universal outcome of failure for all these trials, with exceptions of some small hint of efficacy in only a few cases.

The beneficial effects of NIR light on cells and neurons *in vitro*, together with the demonstrated ability of NIR light to penetrate into the brain, strongly suggest that transcranial PBM should be studied as a therapy for stroke.

18.3.3 PBM for stroke in animal models

Light at 808–810 nm can penetrate the brain and was shown to lead to enhanced production of ATP in the rat cerebral cortex.[51] Findings of

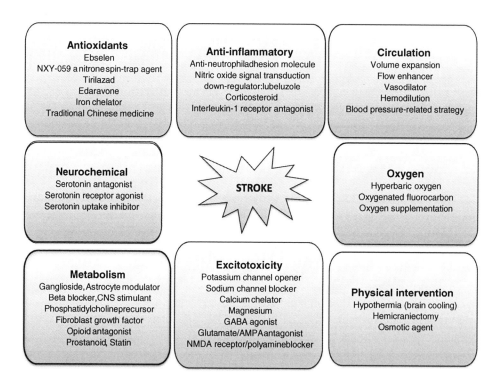

Figure 18.6   Clinical trials of pharmacological and physical therapies for stroke.

increased neurogenesis in the subventricular zone (SVZ) were reported in an ischemic-stroke animal model treated with transcranial laser therapy (TLT).[52] Based on these findings, it is thought that TLT may have multiple mechanisms of action and could be beneficial in acute ischemic stroke.[53]

Although there is no one animal model that identically mimics stroke in humans, the use of animal models is essential for the development of therapeutic interventions for stroke. Outcome measures for animal models involve functional measures and infarct size evaluation. Recommendations from the Stroke Therapy Academic Industry Roundtable (STAIR) for preclinical animal models are for initial studies to be conducted in rat followed by a second species, specifically primates. Ischemia is typically induced by occluding the middle cerebral artery (MCA) in the animal. The MCA is most often used to simulate human stroke because most human strokes are due to occlusion of this vessel or one of its branches.[54] Animals that have been used in ischemia models for various specific reasons include rats, mice, gerbils, cats, rabbits, dogs, pigs, and nonhuman primates. Figure 18.7 shows noninvasive parameter measurement of animal models' skull.

The first animal model for TLT on the brain was reported by Azbel,[55] using a rat model, who found synaptic conductance of rat hippocampal neurons in 1993. in vivo studies have suggested that infrared laser therapy could be beneficial for the treatment of acute myocardial infarction, as shown by Ad and Oron,[56] who demonstrated in 2001 that TLT reduced the loss of myocardial tissue and the severity of acute myocardial infarction following chronic ligation of the left anterior descending coronary artery in laboratory rats. In 2002, Leung et al.[57] used a model of transient cerebral ischemia, TLT-inhibited NO synthase activity, and unregulated expression of TGF beta-1. In 2004, Lapchak[58] showed that laser treatment with 7.5 mw/cm^2 at 6 h post-stroke onset in a rabbit small-clot embolic stroke model (RSCEM) improved behavioral performance and produced a durable effect that was measurable 21 days after embolization. Lapchak[59,60] reported their further research showed

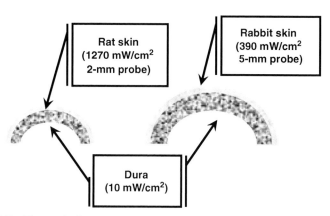

Figure 18.7 Transmission measurements in the skull of different animal models.

TLT improved motor function following embolic strokes in rabbits. In 2006, De Taboada et al.[61] showed in two different animal models a positive impact of infrared laser therapy on the experimental, ischemic stroke treatment outcomes in New Zealand rabbits subjected to a RSCEM, and also in Sprague-Dawley rats (permanent middle cerebral artery occlusion). De Taboada et al.[61] have also shown that laser treatment up to 24 h post-stroke onset in permanent middle cerebral artery occlusion showed significant improvement in neurological deficits which was evident at 14, 21, and 28 days post-stroke when compared with the sham control group. Meanwhile, Oron[52] reported that a noninvasive intervention of TLT issued 24 h after acute stroke may provide a significant functional benefit, with an underlying mechanism possibly being induction of neurogenesis. Currently, the putative mechanism for infrared laser therapy in stroke involves the stimulation of mitochondria, which then leads to the preservation of tissue in the ischemic penumbra and enhanced neuron recovery. The exact mechanistic pathways remain to be elucidated. Figure 18.8 shows how the treatment is performed in a mouse model of stroke.

PBM has been shown to have a cardioprotective effect[104,105] while regulating several biological processes.[106–108] Light can penetrate both the scalp and skull, and reach into the brain. Several clinical and preclinical studies have shown that this process can lead to an improved recovery from stroke.[57] In these studies, stroke was induced in rat and rabbit models, and showed that intervention by PBM within 24 h could have meaningful beneficial effects. For the rat models, stroke was induced by permanent middle cerebral artery occlusion (MCAO) via the insertion of a filament into the carotid artery or via craniotomy.[52,62] Stroke induction in the rabbit models were induced by the RSCEM by injecting a microclot made from blood from a donor rabbit.[59] These studies, along with the treatments and results, are listed in Table 18.1.

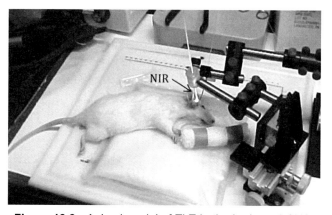

Figure 18.8   Animal model of TLT in the brain and CNS.

Table 18.1 Reports of transcranial PBM used for stroke in animal models.

Subject	Stroke Model	Parameters	Effect	Reference
Rat	MCAO	660 nm; 8.8 mW; 2.64 J/cm^2; pulse frequency of 10 kHz; laser applied at cerebrum at 1, 5, and 10 minutes	Suppression of NOS activity and up-regulation of TGF-β1	Oron[52]
Rat	MCAO	808 nm; 7.5 mW/cm^2; 0.9 J/cm^2; 3.6 J/cm^2 at cortical surface; CW and pulse wave at 70 Hz, 4-mm diameter	Administration of PBM 24 h after stroke onset induced functional benefit and neurogenesis induction	Zhang[62]
Rabbit	RSCEM	808 nm ± 5 nm; 7.5 W/cm^2; 2-minute duration 3 h after stroke, and 25 mW/cm^2 10-minute duration 1 or 6 h after stroke	Improved behavioral performance and durable effect after PBM within 6 h from stroke onset	Lapchak[59]
Rat	MCAO	808 nm; 0.5 mW/cm^2; 0.9 J/cm^2 on brain 3 mm dorsal to the eye and 2 mm anterior to the ear	PBM applied at different locations on the skull improved neurological function after acute stroke	Detaboada[61]
Rabbit	RSCEM	808 nm; 7.5 mW/cm^2; 0.9 J/cm^2; 3.6 J/cm^2 at cortical surface; CW; 300 minutes; pulse at 1 kHz, 2 minutes at 100 Hz	PBM administered 6 h after embolic stroke resulted in clinical improvements in rabbits	Lapchak[58]

18.3.4 Clinical trials for acute stroke

Three clinical trials of PBM have been conducted for human patients suffering from acute stroke. The first study, NEST-1, enrolled 120 patients between the ages of 40 and 85 years of age with a diagnosis of ischemic stroke involving a neurological deficit that could be measured. The purpose of this first clinical trial was to demonstrate the safety and effectiveness of laser therapy for stroke within 24 h.[63] The second clinical trial, NEST-2, enrolled 660 patients, aged 40 to 90, who were randomly assigned to one of two groups (331 to PBM, 327 to sham).[64] The last clinical trial, NEST-3, had 1000 patients enrolled. Patients in this study were not to receive the tissue plasminogen activator, and the study was prematurely terminated by the DSMB for futility.[65] The parameters and results for these three clinical trials are listed in Table 18.2.

18.4 PBM for Traumatic Brain Injury

18.4.1 Introduction

Traumatic brain injury (TBI) includes skull fractures, intracranial hemorrhages, elevated intracranial pressure and cerebral contusions. Unlike stroke, the prevalence of which is tied with an increasing age of onset, TBI is much more common in younger populations. Not only does TBI have a large impact on the healthcare industry but it also causes severe socio-economic problems throughout the world. Every year in the U.S., there are nearly 2 million head injuries, resulting in 283,000 hospitalizations, 53,000 of which lead to death.[94-96] Consequently, Americans living with TBI-related

Table 18.2 Reports of transcranial PBM used for stroke in clinical trials.

Clinical Trial	Number of Subjects	Eligibility Criteria	Parameters of Treatment	Effect	Ref.
NEST-1	120	Patients 40–85 years old with clinical diagnosis of ischemic stroke and measurable neurological deficit. NeuroThera Laser System (NST) within 24 h of stroke onset.	808 nm; 700 mW/cm^2 on shaved scalp with cooling; 1 J/cm^2 at cortical surface; 20 predetermined location, 2 minutes each	This study demonstrated the safety and effectiveness of infrared laser therapy within 24 h of stroke onset.	Lampl[63]
NEST-2	660	Patients 40–90 years old with clinical diagnosis of ischemic stroke within 24 h of onset. NIH stroke scale of 7–22.	808 nm; 700 mW/cm^2 on shaved scalp with cooling; 1 J/cm^2 at cortical surface; 20 predetermined location, 2 minutes each	This trial of TLT within 24 h of stroke onset demonstrated safety, but the efficacy did not merit statistical significance. Mortality and adverse event rate were not adversely affected by TLT.	Zivin[64]
NEST-3	1000	Patients 40–80 years old with clinical diagnosis of ischemic stroke within 24 h of onset. NIH stroke scale of 7–17.	808 nm; 700 mW/cm^2 on shaved scalp with cooling; 1 J/cm^2 at cortical surface; 20 predetermined location, 2 minutes each	Patients were not supposed to receive tissue plasminogen activator. The study was terminated prematurely after 600 patients by the DSMB due to an expected lack of statistical significance.	Zivin[65]

disabilities cost an estimated \$56 billion yearly.[97] Within the next five years, the World Health Organization (WHO) has projected that road traffic incidents, one of the largest causes of TBI, will be ranked just behind ischemic heart disease and unipolar major depression as a cause of morbidity and mortality.[98]

Although the understanding of the pathophysiology underlying the damage following severe brain injury has improved, current treatment options remain limited.[99] The processes and mechanisms that underlie TBI are incredibly complex and are still not well understood. After the initial impact, multiple pathways are activated that result in secondary injury that can spread throughout the brain. These injury processes may include inflammation, an ionic imbalance, excitotoxic damage, oxidative stress, increased vascular permeability, and mitochondrial dysfunction.[100] In turn, these secondary injuries result in brain edema and an increase in intracranial pressure. These physiological changes and disruptions cause neuronal death and a spread of ischemic necrosis, followed by worsening motor and cognitive functionality. Researchers and clinicians should prioritize efforts to improve the outcome and treatment options for TBI patients.[101]

18.4.2 Studies of PBM for TBI in mice

The success of transcranial PBM for stroke has come with an influx of researchers testing this technique in different animal models of TBI. Oron et al.[67] examined the effects of PBM for TBI in mice. A weight-drop device was used to induce a closed-head injury in the mice. An 808-nm diode laser with two energy densities (1.2–2.4 J/cm^2 over 2 minutes of irradiation with 10 and 20 mW/cm^2) was delivered to the head 4 h after TBI was induced. Neurobehavioral function was assessed by the neurological severity score (NSS). There were no significant differences in the NSS between the power densities (10 versus 20 mW/cm^2) or significant differentiation between the control and laser-treated group after 24 and 48 h post-TBI. However, there was a significant improvement, i.e., a 27% lower NSS score, in the laser-treated group after 5 days to 4 weeks. The laser-treated group also showed a smaller loss of cortical tissue than the sham group.[67]

Oron et al.[109] then looked at the long-term effects of varying treatments of different therapies administered at varying time-points in mice with internal (closed-head) injury. Again, a weight-drop device was used along with an 808-nm GaAlAs diode laser with an energy level of 1.2 J/cm^2 (power density of 10 mW/cm^2). Treatments were given at 4, 6, and 8 h post-injury transcranially. Laser treatments at 10 mW/cm^2 at 100 Hz, 600 Hz, and CW 4 h post-injury were conducted in a complementary experiment. For the laser-treated group at 6 h post-injury, the NSS was 3.4 times greater than in the nonirradiated control group. For the laser-treated group at 8 h post-injury, the NSS was 1.8 times greater than the control group. Both groups were evaluated at day 56. The scores for all three varying frequency treatments (100 Hz, 600 Hz, and continuous wave) had 3.5 times greater difference when compared to the untreated control group. The mice receiving PBM with a pulsed wave (PW) at 100 Hz 4 h post-injury made a full recovery (NSS of 0) at day 56. When compared to the control group, the CW and PW laser-treated groups had a significantly smaller lesion size.[109]

Khuman et al.[4] demonstrated that transcranial PBM could improve cognitive function in mice with controlled cortical impact (CCI). The CCI was created by a 3-mm flat-tipped pneumatic piston moving at a velocity of 6 m/s to a depth of 0.6 mm into the brain exposed by a craniotomy. The mice were assigned to one of two groups: an open craniotomy laser-treated group or a transcranial laser-treated group. Within the former group, the mice were irradiated with a low-level laser light with a wavelength of 800 nm at varying energy levels (0, 30, 60, 105, 120, and 210 J/cm^2) at 60–80 minutes post-CCI. The group treated transcranially was exposed to low-level laser light with an energy level of 60 J/cm^2 at varying timing regimens (60–80 minutes post-CCI, 4 h post-CCI or once a day for 7 days after CCI). The Morris water maze (MWM) was utilized to assess cognitive function improvement, whereas motor function was evaluated using the wire grip test. Brain edema, lesion size, and nitrosative stress were also evaluated using a nitrotyrosine ELISA test. Mice in both groups (transcranially or open craniotomy) treated with lasers with an energy level of 60 J/cm^2 showed significant improvements in both the response time to the hidden platform and probe trial performance. An anti-inflammatory effect was also noted in both groups; however, there was no significant difference found in the motor function (days 1–7), lesion size (14 days), brain edema (24 h), and nitrosative stress (24 hours) of the PBM groups and the control.[4]

Quirk et al.[110] evaluated the neuroprotective effects of NIR light using an *in vivo* rodent model of TBI induced via CCI and characterized the changes at the behavioral and biochemical levels. Rats were divided into three different groups: a severe TBI group, a sham surgery group, and a group receiving anesthetization only. Rats in each group were then administered either NIR or no NIR. They received two 670-nm LED treatments (5 minutes, 50 mW/cm^2, 15 J/cm^2) per day for 72 h (biochemical analysis assay) or for 10 days (behavioral assay). During the recovery period, rats were tested for locomotor and behavioral activities using a TruScan device. At the 72-h mark, frozen brain tissue was collected, evaluated for apoptotic markers, and measured for reduced glutathione (GSH) levels. Significant differences between TBI with NIR and without NIR (TBI ±) and between the sham surgery with NIR and without NIR (S ±) were observed. In rats exposed to NIR, there was a significant decrease in Bax pro-apoptotic marker along with a smaller increase in anti-apoptotic marker and GSH levels.[110]

Moreira et al.[111] assessed the effects of PBM following direct CCI to the brain of rodents. The rats were irradiated with 780-nm and 600-nm lasers at energy levels of 3 J/cm^2 and 5 J/cm^2. This study found that laser-treated lesions had smaller tissue loss at 6 h, a significantly higher number of viable neurons at 24 h, and fewer leukocytes and lymphocytes in the first 24 h, while the GFAP staining increased in the control group (but not the PBM group) by 14 days. It was concluded that PBM facilitates wound healing in the brain following CCI by controlling brain damage, preventing neuronal death, and reducing severe astrogliosis.[111]

18.4.3 Effect of different laser wavelengths in PBM for TBI

The following three sections discuss and summarize studies conducted in the laboratory that have investigated the use of PBM to treat TBI in animal models.

Wu et al.[112] explored the effect that varying the laser wavelengths of PBM had on closed-head TBI in mice. Mice were randomly assigned to a PBM-treated group or to a sham group as a control. Closed-head injury (CHI) was induced via a weight-drop apparatus. To analyze the severity of the TBI, the NSS was measured and recorded. The injured mice were then treated with varying wavelengths of laser (665, 730, 810, or 980 nm) at an energy level of

36 J/cm^2 at 4 h. The 665-nm and 810-nm groups showed a significant improvement in NSS when compared to the control group at days 5–28. The results are shown in Fig. 18.9. Conversely, the 730- and 980-nm groups did not show a significant improvement in NSS, and these wavelengths did not produce similar beneficial effects as in the 665-nm and 810-nm PBM groups.[112] The tissue chromophore CCO is proposed to be responsible for the underlying mechanism that produces the various PBM effects. CCO has absorption bands around 665 nm and 810 nm, although it has low absorption bands at 730 nm.[15] This particular study found that the 980-nm wavelength did not produce the positive effects that the 665-nm and 810-nm wavelengths did, but previous studies found that the 980-nm wavelength was active for PBM. Wu et al.[112] proposed that these dissimilar results may be due to the variance in the energy level, irradiance, etc. between the other studies and this particular study.

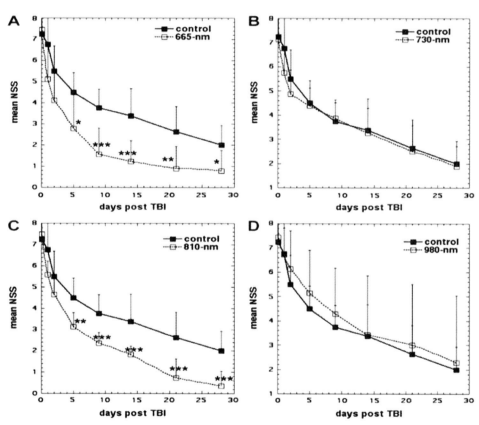

Figure 18.9 Effect of different wavelengths in PBM in closed-head TBI in mice. (a) Sham-treated control vs. 665-nm laser. (b) Sham-treated control versus 730 nm laser. (c) Sham-treated control vs. 810-nm laser. (d) Sham-treated control vs. 980-nm laser. Points are means of 8–12 mice and bars are SD. *P < 0.05; **P < 0.01; ***P < 0.001 (one-way ANOVA).

18.4.4 Effect of pulsing PBM for TBI

A number of studies have investigated the best range of parameters for laser treatment (total energy delivered, irradiance, or power density) and the best wavelengths of lasers that should be used in PBM for the treatment of brain disorders. However, a consensus on whether treatment should be given by CW or PW light—including the parameters for this light—has not been reached. Ando et al.[113] used the 810-nm wavelength parameters from the previous study and varied the pulse modes of the laser in a mouse model of TBI. These modes consisted of either PW laser at 10 Hz or at 100 Hz, or CW laser. For the mice, TBI was induced with a controlled-cortical-impact device via open craniotomy. A single treatment with an 810-nm GaAlAs diode laser with a power density of 50 mW/cm^2 and an energy density of 36 J/cm^2 was given via PBM to the closed head in mice for a duration of 12 minutes at 4 hours post CCI. At 48 hours to 28 days post-TBI, all laser treated groups had significant decreases in the measured NSS when compared to the control. Although all laser-treated groups had similar NSS improvement rates up to day 7, the PW 10-Hz group began to show greater improvement beyond this point, as seen in Fig. 18.10. At day 28, the forced swim test for depression and anxiety was used and showed a significant decrease in the immobility time for

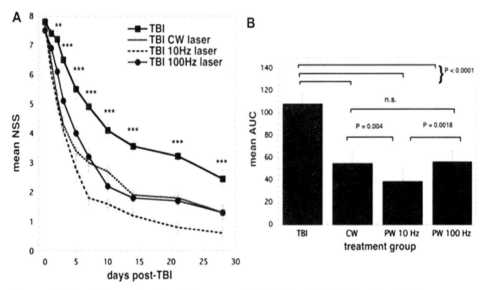

Figure 18.10 Effects of pulsing in transcranial PBM for CCI-TBI in mice. (a) Time course of the NSS of mice with TBI receiving either control (no laser treatment) or 810-nm laser (36 J/cm^2 delivered at 50 mW/cm^2 with a spot size of 0.78 cm^2 in either CW, PW 10-Hz, or PW 100-Hz modes). Results are expressed as mean ± S.E.M ***P < 0.001 vs. the other conditions. (b) Mean areas under the NSS time curves in the 2D coordinate system over the 28-day study for the four groups of mice. Results are means ± SD ($n = 10$).

the PW 10-Hz group. Again, by day 28 and also day 1, there was a significant decrease in the immobility time for the tail suspension test for depression and anxiety found in the PW 10-Hz group.

Both of these test results indicate an antidepressant effect of PBM. Note that severe depression is a major symptom of TBI in human patients. For the PW 10-Hz group at days 15 and 28, the lesion size in the PBM-treated TBI mice significantly decreased when compared to the non-laser-treated control group. These results may suggest a neuroprotective effect of PBM. Overall, the beneficial effects of PBM for TBI, including the antidepressant effects, the degree of injury, and the neuroprotective effects, were found to be more effective with the PW 10-Hz frequency compared to both the 100-Hz frequency and the continuous wave. Ando et al.[114] hypothesized that the PW 10-Hz laser irradiation frequency may be the best frequency to affect the entire brain. The pulsed light may have resonance with existing brain waves, such as theta waves that oscillate at 4 to 10 Hz found in the hippocampus (or a similar region).[115]

18.4.5 Effects of PBM regimen for TBI

The history of all the reported PBM studies has been found a persistent biphasic dose-response relationship that applies not only to cell-culture studies, but also to preclinical studies in animal models and to clinical studies of PBM.[116] Through many previous studies, including the ones discussed earlier, it is largely accepted that there is an optimal level of energy density, power density, and treatment regimen that is needed to create the most beneficial effects with PBM. Choosing suboptimal parameters may lead to a reduction in the beneficial effects and therefore a less-than-effective treatment, or even cause negative effects or adverse reactions.[106]

Xuan et al.[117] studied the effectiveness of varying treatment-repetition regimens of PBM on the neurobehavioral and vestibulomotor function, as well as neuroprotection and neurogenesis via histomorphological analysis and histological evidence. They used an 810-nm laser to deliver PBM to CCI mouse models of TBI. The mice were split into three groups and received PBM (CW 810-nm laser, 25 mW/cm^2 power density, 18 J/cm^2 energy density) either once at 4 h post-CCI, once a day for 3 days, or once a day for 14 days. They found that PBM may have beneficial effects as a treatment of TBI when treated with a single laser treatment and to a greater degree with three laser treatments. These two groups showed significant improvement in the NSS, motion tests, and wire grip test. However, in the group given 14 treatments, there was no significant improvement in any area. This paper also discussed that using PBM (once or three times) on mice with TBI could lead to improved neural function and smaller lesion size, and could possibly protect against neuronal damage in the brain.[117]

18.4.6 PBM has more effect on IEX knockout mice

Mild injury to the brain can sometimes trigger secondary brain injury that can lead to severe post-concussion syndrome. The mechanism behind these series of events is not well understood. Zhang et al.[118] shows that secondary brain injury occurs to a worse degree in mice that had been genetically engineered to the lack of an "immediate early response" gene X-1 (IEX-1) when exposed to a gentle head impact (this injury is thought to closely resemble mild TBI in humans). This secondary injury could be characterized by widespread leukocyte infiltrates and extensive cell death that leads to large amounts of tissue loss. A similar insult in wild-type mice (mice with intact IEX-1) did not produce any secondary injury. Exposing IEX-1 knockout mice to PBM 4 h post-injury suppressed the pro-inflammatory cytokine expression of interleukin (IL)-Iβ and IL-6, but up-regulated TNF-α. The lack of IEX-1 decreased ATP production, but exposing the injured brain to PBM elevated ATP production back to near-normal levels. The protective effect of PBM may be attributed to enhanced ATP production and the regulation of pro-inflammatory mediators. This new model of IEX knockout mice could be a good tool for investigating the pathways of secondary brain injury, as well as the mechanisms behind the beneficial effects of PBM.[118]

18.4.7 PBM in combination with metabolic inhibitors

Vascular damage occurs in injured brains and frequently leads to hypoxia, a result that often explains poor results in the clinic. Dong et al.[119] found that neurons cultured under hypoxia led to high levels of glycolysis, reduced levels of ATP generation, increased formation of ROS, and increased levels of apoptosis. The adverse effects of hypoxia were almost completely reversed after treatment with PBM. PBM maintained the mitochondrial membrane potential, constrained cytochrome c leakage in cells succumbing to hypoxia, and protected these cells from apoptosis. The beneficial effects of PBM were strengthened by combining the treatment with metabolic substrates such as pyruvate and/or lactate, both *in vivo* and *in vitro*. This combinatorial treatment was able to reverse memory and learning deficits in TBI-injured mice back to normal levels as well as leaving the hippocampal region completely protected from tissue loss; a stark contrast to control TBI mice that exhibited severe tissue loss from secondary brain injury. Dong et al.[119] concluded that metabolic modulators could work in concert with PBM to improve its beneficial effects in tissues that have low energy output, such as injured brain tissue.

18.4.8 PBM increases neuroprogenitor cells

Previous studies have shown that treating mice with CCI-induced TBI with PBM using an 810-nm laser after 4 h could significantly improve the NSS while decreasing lesion size. Xuan et al.[112] hypothesized that PBM could improve performance on the Morris water maze (MWM) for learning and memory, and increase neurogenesis in the hippocampus and subventricular zone (SVZ) after CCI TBI in mice. The TBI was created by subjecting the mice to a single right-lateral CCI using a pneumatic impact device with a 3-mm flat-tip rod at a speed of 4.8 m/s with an impact depth of 2 mm. TBI mice were given one of two treatments: one laser treatment 4 h post-TBI or three daily applications (once per day). Both the one-day and three-treatment groups showed an improvement in neurological performance as measured by the wire grip test and by the motion test, especially at 3 weeks and 4 weeks post-TBI. Improvements were found in visible and hidden platform latency and probe tests in MWM at 4 weeks. At 4 days post-TBI, caspase-3 expression was found at lower levels in the region of the lesion, and double-stained BrdU-NeuN (neuroprogenitor cells) was increased in the dentate gyrus and SVZ. Xuan et al.[120] suggested that PBM may improve TBI both by reducing cell death in the lesion and also by stimulating neurogenesis in the hippocampus and the SVZ.

18.4.9 PBM increases BDNF and synaptogenesis

Other studies have shown that applying NIR light to the head of animals with TBI improves neurological function, lessens the size of the brain lesion, reduces inflammation in the brain, and stimulates the formation of new neurons. Xuan et al.[121] examined the expression of brain-derived neurotrophic factor (BDNF) levels in CCI TBI mice treated with PBM. CCI TBI mice were subjected to two treatment regimens: either once 4 h post-TBI or three times daily with an 810-nm CW laser with an energy density of 36 J/cm^2 and a power density of 50 mW/cm^2. The NSS improved when compared to the untreated mice at day 14 and improved further by days 21 and 28. The mice given daily treatments for 3 days showed an even greater improvement when compared to the single-treatment group. After the mice were sacrificed at days 7 and 28 for analysis, it was found that BDNF was up-regulated by laser treatment in the dentate gyrus (DG) of the hippocampus and in the SVZ but not in the perilesional cortex (lesion). A marker of synaptogenesis, Synapsin-1, was up-regulated in the lesion and the SVZ but not in the DG (on day 28, but not on day 7). Xuan and colleagues found that the benefit of PBM to the brain is partly mediated by stimulation of BDNF production, which may encourage synaptogenesis. In turn, these benefits of BDNF suggest that PBM may have a broader application to neurodegenerative and psychiatric disorders.[121]

18.4.10 PBM in humans with TBI

Based on post-mortem observations, red or NIR light can penetrate through the skin and scalp and into the brain tissue 1 cm deep; consequently, the cortex of the brain receives an estimated 2–3% of the incident light. Naeser et al.[122] treated two patients with chronic TBI in a clinical study. In the first case study, the patient reported that her ability to concentrate on tasks for a longer period of time (time able to work at a computer increased from 30 minutes to 4 h), had a better ability to remember what she read, decreased sensitivity when receiving haircuts in the spots where PBM was applied, and improved mathematical skills after undergoing PBM. A 500-mW CW red/NIR LED with a power density of 25.8 mW/cm^2 (area of 19.29 cm^2) was applied to the forehead for a typical duration of 10 minutes (13.3 J/cm^2). After treatment, both TBI patients reported an improvement in sleep and a better ability to control their social behavior.[122] With a LED with a power density of 22.2 mW/cm^2 (area of 22.48 cm^2), the second patient had statistically significant improvements compared to prior neuropsychological tests after 9 months of treatment. The patient had a 2-standard-deviation (SD) increase in tests of inhibition and inhibition accuracy (9th percentile to 63rd percentile on the Stroop test for executive function) and a 1-SD increase on the Wechsler memory scale test for the logical memory test (83rd percentile to 99th percentile).[122]

Both of these reported case studies showed significant improvement in the patient's states of well-being despite variability in a number of different areas, including time of injury (2 years versus 7 years), cause of injury (motor vehicle accident versus injuries resulting from rugby, sky diving, military deployment, and accidental injury), ability to function (vegetative state versus medically disabled versus difficulties in concentration), medications (Concerta prior to LED treatments versus Lexapro changed to Ritalin 3 months into treatments with Provigil versus Armour thyroid replacement, liquid glutathione, and vitamin-B injections given twice weekly), and prior conditions (depression and suicidal thoughts versus PTSD). Naeser reported in open protocol case series that several patients showed improvement in PTSD.[123]

Nawashiro et al.[114] quantified cerebral blood flow using single-photon-emission computed tomography with N-isopropyl-p-iodoamphetamine (IMP-SPECT). In this case study, a single patient who was in a vegetative state following severe head trauma was administered 146 LED treatments over a period of 73 days with a device consisting of a grid of 23 820-nm LEDs (each 13 mW), with a power density of 11.4 mW/cm^2 and an energy density of 20.5 J/cm^2, that was held 5 mm from the head for 30 minutes per treatment. After delivering treatments bilaterally to the forehead, a 20% increase in blood flow in the left anterior frontal lobe was observed. The patient also showed slight movement in the left arm after treatment.

More clinical studies with much larger numbers of patients will be needed in order to better establish the determinants that affect the treatment response to the severity of the injury and the area affected together with studying which neurological functions have been altered. Collaboration among researchers will be necessary for gaining consistency of the results. Including measures such as MRI, IMP-SPECT and neuropsychiatric testing before and after testing will produce accurate and useful quantifications of the extent and location of brain injury, and the respective cerebral blood flow for that area.

18.5 PBM for Neurodegenerative Diseases

18.5.1 Neurodegenerative diseases

A neurodegenerative disease is a disorder caused by the deterioration of certain nerve cells (neurons). Changes in these cells cause them to function abnormally, eventually bringing about their death. The diseases—Alzheimer's disease, Parkinson's disease, and amyotrophic lateral sclerosis, as well as multiple sclerosis—are all due to neuronal degeneration in the CNS.[72] The chronic, unrelenting, and progressive nature of these devastating degenerative diseases has motivated the search for therapies that could slow down or arrest the downward course experienced by most patients; even more desirable would be a therapy that could actually reverse the neuronal damage. Transcranial light therapy is considered to have the potential to accomplish these goals.

18.5.1.1 Parkinson's disease

Parkinson's disease (PD) is a degenerative disorder of the central nervous system that often impairs the sufferer's motor skills, speech, and other functions.[73] Trimmer et al.[74] showed that NIR light therapy (810-nm diode laser, 50 mW/cm^2) can restore axonal transport to normal levels in sporadic PD human transmitochondrial cybrid "cytoplastic hybrid" neuronal cells.

The influence of laser therapy on the course of PD was studied in 70 patients. This influence appeared adaptogenic both in the group with elevated and low MAO B and Cu/Zn SOD activity. Laser therapy resulted in the reduction of neurological deficit and the normalization of the activity of MAO B, Cu/Zn-SOD, and immune indices.[75]

18.5.1.2 Alzheimer's disease

Alzheimer's disease (AD)—also called Alzheimer disease, senile dementia of the Alzheimer type (SDAT) or simply Alzheimer's—is the most common form of dementia.[76] Although the cause of AD is still unknown, impaired oxidative balance, mitochondrial dysfunction, and disordered CCO play important roles in the pathogenesis of the disease.[77,78] British Broadcasting Corporation (BBC) news reported that an experimental helmet made of 700 LEDs capable of delivering NIR light (1070 nm) was being tested by scientists as a treatment for AD. Current treatments for Alzheimer's delay progression of the disease but cannot reverse memory loss.[79]

18.5.1.3 Amyotrophic lateral sclerosis

Amyotrophic lateral sclerosis (ALS) is a progressive, usually fatal, neurodegenerative disease caused by the degeneration of motor neurons, the nerve cells in the CNS that control voluntary muscle movement. As a motor neuron disease, the disorder causes muscle weakness and atrophy throughout the body as both the upper and lower motor neurons degenerate, ceasing to send messages to muscles. Unable to function, the muscles gradually weaken, develop fasciculations (twitches) because of denervation, and eventually atrophy. Mitochondrial dysfunction and oxidative stress play an important role in motor neuron loss in ALS. Light therapy has biomodulatory effects on mitochondria. A study examined the synergistic effect of PBM and riboflavin on the survival of motor neurons in a mouse model of ALS.[80] They used an 810-nm diode laser with an 140-mW output power, 1.4-cm^2 spot area, 120-s treatment duration, and 12-J/cm^2 energy density. The results proved ineffective in altering disease progression in the G93A SOD1 mice using these laser parameters.[80]

18.6 PBM for Psychiatric Disorders

Light therapy has been widely used for some psychiatric disorders for nearly 30 years.[81] Light therapy has been tested in the following psychiatric disorders: seasonal affective disorder (SAD),[82] premenstrual dysphoric disorder,[83] antepartum and postpartum major depressive disorder,[84,85] bulimia nervosa,[86] and adult attention-deficit disorder.[87] These studies used full sunlight and products (such as light boxes) using very intense artificial illumination that are effective. Newer research indicates that a lower intensity of certain wavelengths of light, i.e., the "blue" wavelengths, may be at least as efficacious as using 2,500 lux.[88] Another approach to treating depression and other psychiatric disorders is the use of transcranial magnetic stimulation (TMS), which is a noninvasive method to excite neurons in the brain whereby weak electric currents are induced in the tissue by rapidly changing magnetic fields (electromagnetic induction). In this way, brain activity can be triggered with minimal discomfort, and the functionality of the circuitry and connectivity of the brain can be studied. Repetitive TMS can produce longer-lasting changes. Numerous small-scale pilot studies have shown it could be a treatment tool for various neurological conditions (e.g., migraine, stroke, Parkinson's Disease, dystonia, tinnitus) and psychiatric conditions (e.g., major depression, auditory hallucinations).[89] The success of TMS has suggested that similar stimulation could be applied to brain neurons using transcranial NIR light therapy, but as yet there are no authoritative publications and only anecdotal reports of success.

PBM in various forms has been applied in patients for treating psychiatric disorders such as depression,[90,91] smoking cessation,[92] and alcoholism.[93]

18.7 Conclusion

Transcranial PBM has strong evidence for many beneficial effects on TBI and stroke in both animal models and in patients. Both acute stroke and acute TBI have a growing number of studies being published that show that PBM is an effective means of treating both conditions. The many benefits of transcranial PBM are thought to be based on several different biological mechanisms. Near-infrared PBM functions by improving mitochondrial energy production by stimulating the enzyme CCO and increasing ATP synthesis. Laser therapy can result in neuroprotection and help prevent the spread of brain cell death after injury, as shown in the smaller lesion areas in mice treated with PBM. Protection against toxins, increased cellular proliferation, reduction in apoptosis, and anti-inflammatory and anti-edema effects may contribute to the mechanisms that underlie the beneficial effects of PBM. The most exciting prospect is the possibility that PBM may stimulate both neurogenesis (the ability of the brain to repair itself) and also synaptic plasticity (encourage existing cells to form new synaptic connections), which could lead to the eventual application of this treatment to neurodegenerative diseases such as Alzheimer's disease and Parkinson's disease.

References

1. J. C. Sutherland, "Biological effects of polychromatic light," *Photochem. Photobiol.* **76**(2), 164–70 (2002).
2. F. Antunes, A. Boveris, and E. Cadenas, "On the mechanism and biology of cytochrome oxidase inhibition by nitric oxide," *Proc. Natl. Acad. Sci. U S A* **101**(48), 16774–9 (2004).
3. T. Karu, "Primary and secondary mechanisms of action of visible to near-IR radiation on cells," *J. Photochem. Photobiol. B.* **49**(1), 1–17 (1999).
4. J. Khuman et al., "Low-level laser light therapy improves cognitive deficits and inhibits microglial activation after controlled cortical impact in mice," *J. Neurotrauma.* **29**(2), 408–17 (2012).
5. N. Lane, "Cell biology: power games," *Nature* **443**(7114), 901–3 (2006).
6. I. N. Mungrue, D. J. Stewart, and M. Husain, "The Janus faces of iNOS," *Circ Res* **93**(7), e74 (2003).
7. T. I. Karu and N. I. Afanas'eva, "Cytochrome c oxidase as the primary photoacceptor upon laser exposure of cultured cells to visible and near IR-range light," *Dokl. Akad. Nauk.* **342**(5), 693–5 (1995).
8. T. I. Karu and O. A. Tiflova, "Effect of low-intensity monochromatic visible light on the growth of Escherichia coli cultures," *Mikrobiologiia* **56**(4), 626–30 (1987).
9. R. A. Capaldi, F. Malatesta, and V. M. Darley-Usmar, "Structure of cytochrome c oxidase," *Biochim. Biophys. Acta.* **726**(2), 135–48 (1983).

10. T. I. Karu et al., "Absorption measurements of a cell monolayer relevant to phototherapy: reduction of cytochrome c oxidase under near IR radiation," *J. Photochem. Photobiol. B.* **81**(2), 98–106 (2005).

11. J. Khuman et al., "Tumor necrosis factor alpha and Fas receptor contribute to cognitive deficits independent of cell death after concussive traumatic brain injury in mice," *J. Cereb. Blood Flow Metab.* **31**(2), 778–89 (2011).

12. A. C. Chen et al., "Low-level laser therapy activates NF-κB via generation of reactive oxygen species in mouse embryonic fibroblasts," *PLoS One* **6**(7), e22453 (2011).

13. T. Dai, Y. Y. Huang, and M. R. Hamblin, "Photodynamic therapy for localized infections–state of the art," *Photodiagnosis Photodyn. Ther.* **6**(3–4), 170–88 (2009).

14. T. P. Obrenovitch and J. Urenjak, "Is high extracellular glutamate the key to excitotoxicity in traumatic brain injury?," *J. Neurotrauma.* **14**(10), 677–98 (1997).

15. T. I. Karu, L. V. Pyatibrat, and N. I. Afanasyeva, "Cellular effects of low power laser therapy can be mediated by nitric oxide," *Lasers Surg. Med.* **36**(4), 307–14 (2005).

16. N. L. Lohr et al., "Enhancement of nitric oxide release from nitrosyl hemoglobin and nitrosyl myoglobin by red/near infrared radiation: potential role in cardioprotection," *J. Mol. Cell Cardiol.* **47**(2), 256–63 (2009).

17. H. L. Liang et al., "Photobiomodulation partially rescues visual cortical neurons from cyanide-induced apoptosis," *Neuroscience* **139**(2), 639–49 (2006).

18. M. T. Wong-Riley et al., "Photobiomodulation directly benefits primary neurons functionally inactivated by toxins: role of cytochrome c oxidase," *J. Biol. Chem.* **280**(6), 4761–71 (2005).

19. J. T. Eells et al., "Therapeutic photobiomodulation for methanol-induced retinal toxicity," *Proc. Natl. Acad. Sci. U S A* **100**(6), 3439–44 (2003).

20. A. R. Coombe et al., "The effects of low level laser irradiation on osteoblastic cells," *Clin. Orthod. Res.* **4**(1), 3–14 (2001).

21. N. Hemvani, D. S. Chitnis, and N. S. Bhagwanani, "Helium-neon and nitrogen laser irradiation accelerates the phagocytic activity of human monocytes," *Photomed. Laser Surg.* **23**(6), 571–4 (2005).

22. S. L. Malinovskaya, V. A. Monich, and A. A. Artifeksova, "Effect of low-intensity laser irradiation and wideband red light on experimentally ischemized myocardium," *Bull. Exp. Biol. Med.* **145**(5), 573–5 (2008).

23. A. C. Chen et al., "Effects of 810-nm laser on murine bone-marrow-derived dendritic cells," *Photomed. Laser Surg.* **29**(6), 383–9 (2011).

24. A. M. Rocha Junior et al., "Low-level laser therapy increases transforming growth factor-beta2 expression and induces apoptosis of epithelial

cells during the tissue repair process," *Photomed. Laser Surg.* **27**(2), 303–7 (2009).

25. P. S. Bossini et al., "Low-level laser therapy (670 nm) on viability of random skin flap in rats," *Lasers Med. Sci.* **24**(2), 209–13 (2009).

26. A. V. Corazza et al., "Photobiomodulation on the angiogenesis of skin wounds in rats using different light sources," *Photomed. Laser Surg.* **25**(2), 102–6 (2007).

27. K. M. Pearson-Fuhrhop, J. A. Kleim, and S. C. Cramer, "Brain plasticity and genetic factors," *Top Stroke Rehabil.* **16**(4), 282–99 (2009).

28. S. Wan et al., "Transmittance of nonionizing radiation in human tissues," *Photochem. Photobiol.* **34**(6), 679–81 (1981).

29. E. Salomatina et al., "Optical properties of normal and cancerous human skin in the visible and near-infrared spectral range," *J. Biomed. Opt.* **11**(6), 064026 (2006).

30. V. V. Lychagov et al., *Experimental study of NIR transmittance of the human skull*, in *SPIE*, V. V. Tuchin, Editor. The International Society for Optical Engineering: San Jose, CA, USA. 200–204 (2006).

31. P. A. Wolf, "An overview of the epidemiology of stroke," *Stroke* **21**(9 Suppl), II4-6 (1990).

32. W. Rosamond et al., "Heart disease and stroke statistics–2008 update: a report from the American Heart Association Statistics Committee and Stroke Statistics Subcommittee," *Circulation* **117**(4), e25–146 (2008).

33. A. Durukan and T. Tatlisumak, "Acute ischemic stroke: overview of major experimental rodent models, pathophysiology, and therapy of focal cerebral ischemia," *Pharmacol. Biochem. Behav.* **87**(1), 179–97 (2007).

34. L. Edvinsson and D. N. Krause, *Cerebral Blood Flow and Metabolism* Second Edition ed., Philadelphia, PA: Lippincott, Williams and Wilkins. 521 (2002).

35. L. R. Caplan, ed. *Caplan's Stroke: A Clinical Approach* 3 ed., Butterworth-Heinemann: Boston (2000).

36. K. H. Taber, D. L. Warden, and R. A. Hurley, "Blast-related traumatic brain injury: what is known?," *J. Neuropsychiatry Clin. Neurosci.* **18**(2), 141–5 (2006).

37. A. M. Palmer et al., "Traumatic brain injury-induced excitotoxicity assessed in a controlled cortical impact model," *J. Neurochem.* **61**(6), 2015–24 (1993).

38. H. Pasantes-Morales and K. Tuz, "Volume changes in neurons: hyperexcitability and neuronal death," *Contrib. Nephrol.* **152**, 221–40 (2006).

39. M. Ahmad et al., "Stimulation of prostaglandin E2-EP3 receptors exacerbates stroke and excitotoxic injury," *J. Neuroimmunol.* **184**(1–2), 172–9 (2007).

40. C. Matute et al., "Excitotoxic damage to white matter," *J. Anat.* **210**(6), 693–702 (2007).

41. Y. Ikeda and D. M. Long, "The molecular basis of brain injury and brain edema: the role of oxygen free radicals," *Neurosurgery* **27**(1), 1–11 (1990).

42. L. Cherian and C. S. Robertson, "L-arginine and free radical scavengers increase cerebral blood flow and brain tissue nitric oxide concentrations after controlled cortical impact injury in rats," *J. Neurotrauma.* **20**(1), 77–85 (2003).

43. H. Adams et al., "Guidelines for the Early Management of Patients With Ischemic Stroke - 2005 guidelines update - A scientific statement from the Stroke Council of the American Heart Association/American Stroke Association," *Stroke.* **36**(4), 916–923 (2005).

44. P. Sandercock et al., "The third international stroke trial (IST-3) of thrombolysis for acute ischaemic stroke," *Trials.* **9**(1), 37 (2008).

45. O. Barushka, T. Yaakobi, and U. Oron, "Effect of low-energy laser (He-Ne) irradiation on the process of bone repair in the rat tibia," *Bone* **16**(1), 47–55 (1995).

46. G. A. Donnan et al., "Trials of streptokinase in severe acute ischaemic stroke," *Lancet.* **345**(8949), 578–9 (1995).

47. A. Furlan et al., "Intra-arterial prourokinase for acute ischemic stroke. The PROACT II study: a randomized controlled trial. Prolyse in Acute Cerebral Thromboembolism," *JAMA.* **282**(21), 2003–11 (1999).

48. J. L. Saver, "Time is brain–quantified," *Stroke.* **37**(1), 263–6 (2006).

49. W. Hacke et al., "Association of outcome with early stroke treatment: pooled analysis of ATLANTIS, ECASS, and NINDS rt-PA stroke trials," *Lancet.* **363**(9411), 768–74 (2004).

50. M. D. Ginsberg, "Neuroprotection for ischemic stroke: past, present and future," *Neuropharmacology.* **55**(3), 363–89 (2008).

51. J. Streeter, L. De Taboada, and U. Oron, "Mechanisms of action of light therapy for stroke and acute myocardial infarction," *Mitochondrion.* **4**(5–6), 569–76 (2004).

52. A. Oron et al., "Low-level laser therapy applied transcranially to rats after induction of stroke significantly reduces long-term neurological deficits," *Stroke.* **37**(10), 2620–4 (2006).

53. Y. Lampl, "Laser treatment for stroke," *Expert Rev Neurother* **7**(8), 961–5 (2007).

54. M. Philip et al., "Methodological quality of animal studies of neuroprotective agents currently in phase II/III acute ischemic stroke trials," *Stroke.* **40**(2), 577–81 (2009).

55. D. I. Azbel et al., "The effect of the blood serum from patients subjected to intravenous laser therapy on the parameters of synaptic transmission," *Biull. Eksp. Biol. Med.* **116**(8), 149–51 (1993).

56. N. Ad and U. Oron, "Impact of low level laser irradiation on infarct size in the rat following myocardial infarction," *Int J Cardiol* **80**(2–3), 109–16 (2001).

57. M. C. Leung et al., "Treatment of experimentally induced transient cerebral ischemia with low energy laser inhibits nitric oxide synthase activity and up-regulates the expression of transforming growth factor-beta 1," *Lasers Surg. Med.* **31**(4), 283–8 (2002).

58. P. A. Lapchak, J. Wei, and J. A. Zivin, "Transcranial infrared laser therapy improves clinical rating scores after embolic strokes in rabbits," *Stroke.* **35**(8), 1985–8 (2004).

59. P. A. Lapchak et al., "Transcranial near-infrared light therapy improves motor function following embolic strokes in rabbits: an extended therapeutic window study using continuous and pulse frequency delivery modes," *Neuroscience.* **148**(4), 907–14 (2007).

60. P. A. Lapchak and D. M. Araujo, "Advances in ischemic stroke treatment: neuroprotective and combination therapies," *Expert Opin. Emerg. Drugs.* **12**(1), 97–112 (2007).

61. L. Detaboada et al., "Transcranial application of low-energy laser irradiation improves neurological deficits in rats following acute stroke," *Lasers Surg. Med.* **38**(1), 70–3 (2006).

62. L. Zhang et al., "Quantitative measurement of motor and somatosensory impairments after mild (30 min) and severe (2 h) transient middle cerebral artery occlusion in rats," *J. Neurol. Sci.* **174**(2), 141–6 (2000).

63. Y. Lampl et al., "Infrared laser therapy for ischemic stroke: a new treatment strategy: results of the NeuroThera Effectiveness and Safety Trial-1 (NEST-1)," *Stroke.* **38**(6), 1843–9 (2007).

64. J. A. Zivin et al., "Effectiveness and safety of transcranial laser therapy for acute ischemic stroke," *Stroke.* **40**(4), 1359–64 (2009).

65. J. A. Zivin et al., "NeuroThera(R) Efficacy and Safety Trial-3 (NEST-3): a double-blind, randomized, sham-controlled, parallel group, multicenter, pivotal study to assess the safety and efficacy of transcranial laser therapy with the NeuroThera(R) Laser System for the treatment of acute ischemic stroke within 24 h of stroke onset," *Int. J. Stroke.* **9**(7), 950–5 (2014).

66. G. M. Teasdale and D. I. Graham, "Craniocerebral trauma: protection and retrieval of the neuronal population after injury," *Neurosurgery* **43**(4), 723–37; discussion 737–8 (1998).

67. A. Oron et al., "low-level laser therapy applied transcranially to mice following traumatic brain injury significantly reduces long-term neurological deficits," *J. Neurotrauma.* **24**(4), 651–6 (2007).

68. S. Rochkind et al., "Transplantation of embryonal spinal cord nerve cells cultured on biodegradable microcarriers followed by low power laser irradiation for the treatment of traumatic paraplegia in rats," *Neurol. Res.* **24**(4), 355–60 (2002).

69. S. Rochkind et al., "Efficacy of 780-nm laser phototherapy on peripheral nerve regeneration after neurotube reconstruction procedure (double-blind randomized study)," *Photomed. Laser Surg.* **25**(3), 137–43 (2007).

70. K. R. Byrnes et al., "Light promotes regeneration and functional recovery and alters the immune response after spinal cord injury," *Lasers Surg. Med.* **36**(3), 171–85 (2005).

71. X. Wu et al., "810 nm Wavelength light: an effective therapy for transected or contused rat spinal cord," *Lasers Surg. Med.* **41**(1), 36–41 (2009).

72. R. M. Friedlander, "Apoptosis and caspases in neurodegenerative diseases," *N. Engl. J. Med.* **348**(14), 1365–75 (2003).

73. J. Jankovic, "Parkinson's disease: clinical features and diagnosis," *J. Neurol. Neurosurg. Psychiatry.* **79**(4), 368–76 (2008).

74. P. A. Trimmer et al., *Reduced axonal transport in Parkinson's disease cybrid neurites is restored by light therapy, in Mol Neurodegener.* (2009).

75. L. V. Komel'kova et al., *Biochemical and immunological induces of the blood in Parkinson's disease and their correction with the help of laser therapy*, Patol Fiziol Eksp Ter, (1): 15–8 (2004).

76. D. J. Selkoe, "Alzheimer's disease: genes, proteins, and therapy," *Physiol. Rev.* **81**(2), 741–66 (2001).

77. M. A. Smith et al., "Oxidative stress in Alzheimer's disease," *Biochim. Biophys. Acta.* **1502**(1), 139–44 (2000).

78. P. G. Sullivan and M. R. Brown, "Mitochondrial aging and dysfunction in Alzheimer's disease," *Prog. Neuropsychopharmacol. Biol. Psychiatry.* **29**(3), 407–10 (2005).

79. *Alzheimer's helmet therapy hope* [BBC News] 1/25/2008 [cited 2009 2/25/ 2009]; Health:[Available from: http://news.bbc.co.uk/go/pr/fr/-/2/hi/health/ 7208768.stm.

80. H. Moges et al., "Light therapy and supplementary Riboflavin in the SOD1 transgenic mouse model of familial amyotrophic lateral sclerosis (FALS)," *Lasers Surg. Med.* **41**(1), 52–9 (2009).

81. D. F. Kripke, S. C. Risch, and D. Janowsky, "Bright white light alleviates depression," *Psychiatry Res.* **10**(2), 105–12 (1983).

82. J. S. Terman et al., "Efficacy of brief, intense light exposure for treatment of winter depression," *Psychopharmacol. Bull.* **26**(1), 3–11 (1990).

83. B. L. Parry et al., "Morning versus evening bright light treatment of late luteal phase dysphoric disorder," *Am. J. Psychiatry.* **146**(9), 1215–7 (1989).

84. C. N. Epperson et al., "Randomized clinical trial of bright light therapy for antepartum depression: preliminary findings," *J. Clin. Psychiatry.* **65**(3), 421–5 (2004).

85. M. Corral, A. Kuan, and D. Kostaras, "Bright light therapy's effect on postpartum depression," *Am. J. Psychiatry.* **157**(2), 303–4 (2000).

86. R. W. Lam et al., "A controlled study of light therapy for bulimia nervosa," *Am. J. Psychiatry.* **151**(5), 744–50 (1994).

87. Y. E. Rybak et al., "An open trial of light therapy in adult attention-deficit/hyperactivity disorder," *J. Clin. Psychiatry.* **67**(10), 1527–35 (2006).

88. A. Wirz-Justice et al., "Light therapy in seasonal affective disorder is independent of time of day or circadian phase," *Arch. Gen. Psychiatry.* **50**(12), 929–37 (1993).

89. A. Pascual-Leone et al., *Handbook of Transcranial Magnetic Stimulation*, London (UK): Oxford University Press, 416 2002.

90. J. I. Quah-Smith, W. M. Tang, and J. Russell, "Laser acupuncture for mild to moderate depression in a primary care setting–a randomised controlled trial," *Acupunct. Med.* **23**(3), 103–11 (2005).

91. A. Gur et al., "Effects of low power laser and low dose amitriptyline therapy on clinical symptoms and quality of life in fibromyalgia: a single-blind, placebo-controlled trial," *Rheumatol. Int.* **22**(5), 188–93 (2002).

92. C. Yiming et al., "Laser acupuncture for adolescent smokers–a randomized double-blind controlled trial," *Am. J. Chin. Med.* **28**(3–4), 443–9 (2000).

93. J. Zalewska-Kaszubska and D. Obzejta, "Use of low-energy laser as adjunct treatment of alcohol addiction," *Lasers Med. Sci.* **19**(2), 100–4 (2004).

94. J. Bruns Jr. and W. A. Hauser, "The epidemiology of traumatic brain injury: a review," *Epilepsia* **44**(Suppl 10), 2–10 (2003).

95. J. F. Kraus and D. L. McArthur, "Epidemiologic aspects of brain injury," *Neurol. Clin.* **14**(2), 435–50 (1996).

96. D. M. Sosin, J. E. Sniezek, and D. J. Thurman, "Incidence of mild and moderate brain injury in the United States, 1991," *Brain Inj.* **10**(1), 47–54 (1996).

97. D. J. Thurman et al., "Traumatic brain injury in the United States: A public health perspective," *J. Head Trauma. Rehabil.* **14**(6), 602–15 (1999).

98. S. R. Finfer and J. Cohen, "Severe traumatic brain injury," *Resuscitation.* **48**(1), 77–90 (2001).

99. R. Vink and A. J. Nimmo, "Multifunctional drugs for head injury," *Neurotherapeutics.* **6**(1), 28–42 (2009).

100. B. J. Zink, J. Szmydynger-Chodobska, and A. Chodobski, "Emerging concepts in the pathophysiology of traumatic brain injury," *Psychiatr. Clin. North Am.* **33**(4), 741–56 (2010).

101. N. Marklund and L. Hillered, "Animal modelling of traumatic brain injury in preclinical drug development: where do we go from here?," *Br. J. Pharmacol.* **164**(4), 1207–29 (2011).

102. J. Marler, "Tissue plasminogen activator for acute ischemic stroke. The National Institute of Neurological Disorders and Stroke rt-PA Stroke Study Group," *N. Engl. J. Med.* **333**(24), 1581–7 (1995).

103. T. Thom et al., "Heart disease and stroke statistics–2006 update: a report from the American Heart Association Statistics Committee and Stroke Statistics Subcommittee," *Circulation.* **113**(6), e85–151 (2006).

104. U. Oron et al., "Low-energy laser irradiation reduces formation of scar tissue after myocardial infarction in rats and dogs," *Circulation.* **103**(2), 296–301 (2001).

105. T. Yaakobi et al., "Long-term effect of low energy laser irradiation on infarction and reperfusion injury in the rat heart," *J. Appl. Physiol. (1985)* **90**(6), 2411–9 (2001).

106. H. Chung et al., "The nuts and bolts of low-level laser (light) therapy," *Ann. Biomed. Eng.* **40**(2), 516–33 (2012).

107. M. J. Conlan, J. W. Rapley, and C. M. Cobb, "Biostimulation of wound healing by low-energy laser irradiation. A review," *J. Clin. Periodontol.* **23**(5), 492–6 (1996).

108. N. Mirsky et al., "Promotion of angiogenesis by low energy laser irradiation," *Antioxid. Redox. Signal.* **4**(5), 785–90 (2002).

109. A. Oron et al., "Near infrared transcranial laser therapy applied at various modes to mice following traumatic brain injury significantly reduces long-term neurological deficits," *J. Neurotrauma.* **29**(2), 401–7 (2012).

110. B. J. Quirk et al., "Therapeutic effect of near infrared (NIR) light on Parkinson's disease models," *Front Biosci. (Elite Ed).* **4**, 818–23 (2012).

111. M. S. Moreira et al., "Effect of phototherapy with low intensity laser on local and systemic immunomodulation following focal brain damage in rat," *J. Photochem. Photobiol. B.* **97**(3), 145–51 (2009).

112. Q. Wu et al., "Low-level laser therapy for closed-head traumatic brain injury in mice: effect of different wavelengths," *Lasers Surg. Med.* **44**(3), 218–26 (2012).

113. T. Ando et al., "Comparison of therapeutic effects between pulsed and continuous wave 810-nm wavelength laser irradiation for traumatic brain injury in mice," *PLoS One* **6**(10), e26212 (2011).

114. H. Nawashiro et al., "Focal increase in cerebral blood flow after treatment with near-infrared light to the forehead in a patient in a persistent vegetative state," *Photomed. Laser Surg.* **30**(4), 231–3 (2012).

115. B. S. Sushko, P. Lymans'kyi Iu, and S. O. Huliar, "Action of the red and infrared electromagnetic waves of light-emitting diodes on the behavioral manifestation of somatic pain," *Fiziol. Zh.* **53**(3), 51–60 (2007).

116. Y. Y. Huang et al., "Biphasic dose response in low level light therapy," *Dose Response* **7**(4), 358–83 (2009).

117. W. Xuan et al., "Transcranial low-level laser therapy improves neurological performance in traumatic brain injury in mice: effect of treatment repetition regimen," *PLoS One* **8**(1), e53454 (2013).

118. Q. Zhang et al., "Low-level laser therapy effectively prevents secondary brain injury induced by immediate early responsive gene X-1 deficiency," *J. Cereb. Blood Flow Metab.* **34**(8), 1391–401 (2014).

119. T. Dong et al., "Low-level light in combination with metabolic modulators for effective therapy of injured brain," *J. Cereb. Blood Flow Metab.* **35**(9), 1435–44 (2015).

120. W. Xuan et al., "Low-level laser therapy for traumatic brain injury in mice increases brain derived neurotrophic factor (BDNF) and synaptogenesis," *J. Biophotonics.* **8**(6), 502–11 (2015).

121. W. Xuan et al., "Transcranial low-level laser therapy enhances learning, memory, and neuroprogenitor cells after traumatic brain injury in mice," *J. Biomed. Opt.* **19**(10), 108003 (2014).

122. M. A. Naeser et al., "Improved language in a chronic nonfluent aphasia patient after treatment with CPAP and TMS," *Cogn. Behav. Neurol.* **23**(1), 29–38 (2010).

123. M. A. Naeser et al., "Significant improvements in cognitive performance post-transcranial, red/near-infrared light-emitting diode treatments in chronic, mild traumatic brain injury: open-protocol study," *J. Neurotrauma.* **31**(11):1008–17 (2014 Jun 1) [doi: 10.1089/neu.2013.3244].

Chapter 19
Intravascular Laser Irradiation of Blood

Daiane Thais Meneguzzo, Leila Soares Ferreira, Eduardo Machado de Carvalho, and Cássia Fukuda Nakashima

19.1 Introduction

Intravascular laser irradiation of blood (ILIB) is a systemic low-level laser modality that aims the irradiation of the blood. The process was first reported by Russian scientists in the 1970s and consists of laser blood irradiation through a fiber optic inserted in a vascular channel, usually a vein in the forearm. ILIB irradiation takes about 30 minutes, time assumed to be sufficient for the whole blood to receive light and enable a systemic effect. Thus, the components of the blood, i.e., blood lipids, platelets, immune system, and red cells, are the main targets.

Although the mechanisms of ILIB are uncertain and need to be assessed by further randomized controlled trials and clinical reports, many studies from Russia show the favorable effects of the technique. ILIB has been studied for a wide range of medical conditions, including diabetes mellitus, asthma, chronic hepatitis, multiple sclerosis, cardiovascular diseases, hypertension, and autoimmune diseases.[1–6]

This chapter presents a summary of the main indications and effects of ILIB in order to introduce this promising "new" treatment modality. The goal is to stimulate new research into the mechanisms of action and propose that further randomized clinical studies should be conducted. New forms of noninvasive systemic irradiation have already been developed, and they appear to be promising, such as modified and intranasal ILIB techniques.

19.2 History of ILIB

In the 70s, the Russians began research into ILIB with a helium-neon (HeNe) laser, at a wavelength of 632.8 nm, based on the works of Mester et al.[6] This method was originally developed for the treatment of cardiovascular diseases. Furthermore, improvements to the blood rheologic properties and microcirculation, as well as a reduction of the infarction area, have been proved. Basic research into the mechanisms of action of the laser also saw a significant increase, showing the anti-oxidant effect of ILIB therapy by reactivation of the superoxide dismutase (SOD) enzyme.[7] SOD is a key enzyme that controls the levels of free radicals, leads to hemostasis, and prevents many systemic diseases.

The first laser used was a HeNe laser (632.8 nm) with a power of 1–3 mW and a period of exposure of 20–60 minutes. The technique inserts an intravenous catheter in one of the upper limbs, coupled to an optical fiber that irradiates blood with laser light directly and continuously at the application site, distributing that irradiated blood through the circulation throughout the body (Fig. 19.1). The treatments are usually conducted once or twice a day, up to ten appointments.

Most of the Russian studies published since the 70s using the ILIB technique were little known in the West because of decades of political separation, and they were therefore regarded with disapproval. Thus, ILIB suffered decades of discredit due to the lack of scientific evidence regarding the mechanisms of action of laser therapy. At that time, laser therapy was very unclear and empirical, and only the group of the cell biologist Tina Karu was studying the mechanisms of action.

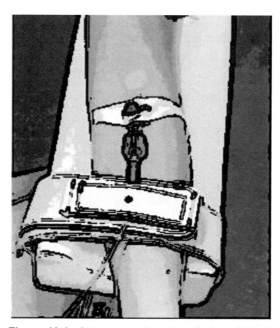

Figure 19.1   Intravenous laser irradiation of blood.

New studies and clinical findings published in Russian magazines contribute to the permanence of ILIB and encourage more scientists to research about it. Many Western studies of great scientific importance in the laser field brought a better understanding of the mechanisms of action of laser therapy to elucidate many of the effects previously reported by the Russians.[7,8]

Among the laser-therapy mechanisms known today, this chapter highlights the light action on the cell membrane, a mechanism that may explain the activation of immune cells, mast cell degranulation, and modulation of lipids and other blood components; light shutdown of NO from hemoglobin, which improves oxygenation of the blood and vasodilatation; and cell biostimulation by light absorption of mitochondrial enzymes (mainly cytochrome c oxidase), which reactivates the cellular metabolism (ATP, ROS, TNF-α) and acts on red and endothelial cells. The induction of an electric field polarizes blood substances to the center of the vessel, temporarily increasing blood flow,[9] and the reactivation of the endogenous SOD enzyme[7] prevents many systemic diseases due to its anti-oxidant activity. It is believed that the SOD effect is the main mechanism of action of ILIB, and therefore this techinique is also claimed as an anti-oxidant and anti-aging therapy.

19.3 Antioxidant Action of ILIB

In the body, cells produce free radicals during the oxygen-combustion process that convert the nutrients absorbed from food into energy. External factors may also contribute to the increased formation of these molecules: environmental pollution; x-ray and UV radiation; cigarettes; alcohol; pesticide residues; substances present in foods and beverages (chemical additives, preservatives, hormones); stress; and the consumption of saturated fats and animal fat.

The interaction of numerous free radicals with the biological system, regardless of their source, can result in significant health consequences, contributing to the development of certain pathologies such as aging itself, Parkinson's, cancer, arthritis, and cardiovascular and cardiorespiratory complications, among others.

To combat these damaging effects, the body uses its defense system. The enzyme system is the main way of combating free radicals by preventing their formation or neutralizing them. Among the enzymes involved in the enzymatic defense system of the body, the SOD enzyme plays the primary role. SOD inhibits the superoxide ion, which is the first free radical formed from molecular oxygen and serves as a substrate for triggering the formation of radicals more harmful, such as hydroxyl (OH).

SOD is the fifth most abundant enzyme in the body. However, in some pathological situations, e.g., blood acid conditions, inflammation, and chronic diseases, the enzyme can be deactivated. Laser radiation of the inactive SOD proved capable of reactivating the enzyme, even with acidic pH conditions within which the inactivation occurs in pathological situations.[7] Thus, ILIB could reverse the oxidative stress present in various diseases.

Treatment with ILIB is aimed at treating the patient for functional recovery of its antioxidant enzyme system, balancing the individual as a whole, to provide a functional optimization of each system. The effects of ILIB and the diseases treated by the ILIB technique are summarized in Tables A.4 and A.5, respectively.

19.4 Modified ILIB Techniques

The original ILIB technique introduced by the Russians presents a great disadvantage: the invasive way in which irradiation occurs. Recent Chinese literature and clinical practice in Brazil have suggested other forms of systemic noninvasive irradiation, such as intranasal laser irradiation and skin irradiation performed on the wrist. This modification in the form of irradiation allows more frequent use of the technique and expands its applicability to patients in their own home (home care treatment).

19.4.1 Intranasal irradiation

From 1989 on, many Russian groups have studied the therapeutic effects of intranasal laser photobiomodulation (ILPBM) on the local inflammation in vasomotor rhinitis.[66] In the mainland of China, ILPBM has been studied to treat internal diseases; special treatment began in 1998 and was called intranasal low-intensity laser therapy (ILILT).

The technique involves attaching a diode laser device (mainly 650–660 nm) with power of 10–30 mW inside the nose (Fig. 19.2). The treatment protocol varies from 15 to 30 minutes per day, daily or not, for 10 days (consecutively or not). There are four suggested pathways mediating the ILILT: the olfactory nerve, blood cells, meridians in traditional Chinese medicine, and the autonomic nervous system. ILILT has been applied to treat cerebral injury,[67] allergic rhinitis,[68] the blood-stasis syndrome of coronary heart disease, myocardial infarction, and brain diseases such as insomnia, intractable headache, Alzheimer's disease, diabetic peripheral neropaty, and acute ischemic cerebrovascular disease.[69]

19.4.2 Wrist skin irradiation

The advancement of technology has produced more powerful diode lasers, which contributed to the notion (introduced by Brazilian researchers a few years ago) of noninvasively irradiating the skin on the wrist to reach the blood vessels. The idea was supported by local industry that developed a special device to perform this modified ILIB (MILIB) technique (Fig. 19.3). This

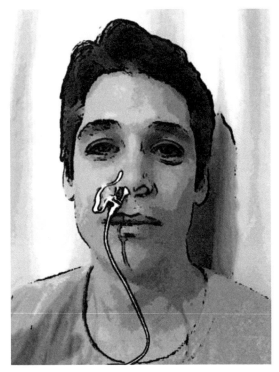

Figure 19.2 Intranal laser irradiation.

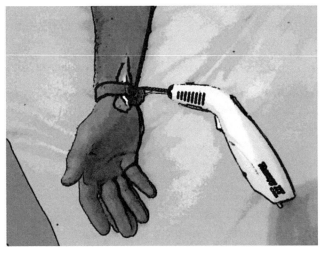

Figure 19.3 Wrist-skin laser irradiation with modified ILIB.

technique and its benefits became known either by health professionals and between patients. Among the advantages of the traditional ILIB technique, patients reported improvements in sleep quality, improved emotional state, and increased sports performance and physical and mental disposition in general. These effects, however, have not been published yet.

The MILIB technique comprises a low-level red (660 nm) diode laser with a power of 60–100 mW. The laser optical fiber is placed on the skin of the wrist region (acupuncture point region lung 8) secured with the aid of an elastic band. The irradiation is performed for 30 minutes continuously, and the dosage varies from once a week for ten weeks up to daily application for 10 days, depending on the type of disease.

All of these new ILIB techniques need to be better studied and researched. Further investigations of the irradiation time, amount of light, and rate of light absorption by the irradiated blood vessels are required.

19.5 ILIB Side Effects and Contraindications

There is no information in the literature about the side effects of ILIB. However, the contraindications of laser therapy itself should be considered for ILIB, especially the use of laser in patients without diagnosis, with blood tumors, pregnant women, and pre-surgery period (ILIB can increase bleeding).

References

1. A. A. Spasov, V. V. Nedogoda, K. Konan, and A. F. Kucheriavenko, "Effect of the intravenous laser blood irradiation on efficacy of drug preparations," *Eksp. Klin. Farmakol.* **63**(5), 65–67 (2000).
2. P. G. Shval'b, A. Zakharchenko, A. A. Sigaev, and M. I. Kataev, "Intravenous laser irradiation of the blood in occlusive vascular diseases of the extremities," *Sòv. Med.* **3**, 21–23 (1990).
3. N. M. Burduli and O. M. Aleksandrova, "Effect of intravenous laser blood irradiation on endothelial dysfunction in patients with hypertensive disease," *Klin. Med. (Mosk)* **87**(6), 22–25 (2009).
4. T. G. Sarycheva, E. B. Tsybzhitova, O. V. Popova, and O. V. Aleksandrov, "Morphometry and electrophoretic mobility of red blood cells from patients with asthma in the intravenous blood laser irradiation," *Klin. Lab. Diagn.* **3**, 13–14 (2009).
5. A. S. Shakhova, A. G. Kulikov, and I. M. Korsunskaia, "The application of intravenous laser irradiation of the blood for the combined treatment of psoriasis," *Vop. Kurortol. Fizioter. Lech. Fiz. Kult.* **1**, 24–28 (2012).
6. E. Mester, T. Spiry, B. Szende, and J. G. Tota, "Effect of laser radiation on the wound healing," *Z. Exp. Chir.* **4**(5), 307–312 (1971).
7. Y. A. Vladimirov, A. N. Osipov, and G. I. Klebanov, "Photobiological principles of therapeutic applications of laser radiation," *Biochemistry (Mosc)* **69**(1), 81–90 (2004).

8. H. Chung, T. Dai, S. K. Sharma, Y. Y. Huang, J. D. Carroll, and M. R. Hamblin, "The nuts and bolts of low-level laser (light) therapy," *Ann. Biomed. Eng.* **40**(2), 516–533 (2012).

9. A. Amat, J. Rigau, R. W. Waynant, I. K. Ilev, and J. J. Anders, "The electric field induced by light can explain cellular responses to electromagnetic energy: a hypothesis of mechanism," *J. Photochem. Photobiol. B.* **82**(2), 152–160 (2006).

10. E. V. Lebed'kov, P. I. Tolstykh, L. F. Marchenko, T. I. Turkina, and V. T. Krivikhin, "The effect of the laser irradiation of the blood on its lipid and phospholipid components in diabetes mellitus," *Voen. Med. Zh.* **319**(10), 37–38 (1998).

11. M. V. Poluéktova, I. L. Kharchenko, M. A. Kaplan, N. I. Sokol, L. M. Ershova, O. V. Borgul', T. V. Chirkova, and O. A. Vorob'eva, "The development of method of intravenous laser irradiation of blood with green laser in patients with hyperlipidemia," *Klin. Lab. Diagn.* **8**, 15–17 (2011).

12. S. F. Huang, Y. A. Tsai, S. B. Wu, Y. H. Wei, P. Y. Tsai, and T. Y. Chuang, "Effects of intravascular laser irradiation of blood in mitochondria dysfunction and oxidative stress in adults with chronic spinal cord injury," *Photomed. Laser. Surg.* **30**(10), 579–586 (2012).

13. A. V. Babaev, D. E. Gogolev, O. V. Reiner, I. M. Korochkin, A. V. Fandeev, V. Y. Pivovarov, Y. N. Fedulaev, and K. M. Drachan, "Effect of intravenous low-intensity laser irradiation of the blood on clinical and laboratory parameters of hepatocellular insufficiency," *Bull. Exp. Biol. Med.* **153**(5), 754–757 (2012).

14. D. I. Azbel', T. A. Zapara, I. Iu. Kuznetsova, A. S. Ratushniak, S. M. Shergin, A. M. Shurgaia, and M. B. Shtark, "Changes in the neural activity of the blood serum from patients with ischemic heart disease. Biull.," *Eksp. Biol. Med.* **116**(8), 161–163 (1993).

15. R. M. Safafov, E. K. Ianenko, L. P. Nikitinskaia, S. A. Golovanov, V. V. Drozhzheva, T. A. Kon'kova, and A. P. Danilkov, "The dynamic level of beta 2-microglobulin, the basic lipid peroxidation indices and middle molecules in the blood and urine in patients with acute calculous pyelonephritis against a background of endovascular helium-neon laser therapy," *Urol. Nefrol. (Mosk)* **1**, 11–13 (1997).

16. A. N. Karneev, E. Iu. Solov'eva, and A. I. Fedin, "Correction of free-radical processes in patients with chronic brain ischemia with intravenous laser irradiation of blood," *Vopr. Kurortol. Fizioter. Lech. Fiz. Kult.* **3**, 22–26 (2007).

17. Iu. N. Sirenko, S. Iu. Savitskiĭ, S. S. Krasnitskiĭ, A. V. Shabil'ianov, and L. I. Popova, "The use of low-intensity laser irradiation of the blood in myocardial infarction," *Sov. Med.* **3**, 18–21 (1990).

18. L. V. Prokopova, A. A. Losev, and Iu. I. Ursol, "Effect of intravascular laser therapy on the rheologic properties of blood in children with bilateral destructive pneumonia," *Klin Khir.* **6**, 7–9 (1992).

19. P. G. Shval'b, A. E. Kachinskiĭ, V. I. Kolobaev, and M. I. Kataev, "Intravenous laser irradiation of the blood in severe forms of chronic venous insufficiency," *Vestn. Khir. Im. I. I. Grek.* **149**, 78–80 (1992).

20. A. G. Brill, B. Shenkman, G. E. Brill, I. Tamarin, R. Dardik, V. F. Kirichuk, N. Savion, and D. Varon, "Blood irradiation by He-Ne laser induces a decrease in platelet responses to physiological agonists and an increase in platelet cyclic GMP," *Platelets* **11**(2), 87–93 (2000).

21. N. R. Paleev, V. I. Karandashov, M. A. Voronina, and I. A. Fin'ko, "Changes in the blood rheological properties in the transcutaneous irradiation of the ulnar vascular fascicle with a helium-neon laser," *Biull. Eksp. Biol. Med.* **116**(10), 428–430 (1993).

22. X. Gao, P. K. Zhi, and X. Wu, "Low-energy semiconductor laser intranasal irradiation of the blood improves blood coagulation status in normal pregnancy at term," *Nan. Fang. Yi Ke Da Xue Xue Bao.* **28**(8), 1400–1401 (2008).

23. A. E. Dmitriev, V. A. Iudin, N. A. Arapov, and V. A. Martynov, "Effect of intravascular laser irradiation of the blood on blood cells in pancreatitis," *Klin. Med. (Mosk)* **67**(5), 108–110 (1989).

24. I. H. Kupnovyts'ka, "Laser irradiation of the blood in patients with refractory tachyarrhythmias," *Lik. Sprava.* **10**, 38–41 (1992).

25. V. T. Palćhun, A. S. Lapchednko, and A. G. Kucherov, "Intravascular laser irradiation of the blood in the treatment of suppurative septic complications in otorhinolaryngology," *Vestn. Otorinolaringol.* **2**, 8–10 (1995).

26. V. N. Koshelev and Iu. V. Chalyk, "Intravascular laser irradiation of blood in treatment of traumatic abdominal organs injuries," *Khirurgiia (Mosk)* **5**, 40–42 (1998).

27. V. L. Hanul, S. L. Zaĭtsev, S. I. Kirkilevs'kyĭ, and F. V. Fil'chakov, "Intravascular laser irradiation of the blood in complex treatment of the patient with esophageal cancer," *Klin. Khir.* **5**, 27–29 (1999).

28. V. V. Stupak and E. N. Rodiukova, "The possibility of immunocorrection in spinal-spinal cord trauma by using intravenous laser irradiation," *Zh. Vopr. Neirokhir. Im. N. N. Burdenko.* **1**, 20–25 (1999).

29. I. K. Dedenko, "Effect of intravenous laser irradiation of blood on the homeostasis in patients with hemorrhagic pancreatitis," *Klin Med (Mosk)* **67**(8), 70–73 (1989).

30. I. K. Marchuk and V. N. Kuzmich, "Intravascular laser irradiation of the blood in the combined treatment of chronic suppurative lung diseases," *Klin. Khir.* **6**, 9–10 (1993).

31. I. G. Alizade and N. T. Karaeva, "Experience in the use of autotransfusions of laser-irradiated blood in treating hypertension patients," *Lik. Sprava.* **5–6**, 29–32 (1994).

32. V. D. Sidorov, D. R. Mamiliaeva, E. V. Gontar', and S. Iu. Reformatskaia, "The interauricular laser therapy of rheumatoid arthritis. Vop. Kurortol. Fizioter," *Lech. Fiz. Kult.* **3**, 35–43 (1999).

33. V. E. Tsvettsikh, V. R. Sultanbaev, B. A. Berdichevskiĭ, N. I. Kazeko, A. A. Ovchinnikov, R. A. Sultanbaev, and A. V. Murychev, "Endovascular Helium-Neon laser irradiation of the blood in the treatment of chronic pyelonephritis," *Urologiia* **6**, 13–15 (1999).

34. D. A. Chiran, M. Weber, L. M. Ailioaie, E. Moraru, C. Ailioaie, D. Litscher, and G. Litscher, "Intravenous laser blood irradiation and tocilizumab in a patient with juvenile arthritis," *Case. Rep. Med.* **2014**, 923496 (2014).

35. V. G. Tsuman, A. E. Mashkov, V. I. Shcherbina, M. S. Surovkina, and N. V. Sinenkova, "Intracavitary laser therapy and its effect on the kallikrein-kinin system of blood in children with pneumothorax," *Vestn. Ross. Akad. Med. Nauk.* **9**, 20–26 (2005).

36. V. V. Polosukhin, "Ultrastructure of the blood and lymphatic capillaries of the respiratory tissue during inflammation and endobronchial laser therapy," *Ultrastruct. Pathol.* **24**(3), 183–189 (2000).

37. N. M. Burduli and A. S. Krifaridi, "The influence of low-intensity laser radiation on the vascular endothelium function and the cytokine system in patients with chronic viral hepatitis," *Vopr. Kurortol. Fizioter. Lech. Fiz. Kult.* **2**, 30–34 (2011).

38. I. V. Grigor'eva, D. R. Rakita, and V. Ia. Garmash, "Effect of endovascular laser irradiation of the blood of patients with diabetic angiopathies," *Probl. Endokrinol. (Mosk)* **37**(6), 28–30 (1991).

39. S. M. Zubkova, E. I. Sorokina, N. A. Kenevich, Iu. Iu. Tupitsyna, and A. A. Minenkov, "The blood antioxidant system in patients with ischemic heart disease undergoing laser therapy," *Vopr. Kurortol. Fizioter. Lech. Fiz. Kult.* **6**, 4–7 (1993).

40. U. R. Farkhutdinov, "Intravascular laser irradiation of blood in the treatment of patients with bronchial asthma," *Ter. Arkh.* **79**(3), 44–48 (2007).

41. D. A. Arnall, A. G. Nelson, L. López, N. Sanz, L. Iversen, I. Sanz, L. Stambaugh, and S. B. Arnall, "The restorative effects of pulsed infrared light therapy on significant loss of peripheral protective sensation in patients with long-term type 1 and type 2 diabetes mellitus," *Acta. Diabetol.* **43**(1), 26–33 (2006).

42. N. M. Burduli and A. S. Krifaridi, "Effect of low-intensity laser radiation on the function of vascular endothelium in patients with chronic viral hepatitis," *Klin. Med. (Mosk)* **87**(1), 49–52 (2009).

43. N. M. Burduli and M. M. Balaian, "The influence of low-intensity intravenous laser irradiation of the blood on the endothelial function in the patients presenting with gastroesophageal reflux disease," *Vopr. Kurortol. Fizioter. Lech. Fiz. Kult.* **5**, 33–35 (2013).

44. I. G. Alizade and N. T. Karaeva, "The effect of plasmapheresis and laser irradiation of the blood on the hemorheological and hemodynamic indices in hypertension patients," *Lik. Sprava.* **3**, 110–111 (1997).

45. D. G. Siposan and A. Lukacs, "Effect of low-level laser radiation on some rheological factors in human blood: an in vitro study," *J. Clin. Laser Med. Surg.* **18**(4), 185–195 (2000).

46. X. Q. Mi, J. Y. Chen, Z. J. Liang, and L. W. Zhou, "In vitro effects of helium-neon laser irradiation on human blood: blood viscosity and deformability of erythrocytes," *Photomed. Laser Surg.* **22**(6), 477–482 (2004).

47. N. A. Iaitskiĭ, E. M. Ageenko, T. E. Davydenko, V. A. Volchkov, O. A. Churzin, and V. D. Zharskaia, "Intravascular laser irradiation of blood in complex treatment of obliterating atherosclerosis of the lower extremity vessels in elderly and senile patients," *Vestn. Khir. Im. I. I. Grek.* **165**(4), 34–37 (2006).

48. V. B. Simonenko, N. I. Siuch, and I. A. Vokuev, "Diagnostic implications of changed red cell count in low-intensity laser radiation of blood in elderly patients with coronary heart disease," *Klin. Med. (Mosk)* **80**(4), 31–33 (2002).

49. A. K. Kirsanova, I. S. Novoderzhkina, V. L. Kozhura, T. L. Berezina, S. V. Dvoretskiĭ, K. V. Talantsev, and N. E. Iakovleva, "Changes in the oxygen balance of the body in the acute period of hemorrhagic shock and after resuscitation under the effect of intravascular helium-neon laser irradiation of the blood," *Anesteziol. Reanimatol.* **5**, 33–35 (1994).

50. O. N. Iakubenia, S. I. Tostik, and G. I. Iakubenia, "Impact of combined magnetic and laser radiation of regional pulmonary blood flow in patients with destructive pulmonary tuberculosis," *Probl. Tuberk.* **6**, 30–32 (1999).

51. N. M. Burduli and A. A. Gazdanova, "Laser Doppler fluometry in assessment of endothelium state in patients with coronary heart disease and its correction by intravenous laser irradiation of blood," *Klin. Med. (Mosk)* **86**(6), 44–47 (2008).

52. N. M. Burduli and S. K. Gutnova, "Types of microcirculation and laser therapy in chronic pancreatitis," *Klin. Med. (Mosk)* **87**(8), 56–61 (2009).

53. N. M. Burduli and D. Ia. Tadtaeva, "The influence of intravenous laser therapy on prostaglandin E2 and F2-alpha dynamics and the state of microcirculation in the patients presenting with gastroesophageal reflux disease," *Vopr. Kurortol. Fizioter. Lech. Fiz. Kult.* **6**, 17–20 (2012).

54. G. V. Tupikin, "Anti-inflammatory and immunosuppressive effects of laser therapy in patients with rheumatoid arthritis," *Ter. Arkh.* **57**(8), 37–9 (1985).

55. N. M. Burduli and I. Z. Aksenova, "The effects of intravenous laser irradiation of blood on the system hemodynamics of patients with chronic obstructive bronchitis exacerbation," *Klin. Med. (Mosk)* **84**(3), 37–39 (2006).

56. Iu. S. Diasamidze, "Impact of photo hemotherapy on blood lipid composition in coronary heart disease," *Klin. Med. (Mosk)* **82**(7), 34–36 (2004).

57. A. P. Vasil'ev, N. N. Strel'tsova, G. G. Shakhov, and V. I. Nikitina, "The effect of laser irradiation of the blood on the adenosine triphosphatase activity of the erythrocyte membranes and on the cardiac activity indices in patients with ischemic heart disease," *Lik. Sprava. 1992.* **6**, 61–64 (1992).

58. N. M. Burduli and D. Ia. Tadtaeva, "Impact of laser therapy on PGE2 level, 24-hour pH-metry changes, and quality of life in patients with gastroesophageal reflux disease," *Ter. Arkh.* **84**(12), 58–61 (2012).

59. N. M. Burduli and S. K. Gutnova, "Effect of intravenous laser irradiation of the blood on plasma content of ceruloplasmin in patients with chronic pancreatitis," *Bull. Exp. Biol. Med.* **149**(6), 697–698 (2010).

60. A. V. Geĭnits, N. T. Gul'muradova, and T. Z. Uspenskaia, "The use of laser beam irradiation by the acute destructive pancreatitis," *Khirurgiia (Mosk)* **7**, 56–61 (2011).

61. N. M. Burduli and N. G. Pilieva, "The dynamics of microcirculation parameters in patients with pneumonia receiving intravenous irradiation of blood as a part of complex treatment," *Klin. Med. (Mosk)* **85**(7), 48–50 (2007).

62. L. V. Komel'kova, T. V. Vitreshchak, I. G. Zhirnova, V. V. Poleshchuk, S. L. Stvolinskiĭ, V. V. Mikhaĭlov, I. V. Gannushkina, and M. A. Piradov, "Biochemical and immunological induces of the blood in Parkinson's disease and their correction with the help of laser therapy," *Patol. Fiziol. Eksp. Ter.* **1**, 15–8 (2004).

63. T. V. Vitreshchak, V. V. Mikhailov, M. A. Piradov, V. V. Poleshchuk, S. L. Stvolinskii, and A. A. Boldyrev, "Laser modification of the blood in vitro and in vivo in patients with Parkinson's disease," *Bull. Exp. Biol. Med.* **135**(5), 430–432 (2003).

64. I. N. Zimon, A. I. Agzamov, V. A. Choroshaev, Iu. I. Kalish, and I. Z. Dalimov, "Effects of intravascular laser irradiation of blood on erythrocyte stereo-ultrastructure in the treatment of generalized suppurative peritonitis," *Khirurgiia (Mosk)* **9–10**, 35–9 (1992).

65. L. I. Rusakova, V. G. Dobkin, and E. S. Ovsiankina, "Efficiency of supra-venous blood laser radiation used in the treatment of disseminated pulmonary tuberculosis in adolescents," *Probl. Tuberk.* **8**, 16–18 (2002).

66. R. K. Tulebaev, Sh. B. Sadykov, V. A. Romanov, and G. Kh. Khalitova, "Indicators of the activity of the immune system during laser therapy of vasomotor rhinitis," *Vestn. Otorinolaringol.* **1**, 46–9 (1989).

67. X. Xiao, Y. Guo, X. Chu, S. Jia, X. Zheng, and C. Zhou, "Effects of low power laser irradiation in nasal cavity on cerebral blood flow perfusion of patients with brain infarction," *Chinese Journal of Physical Medicine and Rehabilitation* **27**(7), 418–450 (2005).

68. Y. S. Yıldırım, T. Apuhan, and E. Koçoğlu, "Effects of intranasal phototherapy on nasal microbial flora in patients with allergic rhinitis," *Iran J. Allergy Asthma Immunol.* **12**(3), 281–286 (2013).

69. C. Y. Liu and P. Zhu (ED). *Intranasal Low Intensity Laser Therapy.* Beijing: People's Military Medical Press, 2009.

Chapter 20
Future Directions and the Path Forward

20.1 Disappointment at Current Lack of Progress

Despite the impressive accomplishments that have steadily accumulated since the 1960s that now consist of the publication of thousands of peer-reviewed papers [that can be retrieved by a PubMed search using the MeSH term "LLLT" and a new MeSH term "photobiomodulation therapy" (PBM)] and hundreds of clinical trials, many of which have been high-quality, randomized, and well-controlled, LLLT has still not reached the stage of acceptance by mainstream medicine. There remains considerable skepticism (and sometimes frank disbelief) amongst biomedical scientists, the medical profession, and the public at large.

The reasons for this skepticism and disbelief are many and various, and they differ depending on the source. Biomedical scientists often refer to a lack of mechanism and the absence of agreement on dosimetry and parameters. Physicians often claim there is a lack of large clinical trials and not enough systematic reviews. Hospital and insurance administrators cannot agree on coverage and reimbursement. Finally (and regrettably), there has been marketing hype, over-promising, and frank misinformation from some of the companies that make devices (lasers, LED arrays, mixed clusters) that are used in the LLLT industry.

20.2 New Indications

20.2.1 Stem cells

It was recently observed that a low-power NIR laser was able to direct the differentiation of dental stem cells to a specific mineralized tissue lineage, dentin.[1] The ability of lasers to induce reparative dentin had been noted previously, but the mechanisms had remained unknown, which prevented the development of effective clinical protocols. This recent study elucidated the molecular mechanism of low-power laser treatments that involved the activation of a latent growth factor, TGF-β1. Using chemical biology and transgenic approaches, this study went on to show that the laser-generated, ROS-activated TGF-β1 was critical for the directed differentiation of endogenous dental stem cells from both human and rodent (mice and rat) teeth. This is clinically very relevant because dentin is a key tissue that maintains vitality of the tooth, and thus the ability to induce dentin prevents the need for root-canal treatments and eventual replacement of nonvital teeth. The limitations of this study included a lack of morphodifferentiation of tubular, regenerated dentin. The newly formed dentin was bone-like (osteodentin) and widespread along the tooth pulp chamber and canals. Better optical-focusing techniques and biochemical strategies to restrict light–tissue interactions could drive the ideal regenerative response instead of the current reparative process observed. More recently, these observations have been extended to directing the differentiation of mesenchymal stem cells (MSCs) using a sophisticated, scaffold-based model.[2] This system can generate exquisitely precise morphogen fields at both temporal and spatial scales, and it was utilizes to activate latent TGF-β1 with NIR lasers to direct MSC differentiation to dentin. Other studies have shown the ability of LLLT/PBM treatments to mobilize MSCs from bone marrow[3] to aid in the healing of damage to the cardiac,[4] liver,[5] and kidney.[6]

20.2.2 Transcranial LLLT for brain disorders

Remarkable results have been found recently in neurology using transcranial LLLT, a noninvasive treatment for serious brain diseases or injuries. Transcranial LLLT improves motor recovery after strokes in rats[7] and in humans,[8] significantly reduces the recovery time in traumatic brain injury (TBI) in mice,[9] and can also be used in humans with chronic TBI.[10] Encouraging pre-clinical results have been obtained for some degenerative CNS diseases, such as familial amyotrophic lateral sclerosis,[11] Parkinson's disease,[12] and Alzheimer's disease[13] with this technique.

Rojas et al.,[14] while using a rodent model of toxic optic neuropathy induced by rotenone, a mitochondrial complex-I inhibitor, reported a neuroprotective effect of 633-nm LLLT. Whole-brain cytochrome oxidase and superoxide dismutase activities were also increased by the PBM, suggesting an *in vivo* transcranial effect of LLLT. It showed that PBM acquired by transcranial LLLT can effectively prevent neurotoxic and retinotoxic effects of some neurodegenerative disorders associated with mitochondrial dysfunction due to complex-I inhibition.

Parkinson's disease is mainly characterized by the degeneration of dopaminergic neurons in the central nervous system, including the retina.[15] Considerable evidence supports mitochondrial dysfunction and oxidative stress as key components in the pathogenesis of Parkinson's. LLLT treatment was cytoprotective in the simultaneous and rescue (post-treatment) in a series of studies in mice.[16,17]

The realization that impaired neurogenesis plays an important role in depression[18] suggested that transcranial LLLT (TLT) could have beneficial effects in patients with major depression and anxiety, and this was confirmed in a pilot clinical trial with 10 subjects receiving a single treatment of TLT to the forehead.[19] TLT may be thought to be just in its infancy, but we believe the stage is set for rapid growth, especially in view of the massive and continuing failure of clinical trials of pharmaceuticals for many brain disorders. As the population continues to age and the epidemic of degenerative diseases of aging and other dementias continues to grow, TLT may make a real contribution to patient health.

20.2.3 Ophthalmology

The retina is one of the highest-oxygen-consuming tissues in the human body because photoreceptor cells (rods and cones) have a high concentration of mitochondria.[20] Mitochondrial repair and attenuation of oxidative stress are keys to the long-term survival of the retina. Moreover, retina tissue contains abundant photosensitizers when it is constantly exposed to visible light. These characteristics make the retina very susceptible to LLLT effects, and there are many reports of red and infrared irradiation regenerating damaged retinal tissue. Eells et al.[21] reported the first direct link between the actions of far-red to NIR light on mitochondrial oxidative metabolism *in vitro*. In order to avoid photodamage, additional care must be taken during a LLLT procedure in the eye; the use of a laser could decrease the usability of this procedure. However, the development of new devices using LEDs and standardized dosimetry could lead to an increase of the use of LLLT in ophthalmology.

Age-related macular degeneration is strongly correlated with oxidative stress and mitochondrial debility. Light therapy can affect several of the pathways that lead to macular damage. The targeting of mitochondrial respiration by direct absorption at cytochrome c oxidase leads to secondary and tertiary beneficial effects on cellular metabolism, including anti-inflammatory, anti-oxidant, and anti-apoptotic protection, and recovery from injury. LED therapy has been demonstrated to be a noninvasive, easily administered, and safe treatment with no serious adverse events for age-related macular degeneration.[22] Nevertheless, there is still an urgent need to properly evaluate this treatment modality.

Retinopathy of prematurity (ROP) is a disorder of the developing retina and one of the leading causes of blindness in developed countries. Risk factors for ROP include low birth weight and gestational age, supplemental oxygen therapy, and respiratory distress syndrome. LLLT at 670 nm reduced neovascularization, vaso-obliteration, and abnormal branching patterns of the retinal vessels in ROP.[23]

20.2.4 Autoimmune diseases

Autoimmune diseases arise from an abnormal immune response of the body to substances and tissues normally present in the body, generating lesions or dysfunction of organs or tissues in different places. The treatment of autoimmune diseases typically involves immunosuppressive medication that decreases the immune response. In both autoimmune and inflammatory diseases, the condition arises through aberrant reactions of the human adaptive or innate immune systems. Due to this similar mechanism, LLLT— which is very well developed and recognized in the treatment of inflammations —has been hypothesized to have an important role in the treatment and amendment of symptoms in autoimmune diseases.

Mucous membrane pemphigoid is a heterogeneous group of autoimmune, sub-epithelial, blistering diseases. A combination of topical and systemic steroid treatment is often used when managing patients with mucous membrane pemphigoid. A patient presenting such illness were successfully treated with the application of local corticosteroids and LLLT using an 810-nm diode laser.[24]

Another important perspective for treating autoimmune diseases with LLLT is the treatment of chronic autoimmune thyroiditis. Hofling et al.[25] showed that ten sessions of transcutaneous applications of an 810-nm laser over the thyroid were enough to considerably improve the thyroid function in patients with hypothyroidism caused by chronic autoimmune thyroiditis.

20.2.5 Lung disease

Light therapy has gained support as a nonpharmacological therapy able to down-regulate oxidative metabolism in the respiratory system.[26] Notwithstanding this support, clinical studies about the effect of LLLT on asthma[27] have usually been directed towards improving the quality of life of patients without major concern about the mechanisms, dosimetry, or inflammatory cells and their mediators. LLLT is known to attenuate pro-oxidant reactions that compromise the bronchial reactivity and structure.[28]

One of the difficulties in LLLT procedures for the lungs and airway is light delivery. It used to be conducted invasively with optical fibers inside needles, but there is recent research claiming the transcutaneous efficacy of light delivery to the lungs. The efficacy of LLLT has been proved to treat asthma, tuberculosis, and pleurisy. A possible future treatment could be the prevention of smoking-induced cancer because it is connected with recurrent inflammatory process present in the smoker's lungs. There is a need to characterize an internal form of light delivery as well because the ideal dosimetry can induce and maintain an anti-inflammatory response in both the airway and lungs.

20.2.6 Performance enhancement

The term "performance enhancement" describes the use of PBM in normal, healthy subjects to enhance some natural physiological or cognitive function. Light therapy using lasers and LEDs has recently been used to increase muscle performance in exercises limited by strength or fatigue, and light therapy may have a role to play in preparing athletes who compete in high-performance sports. Recent reviews have reported positive effects of light therapy on muscle performance, highlighting protection from exercise-induced muscle damage; an increased number of repetitions in maximum exertion tests; increased workload, torque, and muscle-fatigue resistance in training programs; and an overview of the main possible mechanisms of action of the light therapy on muscle tissue.[29]

NIR light passes readily through the scalp and skull and a small percentage of the incident power density can arrive at the cortical surface in humans.[30] A study was conducted by Gonzalez-Lima et al.[31] on healthy college students using TLT. A single exposure of the forehead to a CW 1064-nm laser (60 J/cm^2 at 250 mW/cm^2) improved the scores on tests that measured attention, memory, and mood. Reaction time in a sustained-attention psychomotor vigilance task (PVT) was significantly improved in the treated ($n = 20$) versus the placebo control ($n = 20$) groups, especially in high-novelty-seeking subjects. The LED technology is not expensive, and a TLT protocol with LEDs has potential for home treatment.[32]

20.3 New Light Sources

Most physicians have never heard of LLLT, and yet there are already over 1,000 devices on the world market, many of which have no proof of efficacy. There are single-laser beam devices with power outputs ranging from as little 1mW to 10 watts, there are LED clusters comprising a few red emitters to arrays with hundreds of LEDs delivering up to 480 W to treat the whole body.

The first LLLT procedures were performed using lasers, and in the early days of this field researchers were not sure if the PBM processes triggered by light depended on the special properties of laser light [such as monochromaticity (narrow bandwidth), coherence or polarization] or if they could be achieved by other sources of light. Evidence have been found in the last decades that other light sources can produce PBM, and the major determining parameter for effectiveness of LLLT is the wavelength, which must be one capable to be absorbed by a photoacceptor molecule in the host. In recent year many research studies and clinical procedures have been performed with noncoherent light sources like LED, or halogen lamps connected to monochromatic filters. Even more recent are the use of organic light emitting diodes (OLEDs) which extend the possibilities of LLLT since OLED can emit light uniformly from a flexible surface.

20.3.1 Wearable LLLT devices: bandages and clothing

There are a variety of technologies being developed that involve self-emissive devices, rather than employing discrete emitters imbedded in a substrate. For example, devices have been described that use OLEDs, polymer light-emitting diodes (P-LEDs), and thin-film flexible electroluminescent sources (TFEL). Certainly, light therapy bandages based on these technologies have several potential advantages, including volume production, readily customizable temporal and spatial control from the addressing circuitry, and a very thin form factor, which could help conformability. Such bandages still have some issues to solve (minimizing toxicity, handling moisture, and providing sufficient output power) that will likely delay the appearance of such devices in health-care markets.[33]

A good example of a fabric device that exhibits excellent optical and thermal properties was introduced by Shen in 2013.[34] Its optical power density and operating temperature were stable during usage for 10 h. A series of tests were conducted for the safety of the fabric for human-skin contact according to ISO standard ISO 10993-1:2003. The results showed that there was no potential hazard when the luminous fabrics were in direct contact with human skin. Fabrics that integrate with side-emitting polymer optical fibers (POFs) have great potential to be used for phototherapy.

Combined with deformability, the fabric devices can easily fit into 3D contours like the human body with superior permeability to air, low weight, flexibility, and wearing comfort. A POF is a cylindrical dielectric waveguide that is usually used to transport light between the two ends of the fiber by the process of total internal reflection. By creating certain features in the core or at the core–cladding interface of the fiber, the POF emits light sideways, which offers possibilities for large-area 3D illumination.

20.3.2 Implantable LEDs for brain and spine

Brain implants, often referred to as neural implants, are technological devices that connect directly to the brain (usually placed on the surface of the brain or attached to the brain cortex). Brain implants can be used after stroke or other head injuries and diseases. Neural implants—such as deep-brain stimulation and vagus nerve stimulation—are increasingly routine for patients with Parkinson's disease and clinical depression, respectively, proving themselves a boon for people with diseases that were previously regarded as incurable. Current brain implants work to electrically stimulate, block, or record signals from single neurons or groups of neurons in the brain. It is possible to change the electrical or magnetic stimulation to PBM and thus increase the usability of the implants. Implantable LEDs could also be used in the spine in case of spinal cord damage. A preliminary animal study was carried out by Moro et al.,[35] who used an implanted intracranial fiber optic connected to a laser or LED light source to treat Parkinson's disease in MPTP-treated mice.

20.3.3 Swallowable battery-powered LED capsule for GI diseases

The first wireless camera pills created a revolutionary new perspective for engineers and physicians, demonstrating for the first time the feasibility of achieving medical objectives deep within the human body from a ingestible, wireless platform.[36] The 10 years since the first camera pill has been a period of great innovation in ingestible medical devices. A possible innovation in the field of photomedicine could be the development of ingestible LED devices for LLLT because it requires only the simple and noninvasive swallowing of a pill that would be programmed to emit red or NIR light when it reached the affected part of the gut (it could even be retrieved for reuse).

20.4 Marketing Hype

One of the challenges for potential product purchasers and healthcare reimbursement organizations is "industry hype":

- In October 2014, the FDA issued a legal writ against a laser product manufacturer who claimed the devices were intended for the treatment of "over 200 different diseases and disorders, including cancer, cardiac arrest, and HIV/AIDS."
- Some manufacturers claim their devices are effective when applied through clothing.
- There are manufacturers of class-IV laser devices that refer to clinical trials performed with a class-3B laser; these same manufacturers then claim that because 3B laser results are sometimes negative, the extra power of a class-IV laser will be more effective (systematic reviews show that the opposite is true, i.e., over-treatment is more often the problem).
- There are trials that compare one laser versus another where the treatment plan is designed to cause one of them to be ineffective.
- There are pulsed laser devices with a high peak power and very short pulses that achieve a very low average power whose marketing department trumpets that they have a "25-W device," when in reality 25 W is the peak power and the device's effective average power is 5 mW.
- There are claims that more powerful devices can deliver the required energy in less time, which is true, but changing the fluence rate (irradiance) alters the results.

Quite how reimbursement organizations will reconcile such myriad devices—that range from 630–980 nm and 5 mW to 30 W, and claim the same treatment effect—is unclear. It is, perhaps, unsurprising that lasers have not been more widely adopted by medical product purchasers and healthcare reimbursement organizations: industry appears to be its own worst enemy.

20.5 Negative Publication Bias

Publication bias usually refers to the tendency to publish positive trials and ignore those that support the null hypothesis, but there may be a form of negative publication bias whereby journal referees are not familiar with the intervention and discount the results, especially where the results are "too good to be true."

In 2009, the Lancet published a systematic review and meta-analysis[37] of the management of neck pain with low-level lasers, but only after the authors were asked to make seven revisions. At the end of the revision process, the effect sizes had improved, and the authors concluded that in 16 randomized controlled trials (RCTs) including a total of 820 patients, LLLT reduced pain intensity, disability, and recurrence, and that the mean pain intensity reduction (on a visual analog scale) over placebo was 23.4 mm (95% CI: 17.1–29.8 @ 10–22 weeks).

This result is a "big deal" for two reasons: first, there is no drug in any country approved for the treatment of neck pain, and second, the effect size was more than double that for drug therapies for other musculoskeletal disorders.

The four authors concerned (all of whom were university professors), with 206 published papers between them, had not failed to write a good paper; in fact, one of the reviewers stated that the analysis was "exemplary." However, their only failing may have been introducing a therapy the reviewers did not understand and offering a result that was too good to be true.

This story is not a "one off." In 2006, the Cochrane Collaboration updated a systematic review on "Low-level laser therapy for nonspecific low-back pain,"[38] in which the authors reported that "it seems that LLLT has a modest clinical effect on pain intensity and frequency in patients suffering low-back pain if applied for at least two weeks. No side effects were reported. However we conclude that there is insufficient data to draw firm conclusions." This statement was not what Cochrane finally published. The published text deleted the first sentence of the reviewers' statement and concluded that "no side effects were reported. However we conclude that there is insufficient data to draw firm conclusions." An external reviewer protested:

> "I do not endorse this review conclusion, this is probably the only Cochrane review where 5 out of 6 RCTs with acceptable methodological quality and partially or fully positive results which merits a non-positive review conclusion."

This Cochrane review has since been withdrawn.[39]

20.6 The Path Forward

PBM and LLLT face several hurdles to becoming mainstream in health care and research; one is that the field is so broad. Another obstacle, however, affecting PBM devices used as either independent therapies or applied as adjuncts to particular health care procedures is that the developers of PBM devices have become excited about its therapeutic potential for various and different reasons. Those who have gained the clinical knowledge and skills to effectively use these devices have become equally excited, especially because there has been little evidence to date of any contraindications. Despite these early studies and clinical experiences, though, there are still variables that need to be known and understood, such as the duration of light exposure and contraindications for different people or different kinds of situations. Determining these points will help make these interventions easier to use, more predictable, and more effective.

One pathway to general acceptance of PBM treatment, brought up during the the Optical Society of America (OSA) discussion, was the development of a center of excellence specifically devoted to PBM and its applications. Such a light-based health care center could systematically develop and monitor the various biological biomarkers associated with effective healing. It could also help develop and monitor the devices needed to administer light therapy. This approach would require a multi-center system connected to the existing healthcare research, education, and payment systems.

There are a variety of social, ethical, and professional issues surrounding PBM that come into play and must be addressed. The most important issue involves the clarification and proper prioritization of professional thinking and pure marketplace thinking. In short, patients and families place value in collaborative communication and compassion in their caregiver relationships. The business, market, and bureaucratic sides of the profession, however, place more value in competition and regulation. This mix of values needs to be balanced, especially in our current culture, where more attention is paid to individual immediate desires than on improving care and advancing fields of study.

References

1. P. R. Arany, A. Cho, T. D. Hunt, G. Sidhu, K. Shin, E. Hahm et al., "Photoactivation of endogenous latent transforming growth factor-beta1 directs dental stem cell differentiation for regeneration," *Science translational medicine* **6**(238), 238ra69, (2014).
2. P. R. Arany, G. X. Huang, O. Gadish, J. Feliz, J. C. Weaver, J. Kim et al., "Multi-lineage MSC Differentiation via Engineered Morphogen Fields," *Journal of dental research* (2014).
3. H. Tuby, E. Hertzberg, L. Maltz, and U. Oron, "Long-term safety of low-level laser therapy at different power densities and single or multiple applications to the bone marrow in mice," *Photomed. Laser Surg.* **31**(6), 269–73 (2013).

4. H. Tuby, L. Maltz, and U. Oron, "Induction of autologous mesenchymal stem cells in the bone marrow by low-level laser therapy has profound beneficial effects on the infarcted rat heart," *Lasers in surgery and medicine* **43**(5), 401–9 (2011).

5. U. Oron, L. Maltz, H. Tuby, V. Sorin, and A. Czerniak, "Enhanced liver regeneration following acute hepatectomy by low-level laser therapy," *Photomedicine and laser surgery* **28**(5), 675–8 (2010).

6. U. Oron, H. Tuby, L. Maltz, O. Sagi-Assif, R. Abu-Hamed, T. Yaakobi et al., "Autologous bone-marrow stem cells stimulation reverses post-ischemic-reperfusion kidney injury in rats," *American journal of nephrology* **40**(5), 425–33 (2014).

7. A. Oron, U. Oron, J. Chen, A. Eilam, C. Zhang, M. Sadeh et al., "Low-level laser therapy applied transcranially to rats after induction of stroke significantly reduces long-term neurological deficits," *Stroke* **37**(10), 2620–4 (2006).

8. Y. Lampl, J. A. Zivin, M. Fisher, R. Lew, L. Welin, B. Dahlof et al., "Infrared laser therapy for ischemic stroke: a new treatment strategy: results of the NeuroThera Effectiveness and Safety Trial-1 (NEST-1)," *Stroke* **38**(6), 1843–9 (2007).

9. Y. Y. Huang, A. Gupta, D. Vecchio, V. J. Arce, S. F. Huang, W. Xuan et al., "Transcranial low level laser (light) therapy for traumatic brain injury," *J. Biophotonics* doi: 10.1002/jbio.201200077 (2012).

10. M. A. Naeser, R. Zafonte, M. H. Krengel, P. I. Martin, J. Frazier, M. Hamblin et al., "Significant improvements on cognitive performance post- transcranial, red/near-infrared LED treatments in chronic, mild TBI: Open-protocol study," *Journal of neurotrauma* (2014).

11. H. Moges, O. M. Vasconcelos, W. W. Campbell, R. C. Borke, J. A. McCoy, L. Kaczmarczyk et al., "Light therapy and supplementary Riboflavin in the SOD1 transgenic mouse model of familial amyotrophic lateral sclerosis (FALS)," *Lasers Surg. Med.* **41**(1), 52–9 (2009).

12. V. E. Shaw, S. Spana, K. Ashkan, A. L. Benabid, J. Stone, G. E. Baker et al., "Neuroprotection of midbrain dopaminergic cells in MPTP-treated mice after near-infrared light treatment," *The Journal of comparative neurology* **518**(1), 25–40 (2010).

13. L. De Taboada, J. Yu, S. El-Amouri, S. Gattoni-Celli, S. Richieri, T. McCarthy et al., "Transcranial laser therapy attenuates amyloid-beta peptide neuropathology in amyloid-beta protein precursor transgenic mice," *Journal of Alzheimer's disease: JAD.* **23**(3), 521–35 (2011).

14. J. C. Rojas, J. Lee, J. M. John, and F. Gonzalez-Lima, "Neuroprotective effects of near-infrared light in an in vivo model of mitochondrial optic neuropathy," *The Journal of neuroscience: the official journal of the Society for Neuroscience* **28**(50), 13511–21 (2008).

15. P. A. Trimmer, K. M. Schwartz, M. K. Borland, L. De Taboada, J. Streeter, and U. Oron, "Reduced axonal transport in Parkinson's disease cybrid neurites is restored by light therapy," *Molecular neurodegeneration* **4**, 26 (2009).

16. N. El Massri, D. M. Johnstone, C. L. Peoples, C. Moro, F. Reinhart, N. Torres et al., "The effect of different doses of near infrared light on dopaminergic cell survival and gliosis in MPTP-treated mice," *The International journal of neuroscience* (2015).

17. D. M. Johnstone, N. el Massri, C. Moro, S. Spana, X. S. Wang, N. Torres et al., "Indirect application of near infrared light induces neuroprotection in a mouse model of parkinsonism - an abscopal neuroprotective effect," *Neuroscience* **274**, 93–101 (2014).

18. G. Serafini, S. Hayley, M. Pompili, Y. Dwivedi, G. Brahmachari, P. Girardi et al., "Hippocampal neurogenesis, neurotrophic factors and depression: possible therapeutic targets?," *CNS & neurological disorders drug targets* **13**(10), 1708–21 (2014).

19. F. Schiffer, A. L. Johnston, C. Ravichandran, A. Polcari, M. H. Teicher, R. H. Webb et al., "Psychological benefits 2 and 4 weeks after a single treatment with near infrared light to the forehead: a pilot study of 10 patients with major depression and anxiety," *Behav. Brain Funct.* **5**, 46 (2009).

20. D. Y. Yu and S. J. Cringle, "Retinal degeneration and local oxygen metabolism," *Experimental eye research* **80**(6), 745–51 (2005).

21. J. T. Eells, M. M. Henry, P. Summerfelt, M. T. Wong-Riley, E. V. Buchmann, M. Kane et al., "Therapeutic photobiomodulation for methanol-induced retinal toxicity," *Proceedings of the National Academy of Sciences of the United States of America* **100**(6), 3439–44 (2003).

22. B. T. Ivandic and T. Ivandic, "Low-level laser therapy improves vision in patients with age-related macular degeneration," *Photomed. Laser Surg.* **26**(3), 241–5 (2008).

23. J. L. Garcia-Serrano, J. Uberos Fernandez, R. Anaya-Alaminos, A. Jerez-Calero, J. F. Padilla-Torres, M. C. Ramirez-Garcia et al., "'Oxygen with love' and diode laser treatment decreases comorbidity and avoidable blindness due to retinopathy of prematurity: results achieved in the past 12 years," *Pediatrics and neonatology* **54**(6), 397–401 (2013).

24. H. G. Yilmaz, B. Kusakci-Seker, H. Bayindir, and T. F. Tozum, "Low-level laser therapy in the treatment of mucous membrane pemphigoid: a promising procedure," *Journal of periodontology* **81**(8), 1226–30 (2010).

25. D. B. Hofling, M. C. Chavantes, A. G. Juliano, G. G. Cerri, M. Knobel, E. M. Yoshimura et al., "Low-level laser in the treatment of patients with hypothyroidism induced by chronic autoimmune thyroiditis: a randomized, placebo-controlled clinical trial," *Lasers in medical science* **28**(3), 743–53 (2013).

26. V. R. Silva, P. Marcondes, M. Silva, A. B. Villaverde, H. C. Castro-Faria-Neto, R. P. Vieira et al., "Low-level laser therapy inhibits bronchoconstriction, Th2 inflammation and airway remodeling in allergic asthma," *Respiratory physiology & neurobiology* **194**, 37–48 (2014).

27. M. Y. Elseify, N. H. Mohammed, A. A. Alsharkawy, and M. E. Elseoudy, "Laser acupuncture in treatment of childhood bronchial asthma," *Journal of complementary & integrative medicine* **10** (2013).

28. M. C. Oliveira, Jr., F. R. Greiffo, N. C. Rigonato-Oliveira, R. W. Custodio, V. R. Silva, N. R. Damaceno-Rodrigues et al., "Low level laser therapy reduces acute lung inflammation in a model of pulmonary and extrapulmonary LPS-induced ARDS," *J Photochem Photobiol B.* **134**, 57–63 (2014).

29. C. Ferraresi, M. R. Hamblin, and N. A. Parizotto, "Low-level laser (light) therapy (LLLT) on muscle tissue: performance, fatigue and repair benefited by the power of light," *Photonics Lasers Med.* **1**(4), 267–86 (2012).

30. F. Gonzalez-Lima and D. W. Barrett, "Augmentation of cognitive brain functions with transcranial lasers," *Frontiers in systems neuroscience* **8**, 36 (2014).

31. D. W. Barrett and F. Gonzalez-Lima, "Transcranial infrared laser stimulation produces beneficial cognitive and emotional effects in humans," *Neuroscience* **230**, 13–23 (2013).

32. M. A. Naeser, A. Saltmarche, M. H. Krengel, M. R. Hamblin, and J. A. Knight, "Improved cognitive function after transcranial, light-emitting diode treatments in chronic, traumatic brain injury: two case reports," *Photomed. Laser Surg.* **29**(5), 351–8 (2011).

33. A. Kurtz, J. Roddy, M. Bridges, P. Switzer, and R. Connelly, Light therapy bandage with imbedded emitters US Patent Application US 20070233208 (2007).

34. J. Shen, C. Chui, and X. Tao, "Luminous fabric devices for wearable low-level light therapy," *Biomedical optics express* **4**(12), 2925–37 (2013).

35. C. Moro, N. E. Massri, N. Torres, D. Ratel, X. De Jaeger, C. Chabrol et al., "Photobiomodulation inside the brain: a novel method of applying near-infrared light intracranially and its impact on dopaminergic cell survival in MPTP-treated mice," *Journal of neurosurgery* **120**(3), 670–83 (2014).

36. P. McCartney, "Pediatric capsule endoscopy: the pill camera," *MCN The American journal of maternal child nursing* **38**(4), 252 (2013).

37. R. T. Chow, M. I. Johnson, R. A. Lopes-Martins, and J. M. Bjordal, "Efficacy of low-level laser therapy in the management of neck pain: a systematic review and meta-analysis of randomised placebo or active-treatment controlled trials," *Lancet* **374**(9705), 1897–908 (2009).

38. R. Yousefi-Nooraie, E. Schonstein, K. Heidari, A. Rashidian, M. Akbari-Kamrani, S. Irani et al., "Low level laser therapy for nonspecific low-back pain," *The Cochrane database of systematic reviews* **2007**(2), CD005107.
39. R. Yousefi-Nooraie, E. Schonstein, K. Heidari, A. Rashidian, M. Akbari-Kamrani, S. Irani et al., "WITHDRAWN: Low level laser therapy for nonspecific low-back pain," *The Cochrane database of systematic reviews* **2007**(4), CD005107.

Appendix
Review of LLLT Applications

This appendix summarizes the literature cited in previous chapters and their findings.

Table A.1 Photobiomodulation in bone (see Chapter 12).

Reference	Photobiomodulation Parameters	Type of Study	Main Findings
Ozawa et al.[15]	Wavelength: 830 nm Continuous pulse frequency Laser power: 500 mW Irradiation time: 10 minutes Total energy: 299.87 Energy density: 3.82 J/cm^2 Area: 78.5 cm^2	*in vitro*	LLLT may promote a stimulatory effect in cell proliferation and bone formation during the early stages of cell culture.
Aihara et al.[3]	Wavelength: 810 nm Continuous pulse frequency Laser power: 50 mW (max) Irradiation time: 1, 3, 6, 10 minutes per day Total energy: 3.54, 10.63, 21.27, 35.45 J Energy density: 9.33, 27.99, 55.98, 93.30 J/cm^2 Area (cm^2): 0.38	*in vitro*	• Significantly higher proliferation with light doses of 9.33 J/cm^2, 27.99 J/cm^2, and 55.98 J/cm^2. • Increased immunoexpression of RANK (receptor activator of NF-kB) on 2nd, 3rd, 4th, 6th, and 8th days, and higher bone resorption.
Jawad et al.[16]	Wavelength: 940 nm Continuous pulse frequency Laser power: 100, 200, 300 mW Irradiation time: 3, 6 minutes Energy density: 22.92 and 45.85, 45.85 and 91.79, 68.78 and 137.57 J/cm^2	*in vitro*	LLLT dose response in osteoblast proliferation and differentiation.
Tschon et al.[13]	Wavelength: 915 nm Frequency pulsed at 100 Hz Laser power: 575 mW Irradiation time: 48, 96, 144 s Total energy: 9.55, 19.1, 28.65 J Energy density: 5, 10, 15 J/cm^2 Area: 1.91 cm^2	*in vitro*	• LLLT dose response in cell migration. • Increased collagen deposition by osteoblasts in wound-healing model *in vitro.*

(*continued*)

Table A.1 Continued

Reference	Photobiomodulation Parameters	Type of Study	Main Findings
Barushka et al.[17]	Wavelength: 632 nm Continuous pulse frequency Laser power: 6 mW Irradiation time: 2.3 minutes Total energy: 0.868 J Energy density: 31 J/cm^2 Area: 0.028 cm^2	*in vivo*	• Increase in alkaline phosphatase activity on the 6th day. • Tartrate-resistant acid phosphatase (TRAP) increased sharply on the 12th day. • Calcium accumulation had a peak on the 11th day. • Rapid accumulation of reparative new bone in the LLLT group after 10, 13, and 15 days of the bone defect.
Garavello et al.[18]	Wavelength: 632 nm Continuous pulse frequency Laser power: 1 mW Irradiation time: 5, 15 minutes Total energy: 0.29, 0.88 J Energy density: 31.5, 94.5 J/cm^2 Area: 0.0094 cm^2	*in vivo*	• LLLT (94.5 J/cm^2) increased blood vessels after 7 days. • However, both LLLT dosages decreased the number of blood vessels after 14 days. • There was no increase of blood vessels in the control group between 8 and 15 days after the surgical injury.
Batista et al.[19]	Wavelength: 830 nm Continuous pulse frequency Laser power: 100 mW Irradiation time: 120 s Total energy: 6 J Energy density: 210 J/cm^2 Area: 0.028 cm^2	*in vivo*	• Bone repair occurred only in bone without previous radiotherapy, with the LLLT group expressing higher amounts of newly formed bone. • Groups that received radiotherapy were not responsive to LLLT.
Briteno-Vazquez et al.[20]	Wavelength: 850 nm Continuous pulse frequency Laser power: 100 mW Irradiation time: 64 s Total energy: 0.32 J Energy density: 8 J/cm^2 Area: 0.04 cm^2	*in vivo*	• LLLT presented higher bone consolidation (x ray) after 10 days of irradiation. • Histopathological analysis reported an increase in fibroblasts and angiogenesis in the LLLT group.
Batista et al.[21]	Wavelength: 830 nm Continuous pulse frequency Laser power: 100 mW Irradiation time: 120 s Total energy: 6 J Energy density: 210 J/cm^2 Area: 0.028 cm^2	*in vivo*	• Improvement in new bone formation at the early stages of bone healing in the LLLT group when compared with the control (no treatment). • However, there were no LLLT effects on bone healing when applied in a nonsurgical area.
Matsumoto et al.[22]	Wavelength: 735 nm Continuous pulse frequency Laser power: 18 mW Irradiation time: 60 s Total energy: 1.13 J Energy density: 16 J/cm^2 Area: 0.07 cm^2	*in vivo*	LLLT increased the new bone formed tissue and cyclo-oxygenase-2 (COX-2) immunostaining at 14 days.

(*continued*)

Table A.1 Continued

Reference	Photobiomodulation Parameters	Type of Study	Main Findings
Sella et al.[23]	Wavelength: 808 nm Continuous pulse frequency Laser power: 20 mW Irradiation time: 5 s Total energy: 1 J Energy density: 37 J/cm^2 Area: 0.027 cm^2	*in vivo*	• LLLT group decreased inflammatory infiltration at day 13, presented periosteal formation at day 13 and 18, and increased new bone formation at all days (8, 13, and 18). • Immunoexpression of osteocalcin was higher by day 8 in the LLLT group, but the control and LLLT groups presented similar results for the immunoexpression of osteopontin and osteonectin.
Lirani-Galvao et al.[12]	**Laser** Wavelength: 780 nm Continuous pulse frequency Laser power: 30 mW Irradiation time: 150 s Total energy: 4.1 J Energy density: 112.5 J/cm^2 Area: 0.037 cm^2 **Low-intensity pulsed ultrasound** Frequency: 1.5 MHz Intensity: 30 mW, cm^2 Time per session: 20 minutes	*in vivo* (laser vs. ultrasound)	• Higher maximum load at failure (bending test) and higher number of osteoblasts and new bone formation comparing LLLT to the low-intensity-pulsed-ultrasound and control groups. • The low-intensity-pulsed-ultrasound group increased the number of osteoclasts.
Favaro-Pipi et al.[11]	**Laser** Wavelength: 830 nm Continuous pulse frequency Laser power: 30 mW Irradiation time: 47 s Total energy: 0.51 J Energy density: 50 J/cm^2 Area: 0.028 cm^2 **Low-intensity pulsed ultrasound** Frequency: 1.5 MHz Intensity: 30 mW, cm^2 Time per session: 20 minutes	*in vivo* (laser vs. ultrasound)	• Intense newly formed bone area with high vascularized connective tissue in the LLLT group 13 and 25 days after bone defect (injury). • LLLT produced better effects on bone repair compared with low-intensity pulsed ultrasound.
Oliveira et al.[24]	**Laser** Wavelength: 830 nm Continuous pulse frequency Laser power: 100 mW Irradiation time: 34 s Total energy: 3.4 J Energy density: 120 J/cm^2 Area: 0.028 cm^2 **Low-intensity pulsed ultrasound** Frequency: 1.5 MHz Intensity: 30 mW, cm^2 Time per session: 20 minutes	*in vivo* (laser vs. ultrasound)	No difference between both treatments regarding biomechanical analysis and newly formed bone area.
Pires-Oliveira et al.[6]	Wavelength: 904 nm Frequency pulsed at 10 KHz Laser power: 50 mW Irradiation time: 2 s Energy density: 50 mJ/cm^2	*in vivo* (osteoporotic rats)	• Increase in new bone formation with LLLT on the 7th day compared to the control group. • No significant difference between the LLLT and control group on the 21th day.

(continued)

Table A.1 Continued

Reference	Photobiomodulation Parameters	Type of Study	Main Findings
Bossini et al.[25]	Wavelength: 830 nm Continuous pulse frequency Laser power: 100 mW Irradiation time: 17, 34 s Total energy: 1.7, 3.4 J Energy density: 60, 120 J/cm^2 Area: 0.028 cm^2	*in vivo* (osteoporotic rats)	• Both light doses of LLLT increased the amounts of newly formed bone, presented higher deposition of collagen fibers, better organization of collagen fibers, and higher immunoexpression of COX-2 and VEGF (vascular endothelial growth factor). • No difference among LLLT treatments and the control group regarding biomechanical properties of the bone in the three-point bending test.
Bossini et al.[5]	Wavelength: 830 nm Continuous pulse frequency Laser power: 100 mW Irradiation time: 17, 34 s Total energy: 1.7, 3.4 J Energy density: 60, 120 J/cm^2 Area: 0.028 cm^2 Biomaterial: bioactive glass–ceramic (Biosilicate®)	*in vivo* (biomaterials)	Biosilicate® plus LLLT (60 J/cm^2 and 120 J/cm^2) presented larger areas of newly formed bone, higher collagen amounts, higher immunoexpression of VEGF and COX-2, and maximal load in the bending test.
Fangel et al.[26]	Wavelength: 830 nm Continuous pulse frequency Laser power: 100 mW Irradiation time: 34 s Total energy: 3.4 J Energy density: 120 J/cm^2 Area: 0.028 cm^2 Biomaterial: bioactive glass–ceramic (Biosilicate®)	*in vivo* (biomaterials)	• LLLT did not promote improvement in biomechanical properties of the bone when used as the sole therapy. • LLLT applied in conjunction with Biosilicate® increased the maximal load to induce bone fracture and energy absorption without significance in the three-point bending test.
Pinheiro et al.[27]	LLLT, with or without wire osteosynthesis, in conjunction or not with hydroxyapatite and guided regeneration. Wavelength: 780 nm Continuous pulse frequency Laser power: 50 mW Irradiation time: 160 s Total energy: 8 J Energy density: 16 J/cm^2 Area: 0.5 cm^2	*in vivo* (biomaterials)	The group treated with wire osteosynthesis in conjunction with hydroxyapatite and LLLT presented the highest readings, whereas wire osteosynthesis and hydroxyapatite presented the lowest (Raman spectroscopy).
Rasouli Ghahroudi et al.[28]	Wavelength: 810 nm Continuous pulse frequency Laser power: 300 mW Energy density: 4 J/cm^2 Biomaterial: Bio-Oss®	*in vivo* (biomaterials)	• No significant difference among all groups regarding inflammation. • Increase in newly formed bone in LLLT plus Bio-Oss® at 4 (41%) and 8 (47%) weeks, followed by Bio-Oss® at 4 (35%) and 8 (41%), LLLT 4 (27%) and 8 (25%), and control 4 (15%) and 8 (18%) groups.

(continued)

Table A.1 Continued

Reference	Photobiomodulation Parameters	Type of Study	Main Findings
Favaro-Pipi et al.[1]	Wavelength: 830 nm Continuous pulse frequency Laser power: 30 mW Irradiation time: 47 s Total energy: 1.4 J Energy density: 50 J/cm^2 Area: 0.028 cm^2	*in vivo* (gene expression)	• On the 13th day of treatment, there was an up-regulation of BMP-4 (bone morphogenetic protein 4) gene expression in the bone of the LLLT group. • On the 25th day, gene expression of alkaline phosphatase and Runx2 (runt related transcription factor 2) were up-regulated in the LLLT group.
Fernandes et al.[2]	Wavelength: 830 nm Continuous pulse frequency Laser power: 30 mW Irradiation time: 94 s Total energy: 2.8 J Energy density: 100 J/cm^2 Area: 0.028 cm^2	*in vivo* (gene expression)	• LLLT at 12 h and 36 h presented higher inflammatory cells, better tissue organization, and new bone formation on days 3 and 5 post-surgery. • Runx2 was up-regulated at 12 h and 3 days. • Alkaline phosphatase was up-regulated after 36 h and 3 days. • Osteocalcin was also up-regulated after 3 and 5 days.
Tim et al.[29]	Wavelength: 830 nm Continuous pulse frequency Laser power: 100 mW Irradiation time: 34 s Total energy: 3.4 J Energy density: 120 J/cm^2 Area: 0.028 cm^2	*in vivo* (gene expression)	• Compared to the control, the LLLT group did not present infiltrate inflammation, and it presented better tissue organization at 15 and 30 days post-surgery. • The LLLT group presented major amounts of newly formed bone at 15 days. • The immunoexpression of COX-2 was not up-regulated in both groups at all experimental periods. • BMP-9 (bone morphogenetic protein 9) immunoexpression was higher in the LLLT group at 30 days as well as Runx2 in 45 days. • No difference between the groups regarding the immunoexpression of RANKL and no difference regarding the biomechanical properties of the bone in the three-point bending test.
Tim et al.[30]	Wavelength: 830 nm Continuous pulse frequency Laser power: 30 mW Irradiation time: 94 s Total energy: 2.8 J Energy density: 1000 J/cm^2 Area: 0.0028 cm^2	*in vivo* (gene expression)	LLLT up-regulated genes TGF-β, BMP, FGF, and Runx2 corroborate the increased newly formed bone at the surgical site.
Tim et al.[14]	Wavelength: 830 nm Continuous pulse frequency Laser power: 30 mW Irradiation time: 94 s Total energy: 2.8 J Energy density: 1000 J/cm^2 Area: 0.0028 cm^2	*in vivo* (gene expression)	LLLT-modulated gene expression related to inflammation and angiogenesis at 36 h, day 3, and day 7.

(*continued*)

Table A.1 Continued

Reference	Photobiomodulation Parameters	Type of Study	Main Findings
Abdi et al.[31]	Wavelength: 632.8 nm Continuous pulse frequency Laser power: 10 mW Irradiation time: 210, 1166 s Total energy: 2.09, 11.60 J Energy density: 66.8, 369.4 J/cm^2 Area: 0.0314 cm^2	*in vivo* (diabetic rats)	The authors did not find significant results comparing LLLT with the placebo and control groups.
Javadieh et al.[9]	Wavelength: 890 nm Frequency pulsed at 3000 Hz Laser power: 70 W Irradiation time: 530, 265 s Energy density: 23.3, 11.6 J/cm^2 Area: 1 cm^2	*in vivo* (diabetic rats)	LLLT (11.6 J/cm^2) increased the bending stiffness and maximum force until bone fracture.
Bayat et al.[8]	Wavelength: 632 nm Continuous pulse frequency Laser power: 10 mW Irradiation time: 90, 1200 minutes Total energy: 0.9, 12 J Energy density: 28.6, 382.2 J/cm^2 Area: 0.0314 cm^2	*in vivo* (diabetic rats)	• Stiffness by bending test was higher in 382.2-J/cm^2 LLLT and maximum load until bone fracture was higher in 28.6-J/cm^2 LLLT. • 382.2-J/cm^2 LLLT was the best group to significantly increase the density of bone lamellae meshwork in the tibias of diabetic rats.
Patrocinio-Silva et al.[10]	Wavelength: 808 nm Continuous pulse frequency Laser power: 100 mW Irradiation time: 33 s Total energy: 3.3 J Energy density: 120 J/cm^2 Area: 0.028 cm^2	*in vivo* (diabetic rats)	LLLT presented fewer areas of bone resorption (osteoclast activity), increased cortical area, higher immunoexpression of Runx2 and RANKL, and higher bone-mineral content, density, and resistance to fracture (three-point bending test).
AboElsaad et al.[32]	**LLLT with a bioactive glass** Wavelength: 830 nm Continuous pulse frequency Laser power: 40 mW Irradiation time: 60 s Energy density: 4 J/cm^2	Clinical study	• After 3 months, there was a significant reduction in probing depths with LLLT compared to the control (bioactive glass treatment alone) as well as defect fill. • After 6 months, both treatments did not present significant differences.
Angeletti et al.[33]	Wavelength: 830 nm Continuous pulse frequency Laser power (mW): 100 Irradiation time: 84 s Total energy: 8.4 J Energy density: 140 J/cm^2 Area: 0.06 cm^2	Clinical study	LLLT promoted better bone regeneration assessed by digital radiographs and optical density analysis at all post-surgery times (1, 2, 3, 4, and 7 months follow-up).
Chang et al.[34]	Wavelength: 850, 670, 880, 950 nm Continuous pulse frequency Laser power: 1440 mW Irradiation time: 60 s Total energy: 43.2 J Energy density: 1.4 J/cm^2 Area: 31.2 cm^2	Clinical study	LLLT decreased the pain score and had a positive effect on proprioception tests, such as postural stability and limits of stability.

Table A.2 Photobiomodulation in cartilage (see Chapter 13).

Reference	Photobiomodulation Parameters	Type of Study	Main Findings
Jia and Guo[1]	**LLT** Wavelength: 632.8 nm Continuous pulse frequency Laser power (mW): 2, 4, 6, 8, 10, 12 Irradiation time: 390 s Total energy (J): 0.785, 1.57, 2.35, 3.14, 3.92, 4.71 Energy density (J/cm^2): 1, 2, 3, 4, 5, 6 Area: 0.785 cm^2	*in vitro*	• 24 h after LLT, doses of 4–6 J/cm^2 increased the number of cells (proliferation). • Doses of 4–5 J/cm^2 promoted increases in cell growth and synthesis, and the secretion of glycosaminoglycans and collagen type II (extracellular matrix).
Kushibiki et al.[2]	**LLLT** Wavelength: 405 nm Continuous pulse frequency Laser power: 100 mW Irradiation time: 180 s	*in vitro*	• After 14 days, the LLLT group increased collagen content with up-regulation in the gene expression of collagen type II. • The LLLT group up-regulated the expression of aggrecan, SOX-9, and DEC-1.
Kamali et al.[3]	**LLLT** Wavelength: 890 nm Frequency pulsed at 1.5 KHz Laser power: 60 W Irradiation time: 300 s Energy density: 4.8 J/cm^2	*in vivo* (osteo-chondral injury)	LLLT increased the equilibrium stiffness of the knee joint at 8 weeks of treatment, but at 4 and 16 weeks there was no difference between the LLLT and control group regarding instantaneous and equilibrium stiffness of the knee.
Bayat et al.[4]	**LLLT** Wavelength: 632.8 nm Continuous pulse frequency Laser power: 10 mW Irradiation time: 466 s Total energy: 4.6 J Energy density: 148.4 J/cm^2 Area: 0.0314 cm^2	*in vivo* (osteo-chondral injury)	• After 2 weeks of treatment, the control group had accelerated osteochondral healing compared with LLLT. • After 4 and 16 weeks, the LLLT group presented faster healing than the control group.
Bayat et al.[5]	**LLLT** Wavelength: 890 nm Frequency pulsed at 1500 Hz Laser power: 60 W Energy density: 4.8 J/cm^2 Area: 1.0 cm^2	*in vivo* (osteo-chondral injury)	Did not produce significantly better histological outcomes compared with the control group.
Javadieh et al.[6] de Jesus et al.[7]	**LLLT** Wavelength: 632.8 nm Continuous pulse frequency Laser power: 10 mW Irradiation time: 466 s Total energy: 4.6 J Energy density: 148.4 J/cm^2 Area: 0.0314 cm^2	*in vivo* (osteo-chondral injury)	No significant differences between the LLLT and control group regarding the biomechanical properties instantaneous stiffness and maximum force.
de Morais et al.[8]	**LLLT** Wavelength: 685, 830 nm Continuous pulse frequency Laser power: 20 mW Irradiation time: 100 s Total energy: 2 J Energy density: 2.5 J/cm^2 Area: 0.8 cm^2	*in vivo* (arthritis)	• LLLT at 685 nm and 830 nm significantly inhibited edema (23%), vascular permeability (24%), and hyperalgesia (59%). • LEDT had no effects on the arthritis.

(continued)

Table A.2 Continued

Reference	Photobiomodulation Parameters	Type of Study	Main Findings
	LEDT Wavelength: 628 ± 30 nm Continuous pulse frequency Laser power: 20 mW Irradiation time: 100 s Total energy: 2 J Energy density: 2.5 J/cm^2 Area: 0.8 cm^2		
Carlos et al.[9]	**LLLT** Wavelength: 660 nm Continuous pulse frequency Laser power: 10 mW Irradiation time: 10 s Total energy: 0.1 J Energy density: 2.5 J/cm^2 Area: 0.04 cm^2	*in vivo* (arthritis)	• 6 h after injection, treatment with LLLT significantly inhibited total leucocyte influx, including polymorphonuclear and mononuclear cells, and reduced the activity of MMP-2 and MMP-9. • Decreased the release of IL-1β and IL-6 while keeping the percentage of collagen fibers near normal (no zymosan injection) levels.
Alves et al.[10]	**LLLT** Wavelength: 808 nm Continuous pulse frequency Laser power: 50, 100 mW Irradiation time: 40, 80 s Total energy: 4 J Energy density: 142 J/cm^2 Area: 0.028 cm^2	*in vivo* (arthritis)	• Both LLLT treatments decreased collagen type III, MMP-2, and MMP-3, and increased collagen type I at 7, 14, and 21 days • LLLT (50 mW) was more effective at reducing the expression of MMP-9 at all experimental periods.
Alves et al.[11]	**LLLT** Wavelength: 808 nm Continuous pulse frequency Laser power: 50, 100 mW Irradiation time: 40, 80 s Total energy: 4 J Energy density: 142 J/cm^2 Area: 0.028 cm^2	*in vivo* (arthritis)	• LLLT (50 mW) was more efficient than the 100-mW version at reducing cellular inflammation and down-regulating the gene expression of IL-1β and IL-6. • LLLT (100 mW) was more efficient at reducing the gene expression of TNF-α.
dos Santos et al.[12]	**LLLT** Wavelength: 808 nm Continuous pulse frequency Laser power: 50 mW Irradiation time: 40, 80 s Total energy: 2, 4 J Energy density: 71.4, 142.8 J/cm^2 Area: 0.028 cm^2	*in vivo* (arthritis)	• Both LLLT dosages decreased the number of inflammatory cells. • 2-J LLLT decreased the gene expression of IL-1β and increased IL-10. • 4-J LLLT decreased IL-6. • 2-J LLLT was more effective at reducing the gene expression of TNF-α.
Wang et al.[13]	**LLLT** Wavelength: 830 nm Continuous pulse frequency Laser power: 50 mW Irradiation time: 2.6 s Total energy: 0.13 J Energy density: 4.8 J/cm^2 Area: 0.028 cm^2	*in vivo* (arthritis)	• LLLT applied three times a week for 2, 4, 6, and 8 weeks decreased synovitis in the long term (6 and 8 weeks) and damage in the femoral condyle cartilage, and promoted pain relief (6 and 8 weeks). • LLLT decreased the gene expression of catabolic factors at 6 and 8 weeks, and of MMP-1 and MMP-13 at 8 weeks.

(*continued*)

Table A.2 Continued

Reference	Photobiomodulation Parameters	Type of Study	Main Findings
			• LLLT increased the gene expression of TIMP-1 at 6 and 8 weeks and TGF-β at 8 weeks. • Genes related to the extracellular matrix as collagen type II and aggrecan were up-regulated at 8 weeks.
Bublitz et al.[14]	**LLLT** Wavelength: 808 nm Continuous pulse frequency Laser power: 30 mW Irradiation time: 10, 47 s Total energy: 0.3, 1.4 J Energy density: 10, 50 J/cm^2 Area: 0.028 cm^2	*in vivo* (arthritis)	• Comparing the LLLT groups with the control group, there was no difference in the number of chondrocytes and immunoexpression of IL-1β and MMP-13. • The LLLT groups presented better tissue organization, especially with a dose of 10 J/cm^2, and presented higher content of proteoglycans.
Assis et al.[15]	**LLLT** Wavelength: 808 nm Continuous pulse frequency Laser power: 50 mW Irradiation time: 28 s Total energy: 1.4 J Energy density: 50 J/cm^2 Area: 0.028 cm^2 **LLLT** Combined with aerobic exercise on a treadmill with no inclination, a velocity of 16 m, minute, for 50 minutes, day, 3 times a week, for 8 weeks.	*in vivo* (arthritis)	• Descriptive histological analysis revealed that all treated groups (LLLT, exercise, or a combination) had better organization of cartilage and chondrocytes with fewer irregularities, which corroborates with a better OARSI score. • All treated groups showed reduced expression of IL-1β, caspase-3, and MMP-13, with lower expression of caspase-3 in the LLLT-and-exercise group.
Mangueira et al.[16]	**Raman spectroscopy used to evaluate the LLLT effects** Wavelength: 660, 780 nm Continuous pulse frequency Laser power: 30 mW Irradiation time: 10 s Total energy: 0.3 J Energy density: 7.5 J/cm^2 Area: 0.04 cm^2	*in vivo* (arthritis)	• 660-nm LLLT induced larger amounts of collagen type III in histomorphometric analysis. • Principal component analysis and Mahalanobis distance used in Raman spectroscopy revealed higher increments in collagen type II and III in LLLT groups.
Fekrazad et al.[17]	**LLLT and mesenchymal stem cells** Wavelength: 808 nm Continuous pulse frequency Laser power: 30 mW Irradiation time: 20 s Total energy: 0.6 J Energy density: 8.5 J/cm^2 Area: 0.07 cm^2	*in vivo* (arthritis)	• Histological analysis reported no difference between the LLLT and control (only stem cells implanted) group regarding the formation of new cartilage and inflammation. • LLLT increased the formation of new bone.

(continued)

Table A.2 Continued

Reference	Photobiomodulation Parameters	Type of Study	Main Findings
Alfredo et al.[18]	**LLLT and physical exercise** Wavelength: 904 nm Frequency pulsed at 700 Hz Laser power: 60 mW Irradiation time: 50 s Total energy: 3 J Energy density: 6 J/cm^2 Area: 0.5 cm^2	Clinical study	The LLLT treatment promoted better functional activity when compared with the control group (without LLLT), and only the LLLT group reduced pain and increased the range of motion and functional activity.
Alghadir et al.[19]	**LLLT** Wavelength: 850 nm Continuous pulse frequency Laser power: 100 mW Irradiation time: 60 s Total energy: 6 J Energy density: 48 J/cm^2 Area: 0.125 cm^2	Clinical study	• Pain intensity was significantly reduced with LLLT at rest (47%) and during movement (40%). • Functional activity was improved with LLLT.
Al Rashoud et al.[20]	**LLLT** Wavelength: 830 nm Continuous pulse frequency Laser power: 30 mW Irradiation time: 40 s Total energy: 1.2 J Energy density: 4 J/cm^2 Area: 0.28 cm^2	Clinical study	Significant reduction in pain in the LLLT group at 6 weeks and 6 months after intervention, and improvement in knee function at the last treatment session and after 6 months.
Nakamura et al.[21]	**LLLT** Wavelength: 830 nm Continuous pulse frequency Laser power: 1 W Irradiation time: 30 s Total energy: 30 J Energy density: 20 J/cm^2 Area: 1.5 cm^2	Clinical study	• Significant reduction in pain. • No significant improvement in range of motion.
Soleimanpour et al.[22]	**LLLT** Wavelength: 810, 890 nm Frequency pulsed at 3000 Hz Laser power: 50, 30 mW Irradiation time: 120, 588 s Total energy: 6, 17 J Energy density: 6, 10 J/cm^2 Area: 1.000, 1.764 cm^2	Clinical study	Significant reduction in pain of patients with osteoarthritis of the knee when treated with LLLT.
Paolillo et al.[23]	**LLLT with ultrasound therapy (1 MHz, 1 W/cm^2, pulsed 1:1, 50% duty cycle, 3.5 cm^2)** With or without therapeutic exercises for pain relief and hand-grip strength.	Clinical study	• No improvement in hand grip for all groups. • Pain decreased in both the LLLT-and-ultrasound group and the LLLT-and-ultrasound-and-exercise group.

(*continued*)

Table A.2 Continued

Reference	Photobiomodulation Parameters	Type of Study	Main Findings
	LLLT Wavelength: 808 nm Continuous pulse frequency Laser power: 100 mW Irradiation time: 180 s Total energy: 18 J Energy density: 7 J/cm^2 Area: 2.5 cm^2		
Ip and Fu[24]	**LLLT and hyaluronic acid injection** Wavelength: 810 nm Continuous pulse frequency Laser power: 30 mW Irradiation time: 180 s Total energy: 5.4 J Energy density: 3.6 J/cm^2 Area: 1.5 cm^2	Clinical study	Significant reduction in the need for knee-joint replacement surgery with conventional physical therapy plus active LLLT and hyaluronic acid injection every 6 months (1 patient out of 70) compared to conventional physical therapy plus placebo LLLT and saline injection (15 patients out of 70).
Ip[25]	**LLLT with or without conventional physical therapy** Wavelength: 810 nm Continuous pulse frequency Laser power: 30 mW Irradiation time: 180 s Total energy: 5.4 J Energy density: 3.6 J/cm^2 Area: 1.5 cm^2	Clinical study	• In the LLLT-and-physical-therapy group, only one patient needed knee-joint replacement (1 patient out of 50). • 9 patients needed joint replacement in conventional physical treatment (9 out of 50).
Melo Mde et al.[26]	**LLLT with neuromuscular electrical stimulation (18–32 minutes of symmetric biphasic rectangular current, 80 Hz, 400 μs, and a fixed stimulation intensity near the maximal tolerated)** **LLLT** Wavelength: 810 nm Continuous pulse frequency Laser power: 200 mW Irradiation time: 20, 30 s Total energy: 4, 6 J Energy density: 111, 116 J/cm^2 Area: 0.036 cm^2	Clinical study	• Only electrical stimulation or combined therapies promoted increases in muscle thickness (27–29%). • All therapies increased functional capacity during the walk test (5–9%) without any differences between them.

Table A.3 Photobiomodulation in tendons (from Chapter 14).

Reference	Photobiomodulation Parameters	Type of Study	Main Findings
Tsai et al.[2]	**LLLT** Wavelength: 660 nm Continuous pulse frequency Laser power: 50 mW Total energy: 314, 471, 628, 785 J Energy density: 1.0, 1.5, 2.0, 2.5 J/cm^2 Area: 314 cm^2	*in vitro*	• 2-J/cm^2 LLLT increased significantly the number of tenocytes. • All LLLT doses increased the percentage of nitrite concentration. • Doses of 1.0, 1.5, and 2.0 J/cm^2 upregulated the expression of proliferating cell nuclear antigen (PCNA). • Doses of 1.5, 2.0, and 2.5 J/cm^2 increased the expression of cyclins E, A, and B1.
Chen et al.[3]	**LLLT** Wavelength: 904 nm Continuous pulse frequency Frequency range: 5000–7000 Hz Maximum power output: 27 W Laser power: 2.4 mW Pulse duration: 200 ns Total energy: 0.035, 0.07, 0.14, 0.28 J Energy density: 0.5, 1.0, 2.0, 4.0 J/cm^2 Area: 0.07 cm^2	*in vitro*	• 1-J/cm^2 LLLT increased the viability of cells 24 and 48 h after treatment. • Increased amounts of ATP from 30 minutes to 4 h. • Increased intracellular Ca^{2+} at 15 and 30 minutes. • Increased PCNA and collagen type-I expression after 24 h. • Increased TGF-β1 after 72 h.
Neves et al.[4]	**LLLT** Wavelength: 830 nm Continuous pulse frequency Laser power: 40, 60, 80, 100 mW Irradiation time: 21.0, 14.0, 10.5, 8.4 s Total energy: 0.84 J Energy density: 30 J/cm^2 Area: 0.028 cm^2	*in vivo*	• Higher amounts of type-III collagen as the power of light was increased (60–100 mW). • Type-I collagen also increased with 80 mW. • The alignment of the collagen fibers was not improved by LLLT.
Marcos et al.[5]	**LLLT** Wavelength: 810 nm Continuous pulse frequency Laser power: 100 mW Irradiation time: 10, 30 s Total energy: 1, 3 J Energy density: 35.71, 107.14 J/cm^2 Area: 0.028 cm^2	*in vivo*	• 3 J reduced significantly the gene expression of the biochemical markers of inflammation and tissue remodeling. • Preserved the biochemical properties of the tendon, similar to the control group.
Marcos et al.[6]	**LLLT** Wavelength: 810 nm Continuous pulse frequency Laser power: 100 mW Irradiation time: 10, 30 s Total energy: 1, 3 J Energy density: 35.71, 107.14 J/cm^2 Area: 0.028 cm^2	*in vivo*	• 1-J LLLT exhibited a protective effect. • Reduced expression of MMPs. • Recovered mechanical properties of the tendon similar to the control group after 7 days of treatment.
de Jesus et al.[7]	**LLLT** Wavelength: 780 nm Continuous pulse frequency Laser power: 70 mW Irradiation time: 10 s Total energy: 0.7 J Energy density: 17.5 J/cm^2 Area: 0.04 cm^2	*in vivo*	LLLT during days 3 and 7 presented very similar results of IL-1β, COX-2, and PGE2 compared to the control group (without trauma).

(*continued*)

Table A.3 Continued

Reference	Photobiomodulation Parameters	Type of Study	Main Findings
de Jesus et al.[8]	**LLLT** Wavelength: 780 nm Continuous pulse frequency Laser power: 70 mW Irradiation time: 10 s Total energy: 0.7 J Energy density: 17.5 J/cm² Area: 0.04 cm²	*in vivo*	• Photobiomodulation did not affect the alignment of collagen type I and III. • Increased the percentage of collagen type I in LLLT groups treated for 3 and 7 days.
Casalechi et al.[9]	**LLLT** Wavelength: 830 nm Continuous pulse frequency Laser power: 50 mW Irradiation time: 120 s Total energy: 6 J Energy density: 214.28 J/cm² Area: 0.028 cm²	*in vivo*	• By days 7 and 14 of treatment, the LLLT and diclofenac groups had fewer inflammatory cells when compared with the groups without treatment. • By day 14, the LLLT group kept more type-I collagen, whereas the diclofenac group presented the same proportion of collagen type I and III. • The stiffness and strength to rupture was increased in the LLLT group with 14 days of treatment.
Xavier et al.[1]	**LEDT** Wavelength: 880 nm Continuous pulse frequency Laser power: 22 mW Irradiation time: 170 s Total energy: 3.75 J Energy density: 7.5 J/cm² Area: 0.5 cm²	*in vivo*	• LEDT increased the expression of IL-10. • By days 7 and 14, there was an increase of collagen type-I and type-III expression.
Torres-Silva et al.[10]	**LLLT** Wavelength: 660 nm Continuous pulse frequency Laser power: 100 mW Irradiation time: 10, 30 s Total energy: 1, 3 J Energy density: 35.71, 107.14 J/cm² Area: 0.028 cm²	*in vivo*	3-J LLLT reduced the gene expression of IL-6 and TNF-α in the group.
Da Ré Guerra et al.[11]	**LLLT** Wavelength: 830 nm Frequency: continuous (16 s, 2500-W/m² light intensity) or pulsed at 20 Hz (32 s, 1250-W/m² light intensity) Laser power: 100 mW Irradiation time: 10, 30 s Laser power: 40 mW Energy density: 4 J/cm²	*in vivo*	• By day 4, pulsed LLLT decreased significantly the levels of TNF-α. • By day 8, pulsed LLLT increased TGF-β1. • By day 15, LLLT increased NO levels.
Da Ré Guerra et al.[12]	**LLLT** Wavelength: 830 nm Frequency: continuous (16 s, 2500-W/m² light intensity) or pulsed at 20 Hz and 2 KHz (32 s, 1250-W/m² light intensity) Laser power: 40 mW Total energy: 4 J	*in vivo*	• Increments in the concentration of sulfated glycosaminoglycans in LLLT groups by days 8 and 15. • Functional test (CatWalk) was improved with LLLT pulsed at 8 days of treatment compared to the control and continuous-LLLT groups.

(continued)

Table A.3 Continued

Reference	Photobiomodulation Parameters	Type of Study	Main Findings
Pinfildi et al.[13]	**LLLT** Wavelength: 830 nm Continuous pulse frequency Laser power: 80 mW Irradiation time: 14 s Total energy: 1.12 J Energy density: 40 J/cm^2 Area: 0.028 cm^2	*in vivo*	Increased number of mast cells in the LLLT group at 6 h, 12 h, 24 h, and 2 days after tendon injury compared with the sham group.
Ferreira et al.[14]	**LLLT** Wavelength: 830, 660 nm Continuous pulse frequency Laser power: 60 mW Irradiation time: 18.6 s Total energy: 1.14 J Energy density: 40 J/cm^2 Area: 0.028 cm^2	*in vivo*	LLLT (830 or 660 nm) was not able to increase blood vessels in any region of the tendons studied.
Ng and Chung[15]	**LLLT** Wavelength: 660 nm Continuous pulse frequency Frequency range: 10 KHz Laser power: 8.8 mW Irradiation time: 50 s Total energy: 0.44 J Energy density: 3.4 J/cm^2 Area: 0.13 cm^2	*in vivo*	• Increased resistance to rupture in the LLLT group. • Increased resistance to rupture in the combined LLLT and stretching group.
Nouruzian et al.[16]	**LLLT** Wavelength: 632.8 nm Continuous pulse frequency Laser power: 7.2 mW Irradiation time: 2, 3, 8 s Total energy: 0.014, 0.022, 0.06 J Energy density: 2.9, 4.3, 11.5 J/cm^2 Area: 0.00524 cm^2	*in vivo* (diabetic rats)	2.9-J/cm^2 LLLT improved the maximum stress (resistance to stretching).
Aliodoust et al.[17]	**LLLT** Wavelength: 632.8 nm Continuous pulse frequency Laser power: 7.2 mW Irradiation time: 2 s Total energy: 0.014 J Energy density: 2.9 J/cm^2 Area: 0.00524 cm^2	*in vivo* (diabetic rats)	LLLT increased the gene expression of TGF-β1.
Bjordal et al.[18]	**LLLT** Wavelength: 632, 904 nm Continuous pulse frequency Laser power: 7.2 mW Total energy: 0.5 to 7.2 J	Clinical study	LLLT (904 and 632 nm) with light energy ranging from 0.5 to 7.2 J, in conjunction with other therapies or alone, promoted short-term pain relief and less disability caused by lateral elbow tendinopathy.

(continued)

Table A.3 Continued

Reference	Photobiomodulation Parameters	Type of Study	Main Findings
Eslamian et al.[19]	**LLLT** Wavelength: 830 nm Continuous pulse frequency Laser power: 100 mW Irradiation time: 20 s per point Total energy: 4 J Energy density: 4 J/cm^2 Area: 1 cm^2	Clinical study	LLLT promoted short-term pain relief and less disability caused by lateral elbow tendinopathy.
Tumilty et al.[20]	**LLLT** Wavelength: 810 nm Continuous pulse frequency Laser power: 100 mW Irradiation time: 30 s Total energy: 3 J per point, 18 J per session Energy density: 3 J/cm^2 per point, 18 J/cm^2 per session Area: 1 cm^2	Clinical study	No significant benefits regarding pain.

Table A.4   ILIB general effects demonstrated in the literature (from Chapter 19).

ILIB Effects	Literature
Regulation of blood lipids	Lebed'kov et al.,[10] Poluéktova et al.,[11] Huang et al.,[12] Babaev et al.[13]
Normalizing action on lipid peroxidation	Azbel et al.,[14] Safafov et al.,[15] Karneev et al.[16]
Inhibition of platelets aggregation (lessening the likelihood of clot formation)	Sirenko et al.,[17] Prokopova et al.,[18] Shval'b et al.,[19] Brill et al.[20]
Activated platelet aggregation	Paleev et al.,[21] Gao et al.[22]
Activation of immune system (dendritic cells, macrophages and lymphocytes)	Dmitriev et al.,[23] Kupnovyts'ka,[24] Palćhun et al.,[25] Koshelev and Chalyk,[26] Hanul et al.,[27] Stupak and Rodiukova[28]
Immunomodulation	Dedenko,[29] Marchuk and Kuzmich,[30] Alizade and Karaeva,[31] Sidorov et al.,[32] Tsvettsikh et al.,[33] Shakhova et al.,[5] Chiran et al.[34]
Interference in the arachidonic acid cascade/ anti-inflamatory effects	Tsuman et al.,[35] Sidorov et al.,[32] Polosukhin,[36] Burduli and Krifaridi,[37] Shakhova et al.[5]
Normalize hemostase system	Koshelev and Chalyk[26]
Antioxidant defense	Dedenko,[29] Grigor'eva et al.,[38] Koshelev and Chalyk,[26] Zubkova et al.,[39] Tsvettsikh et al.,[33] Vladimirov et al.,[7] Huang et al.,[12] Farkhutdinov,[40] Karneev et al.,[16] Arnall et al.,[41] Burduli and Krifaridi,[42] Burduli and Aleksandrova,[3] Shakhova et al.,[5] Burduli and Balaian[43]
Vasodilatation	Sirenko et al.,[17] Alizade and Karaeva,[31] Alizade and Karaeva[44]
Improves rheological blood characteristics: reduced the erythrocyte sedimentation and blood viscosity	Dedenko,[29] Prokopova et al.,[18] Alizade and Karaeva,[31] Paleev et al.,[21] Palćhun et al.,[25] Alizade and Karaeva,[44] Siposan and Lukacs,[45] Mi et al.,[46] Iaitskii et al.,[47] Sarycheva et al.,[4] Simonenko et al.[48]
Increasing microcirculation	Kirsanova et al.,[49] Iakubenia et al.,[50] Burduli and Gazdanova,[51] Burduli and Gutnova,[52] Burduli and Tadtaeva Dia,[53] Shakhova et al.[5]

Table A.5   Diseases and their ILIB effects in the literature (from Chapter 19).

Disease	ILIB Clinical Effects	Literature
Arthritis	- reduction of rheumatoid blood factor to 1:20 titers - no side effects or complications - reduction of the time of the patients' stay at hospital - anti-inflammatory and immunomodulating action in patients with rheumatoid arthritis - normalization of titer of IgA and IgG levels - synergistic anti-inflammatory effect of ILBI in combination with tocilizumab	Tupikin,[54] Sidorov et al.,[32] Chiran et al.[34]
Asthma	- retained free-radical oxidation defects and the disease symptoms - better morphofunctional parameters of red blood cells	Farkhutdinov,[40] Sarycheva et al.[4]
Atherosclerosis	- better results in morphofunctional state of erythrocytes and hemorheology - ILIB therapeutic effect persisted for 3 months in most patients	Iaitskii et al.[47]
Acute period of hemorrhagic shock and after resuscitation	- improvement of circulation and gas exchange in the lungs and tissue perfusion - activation of regulatory mechanisms of the regional blood-flow redistribution	Kirsanova et al.[49]
Bronchitis	- positive effect on circulatory system by changing hyperkinetic hemodynamics into normokinetic version	Burduli and Aksenova[55]
Chronic brain ischemia	- normalizing action on lipid peroxidation and antioxidant defense	Karneev et al.[16]
Chronic hepatitis and reactive hepatitis	- reduction of the functional activity of thrombocytes in the presence of fibrinogen and adrenaline hydrochloride - improvement of endothelium function - compensation of NO deficit - protection of the organism against free radicals decreases the severity of oxidative stress - normalization in the plasma NO level - marked beneficial effect on the cytokine system	Spasov et al.,[1] Burduli and Krifaridi,[42] Burduli and Krifaridi[37]
Chronic venous insufficiency	- hypocoagulation - lower hematocrit index	Shval'b et al.[19]
Diabetic angiopathies	- decrease in the activity of free radical oxidation - action on anti-peroxide protection enzymes - improvement of issue microcirculation	Grigor'eva et al.[38]
Diabetes	- impact on the blood lipid and phospholipid components and erythrocyte membrane - favorably affects the blood components - hypolipedemic and hypoglycemic effects - decreased concentration of NO in the blood - improves peripheral protective sensation in patients by a mechanism other than an increased NO production	Lebed'kov et al.,[10] Poluéktova et al.,[11] Arnall et al.[41]

(continued)

Table A.5 Continued

Disease	ILIB Clinical Effects	Literature
Coronary heart disease	- changes in erythrocyte number - effects on the blood antioxidative system - increase of microcirculation - increase of endothelial oscillations and capillary blood flow - increase of endothelial functional activity - decrease of membrane toxicity by 43% - decrease the activity of the blood serum components - significant decrease in the levels of total cholesterol, and low-density lipoproteins - increase in the content of high-density lipoproteins - alleviation of pain syndrome - reduction of ventricular arrhythmias frequencies, heart failures, condition recurrences, and mortality rate - reduction of the hypophyseoadrenocortical and aldosteron-renin-angiotensin system activities - reduction of blood levels of dilatants and pro-aggregants (PGF2 alpha, vasopressin, angiotensin II) - increase of vasodilating and anti-aggregation hormones (PGE, PGI2) levels - improvement of PGI2/TxB2 ratio	Simonenko et al.[48] Zubkova et al.[39] Burduli and Gazdanova[51] Azbel et al.[14] Diasamidze[56] Sirenko et al.[17]
Ischemic heart disease	- increase of the activity of ATP-ase - index of erythrocyte deformability - improvement of cardiac function - optimization of the structural–functional organization of the cellular membrane	Vasil'ev et al.[57]
Esophageal cancer	- immunorehabilitation effect - lower post-operative complication rate - mortality reduction - three-year survival rate indices improvement	Hanul et al.[27]
Gastro-esophageal reflux disease	- increase in PGE2 to the levels typical of those in healthy individuals - significant decrease in all esophageal pH-metry parameters - the DeMeester score achieved normal values - all quality-of-life indicators, except for physical function index, significantly improved - elevation of pro-inflammatory prostaglandin levels and the improvement of parameters of microcirculation - normalization of plasma levels of stable NO metabolites regardless of its initial value, either high or low	Burduli and Tadtaeva[53] Burduli and Tadtaeva Dia[58] Burduli and Balaian[43]

(continued)

Table A.5 Continued

Disease	ILIB Clinical Effects	Literature
Hypertension	- drop in the arterial blood pressure - improvement in general condition of the patients, - enhancement of the effectiveness of antihypertensive preparations, - favorable shifts in immunological and hemorheological indices - duration of beneficial clinical effect for up to 4–8 months - drop of arterial pressure - improvement in viscous and elastic properties of blood and its hemodynamic index - significant decrease of Willebrand's factor activity - normalization of the NO level regardless of its initial value	Alizade and Karaeva[31] Alizade and Karaeva[44] Burduli and Aleksandrova[3]
Liver problems	- alleviation of the major clinical symptoms - significant positive changes in biochemical parameters (AST, ALT, bilirubin, alkaline phosphatase, lactate dehydrogenase, and total cholesterol)	Babaev et al.[13]
Pancreatitis	- recovery of lymphocyte activity - increase in the ATP content in erythrocytes - inhibition of blood proteolytic activity - enhancement of free-radical oxidation, kallikrein–kinin system activity, and blood oxygen transport - correction of endotoxic pancreatogenic syndrome - positive shifts in the immunological status, morphofunctional characteristics of the red blood cells and hemoglobin, hepatic and renal functions - improvement of microcirculation regardless of its hemodynamic type - normalization of ceruloplasmin content in the plasma - avoids infection of pancreatic lesions in 67.7% - decreasing in lethality rate of sterile pancreonecrosis from 24.4% to 5.1% and of infected pancreonecrosis from 42.8% to 23.1%	Dmitriev et al.[23] Dedenko[29] Burduli and Gutnova[52] Burduli and Gutnova[59] Geĭnits et al.[60]
Pneumonia	- positive dynamics in microcirculation in addition to conventional medication - pronounced effects on blood rheological characteristics: reduced blood viscosity, improved both viscous–elastic properties and osmotic resistance of erythrocytes - decrease in blood viscosity - hypocoagulative effect of intravascular - normalization of clinico-roentgenologic	Burduli and Pilieva[61] Paleev et al.[21] Prokopova et al.[18]

(continued)

Table A.5 Continued

Disease	ILIB Clinical Effects	Literature
Psoriasis	- increased the levels of anti-inflammatory cytokines - decreased levels of pro-inflammatory cytokines - immunomodulatory effect - stimulates the antioxidative system - improves microcirculation	Shakhova et al.[5]
Parkinson's disease	- reduction of neurological deficit - normalization of the activity of MAO B, Cu/Zn-SOD and immune indices - correlation between humoral immunity and activity of the antioxidant enzymes (SOD, catalase) - interaction between blood cells	Komel'kova et al.[62] Vitreshchak et al.[63]
Pyelonephritis	- stimulates the antioxidant system, in particular, the activity of superoxide dismutase - immunomodulation effect - changes in beta 2-microglobulin, lipid peroxidation, and middle-size molecules in the blood and urine - effective treatment of acute calculous pyelonephritis	Tsvettsikh et al.[33] Safafov et al.[15]
Refractory tachyarrhythmia	- neurohumoral regulation normalization of the barrier and receptor functional of myocardium cell membranes - it overcomes refractivity of tachyarrhythmia to anti-arrhythmic agents	Kupnovyts'ka[24]
Septic complications in otorhinolaryngology	- activation of immune system - improvement of rheological blood characteristics - enhancement of tissue regeneration	Palchun et al.[25]
Spinal cord injury	- immunostimulating effect - higher mitochondrial DNA (mtDNA) copy number - higher white blood cell adenosine triphosphate (WBC ATP) synthesis - higher total antioxidant capacity (TAC) with significantly reduced malondialdehyde (MDA) - reduction of low-density lipoprotein (LDL) - significant increase of high-density lipoprotein (HDL) - alleviation of oxidative stress and mitochondrial dysfunction	Stupak and Rodiukova[28] Huang et al.[12]
Suppurative lung diseases	- more rapid normalization of the indices of morphologic composition of gases and acid–base state of the blood - immunologic status of the organism, functions of external respiration - incidence of postoperative complications reduced by 4% - duration of hospital stay shortened by 8.1 days	Marchuk and Kuzmich[30]

(continued)

Table A.5 Continued

Disease	ILIB Clinical Effects	Literature
Suppurative peritonitis	- stimulates the bone marrow and the organs in which blood elements are stored - increased number of progenitor cells - reduced number of prehemolytic and degenerating forms of red cells in various stages of peritonitis	Zimon et al.[64]
Traumatic abdominal organs injuries	- improvement of the results of conventional treatment and reduction of complications rate - boosts the functional activity of leucocytes - normalization of hemostasis system - antioxidant defense	Koshelev and Chalyk[26]
Tuberculosis	- promotion of pulmonary vascular tone - better microcirculatory blood flow - increased pulse blood perfusion in the affected portion of the lung - enhancement of the conventional treatment efficiency - accelerated positive changes of tuberculosis by 2.5–3.5 months - smooth course of tuberculosis developing less pronounced residual changes in the lung	Iakubenia et al.[50] Rusakova et al.[65]
Infectious-destructive lung diseases	- reversion of the inflammatory process - stabilization of fibroplastic processes	Polosukhin[36]

Index

Michael R. Hamblin is a Principal Investigator at the Wellman Center for Photomedicine, Massachusetts General Hospital, and an Associate Professor at Harvard Medical School. He has interests in photodynamic therapy and photobiomodulation. He has published 396 peer-reviewed articles, is an Editor/Associate Editor for 10 journals, and serves on NIH Study-Sections. He has an h-factor of 85 and >28,000 citations. He has authored/edited 23 textbooks on PDT and photomedicine, including SPIE proceedings. Hamblin was elected as a Fellow of SPIE in 2011, and he received the first Endre Mester Lifetime Achievement Award Photomedicine from NAALT in 2017 and the Outstanding Career Award from the Dose Response Society in 2018.

Cleber Ferraresi graduated with a degree in Physical Therapy (2008) from the Federal University of Sao Carlos (UFSCar-Brazil), followed by a Specialist degree in Exercise Physiology (2009) and a Master's degree in Biotechnology (2010) from UFSCar. He earned his Ph.D. in Biotechnology at the same school (2010–2014), including work at the Wellman Center for Photomedicine, Massachusetts General Hospital, Harvard Medical School (2012–2013) and the Faculty of Applied Health Sciences, University of Waterloo (Canada, 2014). Cleber Ferraresi was a Postdoctoral Research Fellow at the Wellman Center for Photomedicine (2015). He is currently a Professor and Principal Investigator with the Physical Therapy for Functional Health Postgraduate Program at the Universidade do Sagrado Coração (Brazil) and the Biomedical Engineering Postgraduate Program at the Universidade Brasil. He has experience in physical therapy with an emphasis in photobiomodulation combined with physical exercise; fatigue and muscle damage; sports; and tissue healing.

Ying-Ying Huang is an instructor at Harvard Medical School. She was trained as a dermatologist in China. She received her M.D. from the Xiangya Medical School of Central South University in China. She earned her M.S. in Dermatology from Sun Yat-sen University. She received her Ph.D. in Pathology from Guangxi Medical University. She has been at the Wellman Center for 9 years. She has published over 67 peer-reviewed articles and 24 conference proceedings and book chapters. She has an h-factor of 71 and nearly 6000 citations. She is a co-editor of two textbooks of photomedicine. She has co-authored/edited three textbooks on PDT and photomedicine. She is the co-chair of the anitomicrobial photodynamic symposium of the 16th International Photodynamic Association World Congress. Huang's research interests lie in photodynamic therapy (PDT) for infections, cancer, and the mechanisms of photobiomodulation (PBM) on brain disorders.

 **Lucas Freitas de Freitas** graduated from the Biomedical Sciences program at the State University of Londrina - Brazil and received his Ph.D. in Bioengineering at the University of São Paulo - Brazil. Part of his research regarding the ablation of melanomas using gold nanorods decorated with phthalocyanines was performed under the supervision of Dr. Michael Hamblin. de Freitas has experience in cancer phototherapies using nanodevices, biomedical sciences, biochemistry, and pathology, and he is a reviewer of 3 periodicals.

 **James D. Carroll** is the founder and current CEO of THOR Photomedicine Ltd. He began his career as an electronics engineer at Audix Ltd. UK in 1978. He received his degree in Electronics from Harlow Technical College, UK, in 1980. In 1986, he moved to government grant consultancy with a focus on the technology sector. One of his fundraising projects, for Guys Hospital in London, introduced him to basic science science research on lasers and LEDs for stimulating wound healing. He was hired by their laser supplier, Omega Universal Technologies, in 1988 and has been in the industry ever since. Carroll has a particular interest and expertise in the irradiation parameters and dose of low-level laser therapy (LLLT).